CHRISTMAS
ISLAND
CRACKER

An Account
of the Planning and Execution of
The British Thermo-Nuclear Bomb Tests
1957

AIR VICE MARSHAL
WILFRID E. OULTON
CB CBE DSO DFC

Thomas Harmsworth Publishing

London

British Library Cataloguing in Publication Data

Oulton, Wilfrid E.
   Christmas Island Cracker: an account of the planning
   and execution of the British thermonuclear bomb tests,
   1957.
   1. Hydrogen bomb—Great Britain—Testing
   2. Hydrogen bomb—Kiribati—Kiritimati—Testing
   I. Title
   355.8′25119′09964   UG1282.H9

   ISBN 0-948807-04-0

ISBN 0-948807-04-0

Printed in Great Britain by
The Bath Press, Avon

ACKNOWLEDGEMENTS

At the time of Operation 'Grapple', because of the security anxieties, no personal diaries were kept and, for the same reason, even the official records of events were very sketchy. In writing this account it has therefore been necessary to consult a great number of former colleagues and friends who had some connection with the Task Force. By carefully cross-checking each bit of information and getting at least some guidance from the Service Historical Branches of the Ministry of Defence, I believe that this represents an accurate account of the operation. I therefore wish to record my sincere thanks to the following members, past or present, of the Armed Forces, the Civil Service and other organisations who have patiently and with good humoured tolerance done their best to answer my incessant questions.

Johnny Ayshford	Peter Jones
George Bates	John Marman
Robin Begg	Tom Marquis
Chris Birks	Paddy Menaul
Ken Bomford	Freddie Milligan
Dougie Bower	Felix Neville-Towle
Jack Bradley	Barry Newton
Tony Casswell	Bill Penney
Bill Cook	Harry Chapman Pincher
John Cordery	Henry Probert
Sebastian Cox	Dave Roberts
Allen Crocker	Percy Roberts
Ray Davies	Bill Saxby
Harry De Vere	Gus Sinclair
Roly Duck	Eric Smith
Terry Flanagan	John Smith
Ratu Penaia Ganilau	'Butch' Surtees
'Giloh' Giles	Peter Wadsworth
Terry Gledhill	Tony Wallington-Smith
John Goodson	Donald Watts
Peter Gretton	Guy Western
Edward Hamilton-Meikle	Bill Wheeler
Dougie Hammatt	Bill White
Peter Harris	Paul Whitfield
Roger Hicks	Denis Wilson
Les Howard	Paul Wood
Ken Hubbard	John Woollett
Tony Jillings	Laurie Young

To all this it is necessary to add particularly the very great help I have had from John Foster and Ken Grinstead of the AWRE, with the kind approval of the Director.

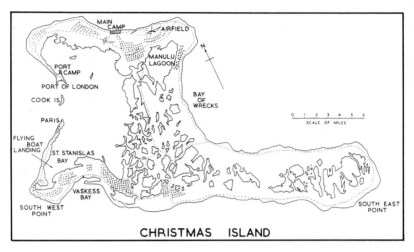

CHRISTMAS ISLAND

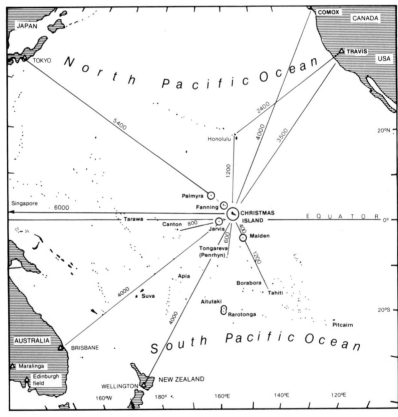

1

The Intruder

Little spurts of the crushed white coral flew into the air as the Land Rover took the left turn into the Main Camp rather too fast, and the rear wheels skidded outwards slightly. At that moment, through a gap in the towering cumulo-nimbus clouds which were sailing by majestically in the twenty-knot easterly Trade Wind, there came a brief burst of brilliant light from the tropical full moon, turning the showers of coral into gleaming silver fountains, contrasting dramatically with the background of dark scrubby bushes at the edge of the track, and illuminating for a moment the faded 'Royal Navy' lettering on the canvas top of the vehicle.

The driver, obviously with no time to spare for any flash of beauty, smartly corrected the skid without slackening speed and drove rapidly down to the lines of darkened, faded grey tents. He turned right between the officers' mess hutments and the seaward row of tents, and pulled up outside the last one, at the windward end of the line.

Leaving the engine ticking over he got out hastily, walked swiftly past the solid, polished wood notice board – 'Task Force Commander' – automatically kicked his feet gently against the standard six-inch high board at ground level across the entrance to the tent to shake off most of the caked coral dust from his desert shoes, took off his work-a-day khaki-topped uniform cap peaked with the gold oakleaves of a Captain (RN), tucked it under his left arm and stepped inside the dark tent.

'Sir!'

'Yes? Who is it? Oh, is that you, Guy?'

'Yes, sir. I'm sorry to have to tell you we've found a ship in the danger area.'

'Bloody Hell!'

The Task Force Commander half-rolled off the bed, put his feet firmly on the floor, shook his head to clear the cobwebs and said:

'Tell me!'

'One of the sea search Shackletons found the ship about forty minutes ago. She's well into the danger area and on her present course and speed would be very near 'Ground Zero' at 'H' hour. May be just coincidence, sir, may be not. The trouble is the Shackleton can get no reaction whatever from the ship, despite having gone through all the procedures laid down in Ops Orders. All we know is she's an old ten-thousand ton Victory ship, the *Effie*, registered in Liberia. The Shack dropped flares and read the name off the stern – nice work! She's on a course which would take her to Panama in about two weeks, so she's probably on auto-pilot and all the crew fast asleep down below. She might have a W/T watch on the international distress frequency, but I suppose we don't want to use that. I think *Cossack* could just get there in time, at the risk of bursting her ancient boilers; so I've warned her to be ready to sail in half an hour. What would you like to do, sir?'

'Right, Guy. Thank you. Please sail *Cossack* as soon as possible. Tell Wykes-Sneyd to take any reasonable risk to reach *Effie* and turn her away. Have that instruction entered in the Ops Room log. Radio silence – except in an emergency – until *Effie* is clear – we can't have an international uproar about this; but tell the Shack to set up homing procedure C to assist *Cossack* and save time. Off you go and I'll join you in the Operations Room in ten minutes.'

'Aye, aye, sir.'

And Captain Guy Western stepped out of the tent, into the Land Rover and was off like a scalded cat back the way he had come.

After a moment to reflect that a clear head would be worth a couple of minutes delay, the Task Force Commander – the TFC as he was usually addressed to save time, or 'Father Christmas' behind his back when time didn't matter – slid his feet into flip-flops, grabbed a towel and trotted some twenty yards to the nearest of a row of shower stalls. This was just a corrugated iron roof and half sides over a cement floor with a duckboard to stand on and a cold water shower rose overhead. The faithful duty land crab, annoyed at being disturbed at two o'clock in the morning, rattled away into a corner. Then a quick deluge of quite cool water. The TFC towelled off as he walked rapidly back to his tent. As he dressed quickly – khaki shirt with shoulder flashes showing the rank of an Air Vice Marshal, Royal Air Force, khaki drill slacks, socks, shoes, uniform beret – he decided that there was at this stage no need to disturb Bill Cook, the Chief Scientist, nor any need or time to call Corporal Beall, his driver, who had already had a hard day.

Behind the TFC's tent, under a rough awning of plaited pandanus leaves, stood the white-painted Super Snipe staff car, clean and well-cared for, but very much the worse for wear and corrosion. He got in, started up, selected reverse gear to back out and engaged the clutch by hauling on a short length of rope tied round the clutch pedal. The clutch return spring had long ago given up the struggle against corrosion and friction caused by the coral dust which got into everything; but the rope round the pedal worked fine – Corporal Beall's invention.

He moved off quietly past the line of tents and their sleeping occupants, most of them exhausted after forty-eight hours of intensive effort and just catching a little sleep before starting again at 5 am. Then he accelerated rapidly away, turning left into the exit road from the Main Camp, then right into the main road which ran from the airfield along the edge of the lagoon to the Headquarters and Joint Operations Centre. For a few seconds he permitted himself the luxury of raging against 'that stupid bloody man, the Secretary of State', who – despite a careful and logical explanation of the vital need for it – had

3

refused to let the international warning 'Notice to Mariners' be sent out in time to keep shipping clear of the designated danger area; and now, in consequence, they were all in this frightful and very dangerous situation. 'Blast the man!'

But there was no time to waste in recrimination. Now if that old destroyer *Cossack* could get there in time, all might still be well. That dashing young Lieutenant Commander Wykes-Sneyd could get there if anyone could and what better ship for the job than *Cossack*? The TFC's grim face relaxed for a moment as he thought of his friend, the sometime Lieutenant Bradwell Turner, then the First Lieutenant of the previous HMS *Cossack*, cutlass in hand, leading a boarding party storming aboard the Nazi prison ship *Altmark* to free more than a hundred British merchant seamen held prisoner on that ship in the Altefjord in 1940.

As he swept alongside the inland lagoon and glanced for a moment at the tall coconut palms silhouetted black against the silver reflections off the water, the white sandy shore, now illuminated by another brilliant flash of moonlight, with the heavy scent of tropical vegetation borne on the strong breeze, he thought for a moment – 'What a waste! What a place for romance, if only there were someone to be romantic with!' Instead he was now faced with this God-awful situation and some uncomfortable decisions to be made in a few minutes and wished to heaven he had never become involved in it. Too late for wishing and, anyway, how *had* he got involved in the first place?

2

Defence Policy in a hurry

It had all begun in London on a chilly Monday afternoon early in February 1956 as he came out of the Government Surplus Clothing shop opposite Charing Cross station, feeling pretty pleased with himself for having got an ex-Navy duffle coat for one of his sons for only half of what it would have cost at the school outfitters. Such a saving was important to an Air Commodore with three sons at boarding schools in the days before educational assistance. But the smug feeling faded sharply as his eye caught the station clock – nearly ten minutes past two. Lordy! He was going to be late for that staff meeting – and after all the fuss he'd made last week about people turning up late! A quick look to his right showed the traffic lights at the end of the Strand at red – just turning red/amber. Tucking the parcel under his left arm, he darted smartly across the road through the slow-moving traffic, handed himself off the massive headlamp of a magnificent $4\frac{1}{2}$ litre Bentley in a manner slightly reminiscent of the rugby football field of twenty-five years earlier, swerved round the back of a taxi, raced towards Lyons Strand Corner House, and grabbing the handrail, swung himself on to the rear platform of a Number 77 red double-decker bus. 'Phew!'

After a pause for breath, and a reflection that it had been a damned stupid impulsive thing to do – his back might have decided to seize up again and he would have been stuck paralysed in the middle of that relentless traffic – he went up to

5

the conductor collecting fares inside and paid his four pence.
'I'll be getting off at the next stop.'

Next problem – whether to get off at the Silver Cross pub at
the top of Whitehall or stay on the bus, hoping to drop off nearer
Horse Guards Avenue at the risk of being carried on to
Parliament Street. He stayed – and luck was with him. As the
bus came level with the two sentries, mounted on their
magnificent black horses outside the archway leading into the
Horse Guards parade ground, it slowed down for traffic coming
from Parliament Square and turning across the road into Horse
Guards Avenue. He swung off the bus platform and walked
rapidly to the steps leading up into the imposing new Air
Ministry building. Up the short escalator which carried
pedestrians over the below-ground ancient Henry VIII's wine
cellar, which they had not been allowed to move when the new
Ministry was being built, to the row of lifts at first floor level.
There was one with the door just closing. He stepped quickly
inside and pressed the button for the fourth floor. A few strides
along the corridor and he glanced at his wrist watch as he turned
into 4027 – his outer office. Two fifteen – just made it!

His secretary, a pleasant and very competent 35-year-old,
looked up from the mirror propped up against the typewriter
and paused in the middle of fixing her hair. For the umpteenth
time he wished she wouldn't do it in the office, but how could
one protest knowing that immediately after work at the end of
every afternoon she rushed off to spend her evenings teaching
deaf children to talk?

'Air Commodore!' – she called.

'Hello, Mrs Harris. Back just in time. Are they all in?'

'No, sir. I've cancelled your meeting. ACAS(Ops) wants to
see you immediately and it's urgent.'

'Any idea as to what it's about?'

'No, sir. Not a clue!'

Hmm! One preferred to have all relevant facts at one's finger
tips before going to see the forthright and somewhat irrascible
Assistant Chief of the Air Staff for Operations; but, lacking that

comfort, at least better not keep the boss waiting. Dropping his hat and parcel on Mrs Harris's desk, he walked quickly back to the elevators – none waiting. So up the stairs two at a time to the awesome sixth floor, where abode the Chief of the Air Staff and his supporting archangels. He entered the outer office and, before he could speak, the secretary turned her head and smiled:

'Good afternoon, Air Commodore. The Air Marshal is waiting for you. Please go straight in.'

'Thank you, Miss Harrison.'

Two quick knocks on the inner door and he went in to the large, quiet office, but with no eyes at this moment for the lovely view of the Embankment Gardens and the river.

'Good afternoon, sir. You wanted me?'

The piercing blue eyes looked up and the rugged pugnacious face behind the desk took on a cheery welcoming smile.

'Hello, Wilf. Come and sit down. I've got a new job for you.' Just a trace left of that Australian accent.

Air Vice Marshal Lees got up and moved over to a couple of armchairs fronted by a low glass-topped coffee table. Broad, stocky, aggressive, he was every inch the fighter ace and leader. A first-class operator – direct, uncompromising and knowing his job inside out.

They sat down and Lees proffered a cigarette, which was refused with a smile and a shake of the head.

'A new job, sir?'

'Yes,' with a wide grin. 'I want you to go out and drop a bomb somewhere in the Pacific and take a picture of it with a Brownie camera.'

'Well, that doesn't sound too difficult at first sight and might be fun.' Then, more cautiously, 'What kind of bomb?'

A pause for a pull on the cigarette.

'A megaton thermo-nuclear device.'

'Good God!'

After a pause for the visitor to regain breath, the quiet Australian voice went on:

'They say that there is going to be an international treaty

banning the testing of nuclear weapons; and if we have not previously demonstrated that we have a serious capability in the deterrent business, Britain will no longer have a leading place in world politics. You know what the Americans are like – great friends as long as you are in the same league, but ruthlessly regardless of a weak ally. As for the Russians, the only thing they understand is a bigger axe than their own. So we have to show that we too have the H-Bomb and are to be reckoned with in the deterrent business.

'I expect you know that Doctor Penney is going to test a kiloton range nuclear fission device in a few months time. That will be at the Monte Bello Islands off Western Australia. Then we have to prove that the device can be made into a bomb and delivered by air, which means a practical demonstration in the middle of the Australian desert. Then finally we have to invent, develop and demonstrate a megaton range nuclear fusion weapon, which is what really counts in World Politics; and we have to do this all by our little selves – we can't just borrow American technology. Also, the fusion process is reckoned to have immense potential economic and industrial application in something called Zeta and we want to be in the lead in peaceful uses of atomic energy. This test is said to be an essential step in the development of those peaceful applications.

'The Prime Minister has given the go-ahead on this programme and top priority for everything to do with it and for whatever steps have to be taken. The only immutable condition is that there shall be no injury to non-British personnel or property. We can't have another "Dagon-sha" incident like the American trouble at Bikini.'

There was a pause while imagination boggled for a while.

'In view of what you said, sir, about the possibility of a test ban, what's the deadline for our H-Bomb demonstration?'

'May of next year.'

'And where is this to take place, sir?'

'I don't know for sure yet. They are talking about either Christmas Island in the central Pacific or the Kerguelen Islands in the southern Indian Ocean.'

'But there is nothing at either of those two places – except possibly the remains of an old wartime fighter reinforcement airstrip at Christmas!'

'That's right. You'll be starting from scratch.'

'Me, sir? What do you want *me* to do?'

'I want you to plan and execute this entire air operation.'

'For God's sake! Why me? Why not your Director of Bomber Ops? Isn't it more of a job for him?'

'No, Wilf. With your scientific background, your experience of setting up an island base in the Azores during the war and having done the US atomic weapons course at Oberammergau, we think you are the chap for the job. So get on with it – starting now. I want you to drop your present job immediately. Who do you think could take it over most quickly?'

After a moment's thought, the Air Commodore replied:

'I suggest Nick Gething from Coastal Command. He's pretty well in the picture of what is going on in the Maritime world and shouldn't have any trouble on the navigation side. I think I must go to Northwood first and take my leave of the AOC-in-C* or there will be umbrage; and we shall in any case need a lot of help from Coastal, so it would be sensible to tell "Chillie" all about this and enlist his support.'

'Oh, no! You can't do that!' exclaimed the Assistant Chief of Staff.

'This is all 'Top Secret Atomic" and information must only be given, at least for the time being, on a "need-to-know" basis. Go and see the AOC-in-C by all means and brief Gething. I'll get the Personnel people to arrange his posting immediately; but not a word to anyone about your new job, unless it is quite essential.'

'Very well, sir. Now, where do I start? Is there any organisation existing? Do I have an office? Secretary? Staff?'

'Nothing at all on the service side. This is a Ministry of

---

* The Air Officer Commanding-in-Chief.

Supply operation and, as I said, you are starting from scratch and you'll have to set up your own team. Maurice Heath in Personnel has been informed that you are to have whatever you need, as far as they are able to do it.'

'From what you say, sir, I am to run the air operation. But what about all the rest? Who is to be in overall command of this programme? What aircraft are we to use for the drop? A megaton is a bit different from a 1,000 pound HE – and it sounds to me as though we have to build a Class I airfield in less than a year. And didn't we lose three Canberras and crews participating in the American tests last year? No radio or radar aids in either of those two areas.'

'Whoa! Steady on! There's a lot of sorting out to be done. There's been some talk that a Mr Bomford of the Atomic Weapons Research Establishment at Aldermaston should be in overall charge, but that is just unrealistic. This is basically the Minister of Supply's baby and the chap responsible for it to the Minister is a Mr Eric Jackson, the Director General in charge of the Atomic Weapons programme. Better go and see him right away and get the full background.'

'I'll do that, sir. Then perhaps we can talk again about the resources we'll need. I'd better get started. It sounds impossible in the time scale, so I shouldn't waste half a day.'

Taking his leave, he made his way back down to the office which was no longer his.

'Mrs Harris, would you please get me Air Vice Marshal Heath in Adastral House on the phone and then Group Captain Gething at Coastal Command.'

The secretary rang back: 'Air Marshal Heath is on the line, sir.'

'Maurice? You may know about it, but if not I can't tell you. I've just had a fearsome job dumped on me by Ronnie Lees and I need personnel help – fast!'

'That's all right, old boy. We're all set to give you whatever you want – as far as we can.'

'For starters, I want a first-class Group Captain, currently au fait with Bomber operations and Canberras, as my chief staff officer. I shall also need people for a small operations headquarters staff – minimum number to do the job, so each one must be worth two of his kind.'

'I've got the form, Wilf. I'll have a look at the Group Captain post immediately and tomorrow I'll send over one of the Establishment boys to draft a special headquarters establishment for you.'

'Thanks a lot, Maurice. Also, although I know it's not really your job, could you fix me a decent staff car right now for my full time use and a good driver, youngish, but able to cope with VIPs and emergencies?'

'I'll get the Organisers to do that for you. Where do you want to stable it?'

'At Northwood, please – nearest to my home.'

It was great to have good friends in a situation like this.

'Next call, Mrs Harris – Group Captain Gething.'

'Hello, Nick. Please don't ask questions because it's all too hot. You'll get the official word later today, but this is just to tip you off that you are to come and take over my present job immediately – I mean tomorrow morning! I'm coming in early to see the AOC-in-C, I hope, and then we could go into the Air Ministry together if that suits you. It would save some time in handing over. But not a word to anyone until you hear from SASO.'*

'Good Lord! That's a bit of a shaker, but very nice! OK. I'll see you in the morning, as you say.'

'To save me time, Nick, would you please ask the ADC to make a date for me to see the C-in-C at nine o'clock tomorrow morning and let Mrs Harris know if it's OK? Thanks.'

'Yes, Wilf. I'll fix that.'

'Next call, Mrs Harris – a Mr Eric Jackson in the Ministry of Supply. He's Director General Weapons Trials or something like that.'

---

* The Senior Air Staff Officer – Chief-of-Staff.

11

Mrs Harris made the connection.

'Mr Jackson? I've just been told I'm to do a job for you. I'm sure you know all about it, but I don't. Sorry about the short notice but can I come and see you immediately please – say, in about twenty minutes?'

'Yes, Air Commodore. We've been waiting to hear from you. Do come over as soon as you wish.'

'Thanks. I'll come right away.'

3

Castlewood House

'Mrs Harris! I'm off to see Jackson and I doubt I'll be back before you go. Please let me know in Jackson's office if I have a date to see the AOC-in-C at Coastal tomorrow morning. If so, I'll be late in – about 10.30. Thanks for everything and I hope you have a good evening with all those kids.'

Grabbing his raincoat and hat, he was off out of the office, down the eight flights of stairs and the escalator, along Horse Guards Avenue into Whitehall, through the traffic across to the bus stop by the Whitehall Theatre with its bill board advertising Brian Rix's latest comedy. A bus would be almost as quick as a taxi if he got one right away – and he did. A few minutes to think, as the bus made its way round Trafalgar Square, along Cockspur Street and up to Piccadilly Circus and Shaftesbury Avenue. He hopped off at St Giles Circus and walked quickly round the back of Castlewood House and into the main entrance of the headquarters of the Ministry of Supply.

At the reception office window, he filled in the visitor's pass form, under the unsmiling eyes of a burly guard who, having checked by telephone, called a blue-overalled woman escort. She led the visitor into an elevator, then along a corridor and through the open door of the outer office of the Director General. The secretary took the pass, studied it for a moment and then:

'Good afternoon, sir. Mr Jackson is expecting you.'

She led him into the inner office – spacious, dark furniture and carpet – dull and gloomy – and a tall, broadly built, fair haired,

13

gentle and academic looking man came towards him with a smile and a hand extended in greeting.

'We're very pleased to see you, Air Commodore. I'm Eric Jackson and we've been anxiously waiting for you. I fear we are very short of time.'

'I'm just as anxious to see you, Mr Jackson, and from the sketchy information I've had so far, I don't see how we are going to do it by the required date. But if we could go through all the background information, we'll get started immediately.'

'First of all,' said Jackson, 'May I introduce Captain Lloyd, who is the Director responsible for atomic trials?'

So this was the famous Frankie Lloyd – medium height, slim build, impeccably but unobtrusively dressed, silver-grey hair well brushed, sharp intelligent face with a seaman's ruddy colouring, piercing blue eyes, a strong personality. The two shook hands and immediately took to each other. It was easy to believe that Lloyd had been widely tipped to become First Sea Lord; but he was an extremely outspoken and straightforward character who did not suffer fools gladly. Either he had been in the wrong job at a vital moment of his naval career or, more likely, he had offended some slower-witted but more senior officer and that had damned him when his name came before the Naval Promotion Board. So, in accordance with Royal Navy practice, not having 'gone up' he was 'out' and now had this job in the Ministry of Supply. Hard luck on Frankie Lloyd, but maybe he was doing an equally important job for the nation.

'I suggest,' said Lloyd, 'that we go down to the Security Area where I can brief you over the chart – if you agree, Mr Jackson?'

Jackson nodded and all three went out and down to the basement, past a security guard and in through a strongroom door which Lloyd unfastened with a bunch of keys secured to his waist belt with a light chain.

Inside was a room, windowless, with steel filing cabinets lined round the walls and a large table in the centre, on which was a chart case.

'Shall I run through the story, Mr Jackson?' asked Lloyd.

'Yes, please.'

'Well forgive me if I tell you what you know already, but to bring you up to speed quickly, when Attlee was PM the Government decided to embark on an atomic weapons programme. The Chiefs of Staff had advised that there was no hope of defending Europe – and hence the UK – with conventional arms only and it was decided to go for the atomic deterrent. The Atomic Weapons Research Establishment at Aldermaston, under the direction of Doctor Penney, has been working on this for several years and you may remember the tests of two early atomic devices.

'We are now all set to do the first tests of a more nearly operational nominal 15 kiloton device at Monte Bello and later on this year a test of an air-dropped prototype weapon in Central Australia. But kilotons don't count for much in the deterrent business nowadays and we must press on with developing a megaton fusion device. Now the Government is suddenly faced with an imminent international ban on testing such weapons in the atmosphere; so the word is – get on with it at top speed and get a megaton test done before June of next year. Hence the panic.

'We've started patching the thing together, beginning with finding a suitable test site, which has to be somewhere where, if a nasty accident occurs, there'll be no significant risk to people downwind of the fall-out and of all the international uproar which that would cause. So we've chosen Christmas Island, about eleven hundred miles south of Hawaii. Britain claims sovereignty, based on Captain Cook's original discovery of the island. The Americans dispute this, but have agreed not to be difficult over our using it for our test.

'If Bill Penney can produce a bomb and make it work, we've no idea what the yield will be or what the local effects will be – including what effect it will have on the aeroplane which does the drop! So the aiming point for the high airburst explosion will not be Christmas Island itself, but Malden Island – a tiny blob of land some four hundred miles south-east of Christmas. Malden will therefore have to be the site for all the instrumentation required to record and measure what actually happens during the explosion; and since we don't know if we'll be able to test only one – or two – or three devices, we must get the maximum of information from each shot and this will mean a vast set-up of cameras, blast and radiation measuring instruments and God knows what else.

'So we have to have an operational base on Christmas Island, with an instrumentation base on Malden, in time to do a test before June of next year. So a lot of air transport will be essential. The route to Singapore and Fiji is clear enough; but it looks as though you'll need an intermediate base between Fiji and Christmas and we have arranged to use Canton Island, which is British and has a runway which the Qantas Constellations use from time to time.'

Lloyd flicked open the chart case on the table to expose a large blue and white chart – a recent, quickly produced job by the Directorate of Military Survey, noted the visitor.

'This is Christmas Island – the largest coral island in the world, but most of it is only about eighteen inches above sea level and not much of it is dry land. There's nothing there, except a lot of coconut palms and from time to time a crowd of Gilbert and Ellice islanders move in to collect the coconut crop. At such times, a New Zealand Colonial Service Officer, Percy Roberts, moves in also, to administer the place, keep order and see that the copra is shipped. He has a small bungalow for residence when he's there and the native population build themselves the typical Polynesian "long house" accommodation. There's a small jetty and Roberts keeps a small motor launch there. I believe he also has a motor vehicle of some kind. Apart from that there is nothing.

'The Americans made a coral strip airfield – Cassidy Field – for ferrying aircraft out to the south-west Pacific during the war, but I understand that this is now overgrown with bush. It may be usable by some rugged types of aircraft.

'The Army – that is the Royal Engineers – have been asked to do all the building and construction work. The Navy will provide

operational support and organise all sea transportation. AWRE*
personnel – a mixture of civilian scientists and RAF and Army
technical people – will set up all the instrumentation, assemble the
device, handle radiation safety and all atomic technical support.
The RAF have been asked to provide air transport, take the
weapon out there, drop it as required, collect samples from the
cloud and get them back to Aldermaston. That's it.'

A silence fell on the little group for a few moments.

'Thank you, Frankie,' said the Air Commodore. 'That all seems
pretty straightforward, but one or two questions occur. Firstly,
has any thought been given as to what type of aircraft is to do the
drop?'

'I understand it has to be a Valiant, because it can't be a
parachute drop because of the need for accuracy.'

'But the Valiant, although it is the first of the new "V-
bombers" isn't in service yet!'

'We just hope it will be available in time. There's nothing else
yet.'

'Then if we are to use a Valiant, Frankie, sure as hell no coral
strip will do. It has to be a minimum two thousand yards of
concrete, very level and smooth, with an LCN† of at least 35 –
that means about six inches of concrete. It normally takes about
two years to build one; and not just a runway. The RAF will
need an extensive aircraft dispersal area similar in strength to
the runway and a lot of technical maintenance facilities as well.
And won't the AWRE boys need a lot of facilities as well?'

'Yes. I think you're right; but we haven't got as far as that yet.'

'Next, you say there must be no risk of fall-out seriously
affecting other people down-wind. How are we going to know
what the wind is? There's no weather forecasting organisation, as
far as I know, in that area and we shall have to set one up. And
what about ensuring that there is no shipping passing through the
dangerous area? That's going to mean a very large search problem

---

* Atomic Weapons Research Establishment (Aldermaston).

† LCN – a number indicating the load bearing strength of a runway.

and some means of shoo-ing shipping out of the area should we find any. And has any estimate been made of how many thousands – or rather tens of thousands – of tons of construction material and fuel and supplies of all kinds are to be put ashore at Christmas and Malden? And how is all this to be landed in the time available? From what you have said, Frankie, this is going to be a massive operation involving large numbers of Navy, Army, Air Force and AWRE people and equipment, up against a time scale which at the moment looks quite impossible. Who is going to be in charge of the whole show and drive it along at high speed?'

At this point, Eric Jackson cut in – having felt a little out of it all so far.

'Ah, Air Commodore, we have at least got that arranged. There is to be a committee, the "Grapple" Committee, headed by General Morgan, the Controller of Atomic Weapons, which will co-ordinate all activities. It will include representatives from every Ministry and Department involved – about thirty people in all, I think. You can be sure that the Grapple Committee will do all the necessary co-ordination.'

The airman stared at the civil servant in disbelief and dismay.

'Grapple? What's that?'

'Oh, haven't I told you? This operation is code-named "Grapple" – just a word out of the list of available code words to be used for security purposes. Incidentally, the word "Grapple" itself is Top Secret for the time being.'

'Well, Mr Jackson, the Grapple Committee will be very helpful, I'm sure, but I don't think it will suffice to get a first class airbase operating on Christmas Island a year from now, nor to conduct a highly hazardous operation without risk to innocent people. Surely it has been recognised that there must be someone in overall command on the spot?'

At this point Lloyd chipped in again.

'You may know that for this next Monte Bello test in a few months time, all the Services support is to be commanded by Commodore Hugh Martell. I don't think any firm decision has been made yet about Grapple, but I've heard it suggested that Admiral Edden might be appointed in overall charge of it.'

'Do you mean Kaye Edden, the Commandant of the Joint Services Staff College?'

'Yes.'

'Right! I'd better go and see him as soon as possible.'

The airman moved over to the chart of Christmas Island and tried to study it, his head reeling under the realisation of the staggering factors inherent in this task. So this was Christmas Island – shaped rather like a lobster claw enclosing a vast internal lagoon. A glance at the scale – about twenty five miles north to south, twenty east to west, perhaps thirty five north-west to south-east. Most of the dry land along the north shore. A small port? – at the western entrance to the main lagoon. Very deep water just offshore – anchorages?

'I should mention,' said Lloyd, 'that we've done a photographic reconnaissance of Christmas and some of the adjacent islands and there is now a good mosaic with the Army engineers planning the building programme. They also need samples of the soil to do their sums on concrete work. We've arranged for a survey ship to make an unobtrusive call to do this and to get the samples flown back from Australia.'

'Thank you. I think, Mr Jackson, that's about as much as I can absorb at one go. I'd better get some direction on the command set-up and work out some rough idea of an operational plan for the air side. Perhaps I could come and see you again in a few days?'

'Please come and see us whenever you want to. There will probably be a meeting of the Grapple Committee next week and you may wish to come to that.'

Taking his leave, the airman headed back to Whitehall, wondered whether to go straight home as it was now after six o'clock, but remembered his parcel and went back to his old office to collect it. Oh, Lord! What about seeing the AOC-in-C at Coastal tomorrow?

Propped on his parcel was a note from Mrs Harris.

'Northwood date OK – 0900 tomorrow. Have fun!'

So up to Trafalgar Square tube station, Bakerloo line to Baker Street, and the good old Metropolitan line to rural Hertfordshire and the sixteen minute walk home to the wifely greeting.

'Hello, darling. Had a good day? Did you get the duffle coat?'

'Yes, dear. It looks just the job; and talking of jobs, they say I'm to move over to a different one, but I don't have the details yet. By the way, don't we have an invitation to the Highland Ball at Latimer on Wednesday?'

'Yes, we have. It's on the hall table. Do you want to go?'

'I'd very much like to go if you can manage it. The dancing is always fun and I want to have a few words with the Commandant, if possible.'

4

Picking up the threads

The Headquarters of the Royal Air Force Coastal Command in Northwood was housed in the old 'Chateau de Madrid', famous in Kate Merrick's time for the wild parties of the jeunesse dorée of the 1920s. Just before and during the 1939/45 war it was the scene of much more urgent affairs, but there always remained a touch of the levity of happier times and it still seemed more like a country house than an operational headquarters of the Royal Air Force.

As he went in and through the still elegant reception hall, with the illuminated war record book on its stand and open to the page of some squadron history to be remembered that day, he met the Senior Air Staff Officer coming down the handsome staircase.

'Good morning, sir' – always very formal at the first encounter of the day, after which they could relax in the easygoing intimacy of many years of serving together.

'Never mind the good morning, Wilf, what's this new job of yours? Come on! Give!'

'New job, Chillie?' he countered, deliberately obtuse.

'Yes! I'm told to send Nick Gething to take over from you immediately, so tell me what it's all about.'

'Oh, Ronnie Lees wants me to do some work for him fairly urgently. It's full time, so I have to hand over Maritime Ops.'

A shrewd look and a knowing smile.

'Oh, so that's all it is, is it?'

No one could fool Air Vice Marshal Chilton and it didn't take him a second to recognise a security situation.

'I'll be coming to tell you more about it later on, Chillie, and asking for a lot of help, I expect.'

'Right-oh. So you've just come to take your leave of the C-in-C, have you? He's ready to see you and Gething can go back with you.'

Two hours later in the Air Ministry:

'Nick, you know the job and you know Mrs Harris and the staff. Instead of my handing over formally, I suggest you just carry on and ask me for help when you need background or whatever. May I share your office for a day or so until I get one for my new job, please? – and I suggest you begin by going upstairs and making your number with ACAS Ops.'

'Right, Wilf, that suits me. Of course go on using the office and I'll go up and see the Boss right away.'

The next thing was to follow a hunch and get to the horse's mouth, to wit the Deputy Director of Bomber Operations, one Group Captain 'Paddy' Menaul, a brilliant but very aggressive young officer. During the war he had reached the acting rank of Group Captain, commanding a bomber base when scarcely out of his teens. He had had to drop rank after the war, of course, but had progressed rapidly and was now back again doing what might at first appear to be a fairly humdrum staff job. In fact with his exceptionally keen and fast brain, he was probably the most knowledgeable man in the RAF as regards the practical side of the American atomic tests and had compiled a vast personal library of background information on both the practical and the theoretical sides of the subject. Slim built, blazing blue Irish eyes, aggressive in manner, ambitious and always 'playing his cards close to his chest', he was not an easy person to know. Fortunately they had both been at the RAF Staff College together, which helped.

'Morning, Paddy.'

'Morning, sir,' – with the manner of one who is very busy with matters of great importance and has no time for banal trivialities. Shutting the door carefully – 'Paddy, relax! I need your help. Do you know about my new job?'

'No, sir. What's that?'

'I'm to run the air side of Grapple.'

All the prickliness vanished immediately in a broad smile.

'Shake! I'm to run the air side of Mosaic – the preliminary test of the trigger device at Monte Bello.'

'Good for you, Paddy. But I'm just an ignorant child in all this. Can you tell me something about what's been going on? I've been to see Jackson and Frankie Lloyd, so I have some broad idea. But can you fill me in?'

'Sure thing.'

He unlocked a steel cupboard and took out two massive folders.

'Here is all the gen on every American test, starting back in July 1945 – eleven years of work and experience which we are trying to catch up on in a few months. You know about the first of Penney's tests at Monte Bello in 1952 and then at Emu in Central Australia?'

'Not much. I was overseas at that time and didn't get to read about it.'

'Not to worry. The situation now is that we're trying to establish quickly a thermo-nuclear capability and a small force is going again to Monte Bello to test a further step in the development programme. I'm running the air side, which involves a lot of air transport up and down the west coast of Australia, a weather service, sampling the cloud after the explosion and tracking the fall-out until it becomes negligible. The whole outfit is to be commanded by a sailor, Hugh Martell, in a ship – an LST called *Narvik*. We are now assembling the air team at Weston Zoyland – a ridiculous place, but I suppose it is at least out of the public eye. Then there's to be a further test, a prototype kiloton weapon which is to be the trigger for the big bang and this will be at Maralinga in the middle of the Australian desert. That's called 'Buffalo' and I don't know yet who is to run it. Lastly your job, probably at Christmas Island, will be to test the real McCoy – the megaton baby which is not even designed yet. I can tell you this: running a test like this safely and to time is a mighty big operation, as the Americans have found to their cost;

23

and I recommend you to get as much gen as you can from their Joint Task Force 7 (which runs their tests) and in particular to talk with Monty Canterbury – Brigadier General, USAF, who is the most competent character in that business.

'You're welcome to look through all my bumff here – please excuse me if I don't take you through it myself, as I'm in a hell of a rush to get my own show going. I'll just say one thing more, though: I think the Navy want to run Grapple and I think that would be wrong. It's going to be a very complex air force problem and we ought to run it.'

'Paddy, thanks a million for all the gen. As to the command set-up, I can't argue with the Chiefs of Staff, whatever they decide; but what I do need – and fast – is that decision; and can I come and see you at Weston Zoyland before you go?'

'Sure thing. Glad to see you as long as you know we'll be hustling.'

So while Menaul with a polite excuse got on with his own work, his visitor settled down quietly in the corner to browse through the collection of documents, reports, extracts from American journals, notes on visits and so on, including reports on the US test in which Japanese fishermen were injured by fall-out; and on the wave of shrill criticism which ensued. And it was clear that there was an enormous difference between the problems of a kiloton range test and those of a megaton or more.

All this was fine, heady, exciting – and worrying – stuff but he had nothing formal to justify or support any actions which he might need to take – and not even an office! So, after brooding awhile, he went to the oracle – the office of the Chief of the Air Staff – and sought out a friend in the S6 department, a collection of 'eminences grises' who really ran the Air Ministry despite what anyone in the Royal Air Force might think. Frank Cooper was tubby, cheerful, unflappable, endowed with a keen intelligence and sharp wit which would take him years later to the very top of the tree; and right now he was a most able string-puller in the abode of the mighty and therefore a possible help in this time of trouble.

'Frank, can I come in?'

'Sure thing, Wilf. Can I do something for you, or why else would you be here?'

'Do you know about my new job?'

'New job, Wilf?' – innocent baby face giving away absolutely nothing.

'If you don't know about it, who does? I'm sure you know damn' well that Ronnie Lees has assigned me to a rather, er, *hot* job and I need help – fast!'

'Well, Wilf, one hears rumours, of course; but what had you in mind?'

'First of all, Frank, I need some authority – something to enable me to give orders and to justify requests for action. Secondly, I need some firm instruction on the command set-up. Who is to be my boss? Thirdly, I need an office, tomorrow, and some more space soon thereafter. Who fixes this for me, and can you – or someone else – instruct him accordingly?'

'As to your first two points, Wilf, I think you are right. Things have been moving too fast without sufficient co-operation between us and another Ministry. The best thing, I think, would be for me to get DCAS (the Deputy Chief of the Air Staff) to hold a meeting to formalise your position and give you proper authority. I think we could fix that for Friday. As for your office, I'm afraid we're having terrible trouble all round finding sufficient office accommodation until the other half of this building is completed. I suggest you go and see Brian Humphries-Davies, Deputy Secretary II. Accommodation comes under his aegis.'

'Thanks, Frank. I'll try Dep Sec II. I don't know him personally, but his brother, Peter, and wife and child, once stayed with us in Washington during the war, so maybe there's a little leverage there. Amusing story that. Peter H-D had instructions to cut our almost non-existent Washington allowances in the interests of economy, when in truth we couldn't afford to eat properly. So when my dear wife wanted to show welcoming hospitality, she took Barbara H-D off to the kitchen for a glass of cooking sherry while I kept Peter talking in the living room without a drink! Anyway, thanks for help and I'll wait to hear from you about DCAS's meeting. Would you care to tip off Dep Sec II to help me?'

Along to Brian Humphries-Davies's office to a friendly welcome. A very pleasant chap with a game leg and a woeful mien.

'I *do* understand, Air Commodore, that you need an office urgently and have top priority and all that, but honestly we haven't got even a broom cupboard. I could find something in an outlying office block, if that would do? Otherwise, short of turning someone out, which would really be impossible at such short notice, I'm afraid I can't help – except to put you on the waiting list.'

'No. It must be here in the centre – at least for the time being.' Then, after a deep breath – 'There *is* one room you could let me have for six days a week, sir – the Air Council Room.'

Astonishment! – and the deafening rattle of a pin dropping.

'You can't be serious!'

'Never more so, sir. The Air Council only meets once a week for half a day at the most. I could fix up some trestle tables and a couple of filing cabinets and some telephones on long leads. Move the whole lot out into a lower corridor first thing Tuesday morning and back again after lunch.'

'Oh, I don't think we could possibly do that,' protested the civil servant.

'Would you like *me* to speak to CAS* about it? – or would it be better if you just didn't know anything about it, but arranged to let me have some trestle tables and so on?'

'Oh, dear! Well, OK; but for God's sake be discreet and I'll try to find something better – or safer! – as soon as possible.'

'Thanks so very much. I'll move in tomorrow morning, out on Tuesday morning and not a word to Bessie as Richard Murdoch used to say – or was it Kenneth Horne? Good day, sir.'

---

* The Chief of the Air Staff.

Back to the D Ops Maritime office.

'Hello, Mrs Harris, is your new boss in? No? Then may I make a few telephone calls, please?'

'Oh, of course, Air Commodore; and Air Marshal Heath wants you to call him.'

'Maurice? You were calling me?'

'Yes, Wilf. First of all your Group Captain post. I reckon Freddie Milligan, at present commanding Bassingbourne - the Canberra base - is the best chap for you, but you can't have him full time until he can be relieved in three weeks. Will you hang on for him? I expect he could come to see you for the odd day, to start thinking about the job.'

'OK Maurice, I'll take your recommendation.'

'Right. I'll fix that. Then I've got a good ADC for you - Squadron Leader Helfer. An excellent war record, first class aeroplane operator and a very polished manner. As for the rest of your needs, I've got one of the Establishment boys standing by to come to see you and work out an outline staff. Then we'll put that into the machine and start getting the posts filled.'

'That's great, Maurice. Thank you so very much. Now we're really moving.'

5

A surprised Task Force Commander

The Joint Services Staff College at Latimer in Buckingham-shire, where selected officers and officials of all the Armed Forces and Civil Services of the UK and the major Common-wealth countries came together to study defence problems, had an enthusiastically supported tradition of Scottish Country Dancing on Wednesday evenings. Many staff and students and their wives were pretty skilled dancers, but there was no lack of good instructors to help those starting from scratch or slow to learn. Once a year the weekly event was turned into a much grander sounding 'Highland Ball', which meant dinner jackets for the men and long dresses for the ladies, some of whom sported a tartan sash for the occasion and looked very dashing.

The Air Commodore and his wife had caught the Scottish country dancing bug years before when he served on the directing staff at Latimer. They were keen to go to the Ball this Wednesday and joined in the fun wholeheartedly, meeting a number of old friends in the process. Taking advantage of the general pause for breath after a particularly energetic Eightsome Reel, he left his wife talking to old acquaintances and went over to pay his compliments to the Commandant of the College. Rear Admiral Kaye Edden, although unobtrusively dressed like all the other men in the anonymity of a dinner jacket, was clearly the Commandant. Of a lean and athletic build, with a strong, dark and intelligent face, he was every inch a senior naval officer in disguise and was evidently much liked by all the staff and students.

'Good evening, sir. I believe you are to be my boss for this little exercise in the Pacific?'

'Good evening to you, too,' replied Edden. 'Glad to see you here again; but no, I don't think so. The suggestion was put to me, but I told the Admiralty that I thought this would be wrong. It is primarily an Air Force show and you should run it, with us in support.'

'I agree, sir, and I think it very good of you to put that view to the Admiralty.'

After a little more chat about the social occasion and mutual friends, the two parted amicably and, with their partners, took up their positions for the start of the next dance – the 'Scottish Reform'!

Well done, the Navy! That was very generous of Kaye Edden, for it would have been a plum assignment in terms of prestige. So now DCAS would have to sort out an Air Vice Marshal to be in overall command and that would certainly share the burdens of this impossible Operation Grapple.

Next day was taken up with a helpful young Squadron Leader from the Directorate of Organisation (Establishments), who would much rather have been out on a flying job, but was conscientiously doing his stint at a desk. There was merit in this arrangement, for he was able to bring the light of recent and up-to-date flying experience to bear on the discussions. Together they sorted out a framework for a small staff of highly competent individuals to cover all aspects of the work with the minimum number of bodies. Names were suggested, of whom some could come in a couple of days, some in a couple of weeks and some could just not be available in time, so the gaps were filled with unknown but highly recommended individuals.

With no one he could talk to as yet and with no authority to take any action, he concentrated for the moment on reviewing the American experiences in atomic tests, as revealed in Paddy Menaul's extensive files, and in pondering the problems involved in setting up a weather forecasting service over a vast area of the Pacific Ocean, navigation facilities, staging posts for aircraft commuting between UK and Christmas Island round three-quarters of the world and many others. Happily, Frank Cooper rang to say that DCAS's meeting was fixed for 10.00 am the following day and Maurice Heath rang to say he had picked out a first-class chap, Flight Sergeant Kitchingman as secretary/shorthand typist and to run the office. Things were moving along quite nicely.

At ten o'clock next morning, the small group assembled in DCAS's outer office – Ronnie Lees (Assistant Chief of Staff for Operations), Ronnie Kent and Frank Cooper from S6 secretariat, a representative from the Finance Branch (the Treasury's watch-dog in the Air Ministry) and the Air Commodore who was to run the Air Force part of the operation. Promptly they were shown into the spacious and deceptively peaceful office of the Deputy Chief of the Air Staff.

Air Marshal Sir Thomas Pike, a tall, scholarly man with the air of an academic rather than that of the fighter pilot he had been, was seated behind his large desk and welcomed them all with a warm smile and a quiet 'Good morning, gentlemen. Please sit down.'

They sorted themselves out into a small semi-circle of chairs facing the desk. Tom Pike, a man of gentle manner which belied the strong character and great integrity resulting from his Quaker background, was always unfailingly courteous but never wasted time. He came straight to the point.

'So, we are to review the initial arrangements for Operation Grapple and to authorise all necessary action to go ahead, in order to achieve the testing of several thermo-nuclear devices – a polite euphemism for H-Bombs – before June of next year. The task of the Navy, Army and Air Force is to create the necessary facilities and carry out the operation to meet the technical requirements of the Atomic Weapons Research Establishment. How do we stand at the moment, ACAS(Ops)?'

Ronnie Lees, equally direct, replied:

'I've put Wilf Oulton in charge of the RAF side of things. I suggest he tells us how far he has got.'

DCAS agreed and turned to the Air Commodore.

'As you probably know, sir, the Ministry of Supply has set up a Grapple Committee, headed by General Morgan, to oversee the whole operation. Christmas Island has been selected as the operating base, with Malden Island, 400 miles to the south-east, as the aiming point and the site for very comprehensive instrumentation and recording. Some preliminary survey has been made but no work has started as yet, as far as I know. There is a derelict airstrip at Christmas, but nothing else other than a visiting District Officer's residence and occasional visits by native plantation workers.'

He summarised quickly the information he had gathered in the past three days and went on:

'The time scale seems impossibly short. We need to have a Class I airfield operational on Christmas Island fifty-one weeks from today – with all that that implies in the way of sea transportation and a vast construction effort by the Army, and as yet I don't even know who is to be in command of the whole operation.'

'Well,' said DCAS, with his gentle smile, '*You* are, aren't you?'

'Me!! G-Good Lord!!!'

'Why? Didn't anyone tell you?' queried DCAS.

'I suppose, sir, in retrospect I can see now that maybe I was given a hint; but everyone is so cagey about this operation that it's usually hard to detect the message and I didn't believe it!'

There was general laughter all round for a moment. Evidently others, too, were having difficulty with the security requirements.

After a deep breath to get over the shock, he continued:

'So am I to understand, sir, that I am to take charge and run the entire operation as from now?'

'Yes.'

'In what rank, sir?'

'We must make you an Air Vice Marshal. Congratulations!'

'Thank you, sir, but in view of the time-scale which I

mentioned, may I assume that rank and appointment as from today?'

'Yes, certainly – get on with it. Cooper, will you please send a minute to the Air Secretary to confirm this.'

'Now,' said DCAS, 'Is there anything else you want me to deal with at this meeting?'

'Yes, sir. Quite apart from meeting the time scale, which will require strong central direction, and without being dramatic, I think this is going to be a very dicey operation indeed, possibly involving loss of life. That and the imperative requirement to avoid injury to civilian life or property – from fall-out for instance – may well involve instant decisions on the spot and no argument. I feel I must have absolute command over all forces – Navy, Army, Air Force and scientists – in the operational area. Further than that, I think I should have clear terms of reference to give me this authority and to specify how far I may go in taking risks.'

'H'm. That's quite a lot to ask,' replied DCAS, 'but I'm bound to say I agree with you. There are administrative and other problems involved in command over the other services – we haven't yet worked out a scheme for a unified inter-service command – and we may have to make you a temporary Rear Admiral and Major General as well. However, we will get something done at Chiefs-of-Staff level to give you clear terms of reference and command over all the forces involved. You haven't had much time to think about it yet, but have you any idea how you will run the build-up and the operation?'

'Yes, sir. I think it best to have four Task Groups – Navy, Army, Air, Scientists – operating under a very small Task Force Headquarters, with the Task Group Commanders doubling as the senior planners in the HQ. The Navy will lead during the sea transportation phase and initial landing, the Army will lead during the construction phase and the Air Group will lead during the operational phase, all operating within the Task Force directive and conforming to the technical needs of AWRE.

'I shall need a good Air Commodore for the Air Task Group. I presume I may fix that with Personnel?'

DCAS agreed and went on:

'Have you any idea of the air effort involved?'

'On first rough reckoning, sir, over and above the Valiant squadron, we shall need a squadron of B6 Canberras for cloud sampling, one of Canberra PR7s fitted with the new Green Satin doppler and perhaps Decca for weather and wind-finding, one or more of Shackletons and a substantial Hastings airlift. No doubt there'll be something more needed as well.'

'Thank you. I think that will be enough for the time being. Let us have another meeting when your plans are a little firmer . . .'

'Mr Kent, there is another matter . . .'

As the little group dispersed, Frank Cooper murmured to the brand new and still rather overwhelmed Task Force Commander:

'That's all pretty clear on this side. It might be a good idea to go over to the Admiralty and see DCNS.'

'Thanks, Frank. I was thinking along that line myself. Likewise the War Office.'

By good luck, the Deputy Chief of Naval Staff, Sir Thomas Pike's opposite number in the Admiralty, was a former colleague with whom the new Task Force Commander had worked very amicably some years previously. So he had no trouble in getting an appointment immediately with Vice Admiral Sir Eric Clifford, a solid, stocky, pipe-smoking, easy-going man with sandy hair and a ruddy weather-beaten complexion, who greeted him with a warm smile and a firm handshake.

'So very nice to see you again and we know all about your new job. So we're giving you Peter Gretton to run the naval side for you.'

The visitor beamed with pleasure.

'That's absolutely great, Admiral. I expect you know we are old friends from Londonderry Joint Anti-submarine School days. That couldn't be better. I'm tremendously pleased – thank you. Shall I make all arrangements through Peter, then?'

'Yes. Do that, and he'll keep me informed and come to me if he's in difficulty. You know we'll do all we can to help, but we're short of everything and it's not going to be easy.'

They chatted on for a few minutes more and then the Task Force Commander made his way out through the labyrinth of corridors heading for the exit into Whitehall. But as he turned out of the doorway into the little courtyard he almost collided with a tall, lean figure hustling in at a rate of knots. Another stroke of luck!

'Peter! How glad I am to see you again. Have you heard the news?'

'Wilf! Good to see you again too. I just got the word and was rushing to intercept you. I'm delighted! But now Judy will have to sew that ruddy Commodore's broad stripe back on my uniforms and she's only just taken it off!'

In response to an interrogative look, he elaborated: 'We've just got back from a tour of duty in Washington.'

Peter Gretton had had a tough war, most of it spent as a very young Escort Group Commander shepherding Atlantic convoys through the hazards of the U-Boat Wolf packs. Having learnt the hard way, he was now completely master of his profession as a seaman Naval Officer. He set himself very high standards and had little patience with those others who were not up to those same standards. As a result, he was usually of a peremptory, abrasive and commanding manner and outspokenly intolerant of inefficiency; but he could charm the birds off the trees if he put his mind to it.

'Peter, I don't have any offices as yet – I've only had the job for a couple of hours. Can you fix yourself up with an office in the Admiralty for the time being – and could we go somewhere and talk?'

After a brief outline of the task ahead, they agreed to meet on Monday morning and the TFC returned to his very snobbish and very temporary office in the Air Ministry. But first he called on Mrs Harris to check for messages.

'Oh, sir, I'm glad to see you. This is Group Captain Milligan, who has been told to report to you.'

A stocky, friendly figure with a cheery smile, who had obviously been hovering around, not knowing quite what to do, greeted him with relief.

'Freddie Milligan, sir. I understand I'm to leave my nice job as Station Commander at Bassingbourn and come to work for you as soon as my relief arrives. I'm having a weekend off so I sneaked away early in the hope of seeing you and finding out what it's all about.'

'Welcome aboard, Freddie,' said the TFC as they shook hands.

'Am I ever glad to see you! Let's go up to our temporary office and I'll tell you about it – and don't faint on me! We're using the Air Council Room for the moment!'

Milligan's eyes nearly popped out of his head, but he gulped and took the news in his stride as they went up to the sixth floor and the Holy of Holies.

A quick explanation of the situation, the task and the security problem and then:

'I want you to act as my chief of staff, but also to run the planning of the air operation until such time as we get an Air Task Group Commander. So start thinking about it; but be very careful with any notes you might make – don't forget the whole thing is Top Secret (Atomic) at the moment, although sooner or later the logistics will have to be downgraded. Come and join me as soon as you can and meanwhile use Mrs Harris's telephone as a communication link. How are you fixed for moving to London?'

'Fortunately, sir, that's no great problem. We have a flat in Gloucester Place, near Baker Street station, for my daughter; so we shall just move in there.'

'That's great. We'd better not get you too involved at this moment. Just concentrate on handing over Bassingbourn as soon as possible. But you could think about one problem. Our target date for the first drop is May next year. How much ahead of that do you think we need to have all the squadrons moved in to Christmas to work up to the highest possible operational standard?'

'I should think about three months, sir, but I'll work on it.'

'Yes. That was my first estimate too; but it implies having the runway and all base facilities built and in operation less than a year from now. That's going to be bloody difficult, but we must try.'

After Milligan had gone he made another call to the Director General of Personnel.

'Maurice, I'm sorry to bother you again, but I need more help. They've dumped the entire job on me now and I need a first class character to run the Air Task Group as an Air Commodore – and fairly soon.'

'Yes, Wilf. We've already got the word from DCAS's office, and I think the right chap for your job is 'Ginger' Weir, who has the additional benefit of having had some connection with the American tests. He's commanding Lindholme at the moment and will have to hand over. Worse than that, he's had a car crash, broken a couple of ribs, written off his Jaguar and won't be fit for duty for a few weeks, but I think it would pay you to wait for him, if you can.'

'That's fine, Maurice. I know Ginger – he was one of my brighter students at Latimer and I formed a high opinion of him. I just hope he can get here soon. Initially it shouldn't be too hard for him physically, just driving a telephone and a desk, as long as he's going to be OK in a couple of months.'

'Right. We'll post him to you in the rank of Air Commodore. What's your other problem.'

'I want a good, practical Specialist Navigator to go out to that place fairly soon as Wing Commander i/c the airfield. It will be pretty rugged at first, so I want someone with initiative and good power of command and able to liaise happily with the Army and Navy.'

'OK, Wilf, we'll see what we can find for you.'

'Thanks a lot, Maurice.'

Suddenly it all seemed too much, and he had a splitting headache. Looking at his watch – nearly five o'clock – whatever happened to lunch? – if he moved quickly maybe he could coax a cup of tea from Mrs Harris before she left. So off flying helter-skelter down the stairs to the fourth floor.

'Yes, of course, Air Marshal. I'll fix you one right away. Air Commodore Gething has gone to Northwood, so why don't you go and have it in your old office?'

'Good idea, Mrs Harris. Thank you.'

He went and poked around in the bottom left-hand drawer of his old desk and found a forgotten ball of string. Going over to the large Mercator projection world map which covered one wall of the office, he checked off distances to Christmas Island, Pacific Ocean, and not to be confused with Christmas Island, Indian Ocean, Malta – Ismailia – Karachi – Calcutta – Singapore – Darwin – Brisbane or Townsville? – Fiji – Canton Island – Christmas. It was a hell of a long way – three quarters of the way round the world. Of course, there was already a weekly Hastings service through Darwin and Alice Springs to Adelaide, and that could perhaps be extended through Fiji; but they would only have a small amount of spare capacity. Christmas would need at least a full Hastings load every week. And what about staging post facilities, engineering support, spares for at least five different types of aircraft and God knows what else along that eighteen thousand mile route?

It was too much for one day. Switch off and go home. But it was one day gone. Only three hundred and fifty-seven days left to get a squadron of Valiant bombers on a Class I runway at Christmas.

During the sixteen minute walk home from the station he wondered mischievously how to break some of the news to his wife. He let himself in through the kitchen door, patted the head of the elderly elkhound bitch who rose to greet him and in a fruity and pompous voice addressed the dark-haired slim-figured lady busy stirring a saucepan at the cooker:

37

'Good evening, Mrs Air Vice Marshal!'

'WHA-A-T! Are you joking?'

'No, darling. They've made me an AVM – only acting, of course, but it will help with the bank overdraft.'

A big hug and a kiss. 'This is wonderful! But,' rather anxiously, 'you don't get it for nothing. Are you happy about it? Are you pleased about the job? Can you tell me what it is now? Oh, never mind – it's wonderful. Let's have a drink and celebrate. Ooooh! My carrots! They're ruined!'

'Yes. Yes. No, not yet, I'm afraid. Gin and tonic or sherry?'

6

Ecclesiastical inspiration – 'Go west, young man!'

Sunday morning usually meant the eleven o'clock service in the church on the village common and a mingling of the farming and stockbroking communities with the local townspeople. They unobtrusively took seats at the end of a pew, where a shaft of wintry sunshine took a little of the chill off the not-too-well heated church and conveyed some over-optimistic early promise of Spring.

When it came to the time for the sermon and the vicar ascended to the pulpit and announced his text – something from St Paul's First Epistle to the Corinthians (a pity it wasn't his favourite quote 1 Corinthians 14, Verse 8) the thought occurred to the two-day old Task Force Commander that there was certainly going to be no place for any 'uncertain sounds' in the next fifteen months – or for mentally slouching-around, instead of thinking clearly about a problem and making up his mind. This route to Christmas Island, for instance, using Canton Island. From the Flight Guide which he had glanced at, there was just a modest runway and a few buildings. No room for parking any significant number of aircraft, no space for more buildings or a major fuel installation, and the runway flooded under extreme conditions of wind and tide. Very dicey as a main link in the chain.

Next point, there was not enough time to build up second-line servicing for all types of aircraft at Christmas. They could probably cope with the Valiants. The Canberras could be serviced in Australia in the aftermath of Monte Bello and Maralinga – or in New Zealand, perhaps. But the Shackletons would have to traipse three quarters of the way round the world for major servicing in the UK and then back again; and it would take a Hastings AOG delivery ten days to come through on the Australia route and on via Fiji and Canton. What kind of a rapid supply route was that?

Then the flash of inspiration came. For God's sake! Oops! Very sorry, God! and in church too! Why *three* quarters of the way round? Why not *one* quarter, via Canada and Hawaii? The Americans had already shown a co-operative spirit in not quibbling over our using the disputed Christmas Island; there was a lot of USAF/RAF co-operation over war plans, training, etcetera, etcetera, and the 'special relationship' thing. Of *course* they would agree and Hickam Air Force Base – the military side of Honolulu International Airport – could provide all the services and sophisticated facilities we might need in the Pacific area without even noticing the extra work load.

Full of enthusiasm and forgetting where he was for a moment, he started up from his seat. Fortunately he caught the look of surprise and interrogation in the hazel eyes beside him and sheepishly sank back again on to the pew without upsetting the preacher's oratory or the attention of the congregation. Regrettably his mind was not on the rest of the service and he wasn't able to give a convincing reply to the 'What was all that about?' as they went out into the chilly open air, greeted a few friends and returned home.

How to fix it, though? Through the Ministry of Supply's Grapple Committee? – or through the RAF/USAF old chums net? Or both? Which brought him back to St Paul. Why stop at Verse 8? Verse 9 was equally apposite in dealing with a four-dimensional task force using at least four different languages, with an Anglo-American angle into the bargain.

7

The Navy Team

At eight o'clock next morning, letting himself out of the house to walk to the station for the 8.16 to town, he was first surprised and then delighted to find a black Super Snipe staff car waiting on the gravel driveway outside the front door. Beyond the car, the back of a sturdy figure in RAF blue, hands in pockets, service cap pushed back on his head, enjoying the fine view across the valley.

'Good morning, Corporal!'

The figure whirled round, hands out of pockets, pulled his cap straight, saluted and grinned.

'Sorry, sir. Didn't hear you coming. Corporal Beall, sir. I am to be your driver and this car is allotted to you.'

'Well, Corporal Beall, I'm glad to have you as my driver and certainly glad to have the staff car. Clever of you to find your way to my home. It *is* a nice view, isn't it? It's a bit of a waste, though, using the car to drive me from here to the Air Ministry, but we'll work out a more economical routine later. Let's be off to London now. I'll ride in front with you this morning and you can tell me about yourself.'

'Yes, sir' – opening the passenger door to see his new boss seated, then smartly round to his own driver's seat. The car moved off smoothly along the drive and into the main road.

'Now, Corporal Beall, this is going to be a pretty intense job, probably a lot of early and late work and certainly overseas for some months next year. Is that all right for you, from your domestic point of view? Are you married?'

41

'Yes, sir. I am married, but my wife has gone to stay with her mother while I get settled into this new job and I'd like to get some overseas service.'

So that was OK. The car was elderly, but in good condition. Corporal Beall was obviously a good driver and a cheerful fellow to have around. So far so good, this Monday morning, and they reached the Air Ministry in just over the hour. Good going, in rush hour traffic. After a call on Mrs Harris to pick up messages – and feeling a little conscience stricken in imposing an extra load of work on her – the TFC walked quickly across Whitehall to the Admiralty building for the first meeting on the Navy's part in the Grapple programme.

The newly appointed Navy Task Group Commander, Commodore Peter Gretton, was on the ball as always and had a messenger waiting at the entrance door of the courtyard entrance to conduct the TFC without delay to a small austere conference room. He greeted the Task Force Commander in his usual abrupt and direct manner.

'Good morning, Wilf. May I introduce the first few members of the Navy team? This is Captain Guy Western, who will be my chief of staff. This is Paymaster Lieutenant Commander Thatcher, who will look after the logistic planning; and this is Lieutenant Wallington-Smith who will be my secretary.

The TFC shook hands with each in turn and liked what he saw. Captain Western was of medium height but well built, a quiet unobtrusive manner, yet with a confident look about him which told that he knew his job and did not need to shout about it. Thatcher, quiet, amiable, confident but very courteous, looked to be a very reliable type. Wallington-Smith was a bubblingly exuberant young officer, very self-confident, bright and sharp, loquacious. Altogether a good team and obviously keen.

On the table were laid out a chart of the central Pacific, the map of Christmas Island seen in Frankie Lloyd's office and a similar one of Malden Island.

'Where would you like to sit, Wilf? – and would you like to

give us an outline of the operation as you see it so far?'

They grouped themselves informally round the table and the TFC gave a short account of what he had learned in the past week. He continued:

'It seems to me that the biggest problem at the moment is the very short time scale. To achieve the political aim of a successful test in May of next year, the whole – or at least most – of the Air Task Group must be in position at Christmas and ready to start the work-up phase by 1st February, I reckon. If you're interested in the reasons, I'll go through them with you at a later date, but let's work on that for the time being.

'This means that by the end of January we must have a brand new Class I runway and aircraft hard-stands ready for use, with extensive operational and technical facilities. This would normally be regarded as a two year job. We shall also have to create a weather-reporting network, which will mean detachments with heavy equipment on a number of widely dispersed islands and all their logistic support.

'At the same time the scientists will have a big requirement for specialised technical buildings and laboratories with the usual domestic facilities at Christmas and a hefty instrumentation set-up on Malden. To provide all this in a short time, the army engineers will have to have a vast amount of heavy plant, construction material of all kinds and a great deal of heavy motor transport, which also means a great deal of fuel. I don't know what all this is going to add up to, but I would guess at three thousand personnel ashore plus your own chaps on board and many thousands of tons of equipment and material to be put ashore. We obviously need to start work on site as quickly as possible – within two months, I reckon. I'm going to see the AWRE lot tomorrow and the sappers on Thursday. By then we should have more information. But now let's hear how you think we might get all this stuff and all the troops, ashore at Christmas and Malden, ready to start the construction programme.'

Guy Western came in, rather diffidently at first:

'Well, sir, I've had a quick look at such information as we have in the Admiralty about both Christmas and Malden. The first trouble about Christmas is that, at present, no sea-going vessel of any size can go alongside the small jetty – or what's left of it. During the war, the Americans dredged a channel good enough for fuel carriers and small cargo boats; but that has silted up and it would take us quite some time to get hold of a dredger, get it out there and clear the channel again. We might be able to hire that big Dutch dredger which operates out of Singapore, but it would take a long time to get it released from its present commitments, tow it to Christmas and then clear the channel. So it looks like barges or LCMs for unloading from cargo ships at anchor off the entrance to the lagoon and dumping the stuff ashore at this little port area at London,' indicating the place on the map. 'That's going to be a slow business, I'm afraid.'

The TFC turned to Commodore Gretton:

'Peter, in your visits round navy establishments in the States, did you come across some six-foot sided cubic steel tanks which could be bolted together to make a barge of any required size?'

'Yes, I did, and very useful they were. But I don't think we have any here.'

Lieutenant Commander Thatcher spoke up for the first time:

'Not in the Royal Navy, sir, but the army does, I think, as part of their sea transportation set-up.'

'Well, if we could lay hands on a couple of such barges, that would ease things considerably. Maybe we could even fit outboard motors and make them self-propelled. We'll contact the army about that.'

'Good. At the same time, could you see if there's any chance of getting some DUKWs – you know, the army's amphibious boats on wheels, used in follow-up assault landings and some river crossings during the war. They could deliver from ship direct to sites ashore and save a lot of time.'

'If there are any still around,' replied Gretton, 'they would certainly be very useful. We'll try.'

'OK. Let's wait and see what you can turn up. Now, once the sappers get there, there'll be the problem of feeding them and that of water supply. They'll presumably take their own tented accommodation and domestic facilities; but what do we do about supply by sea? – the total logistic support?'

Gretton rubbed his chin, thought for a moment and replied:

'We'll have to have a Royal Fleet Auxiliary ship – maybe more than one later on – to supply food and general stores as required, plus a water carrier, plus something better than forty gallon barrels for the large quantities of fuel needed. We *must* clear the channel as soon as possible so that we can at least get water and fuel barges alongside the jetty at London; so we must get a small dredger out there early on, which means a heavy lift ship and there are only a few in the world. Of course there'll have to be a troopship – or perhaps two – for the army engineers and if you want to put heavy equipment ashore at various islands we need an LST. We'd better get out a first draft of a complete shipping plan and then we can go through it at your next meeting.'

'That's fine, Peter. Could we do that today week, do you think?' Gretton looked enquiringly at Western and Thatcher, who nodded assent.

'Yes, I think so.'

'Could we then,' continued the TFC, 'take a first look at the operation itself and at possible requirements for ships during the actual tests? I haven't been to AWRE yet – I hope to go tomorrow, as I said – but I'm pretty sure that, from the Air Force point of view, this is going to be a very hairy exercise and we shall need everything possible in the way of belt and braces, both to minimise risks and to ensure accuracy in the drops.

'I need ground to air tracking radar and close radio control of all aircraft in the Malden area. The Valiant during the run-in to the drop must be accurately monitored and possibly be vectored on to the target. We shall need close control of the sampling Canberras and of the photographic aircraft in the area. We may also need rapid air transport from the Malden area to Christmas. So our first requirement is for an aircraft carrier. Is that possible?'

Gretton and Western looked at one another for a moment before replying.

'I'm not yet fully in the picture,' said Gretton, 'but I think it will be very difficult. We're not fulfilling our NATO commitments even as it is, I understand, and to take one of our operational carriers away for six months may not be acceptable.'

'We *could* get one out of reserve, sir,' ventured Captain Western.

'It would need a charge of dynamite behind the dockyard people to get it ready in time, but I think it might be done. Finding a full complement won't be easy either, with our present manpower shortages; but with the priority of this job we can probably manage it. Perhaps, sir, you could speak to the Controller* to start the ball rolling?'

Commodore Gretton nodded, 'Right, I'll do that today.'

'Assuming then that we get a carrier – as I profoundly hope we can – there is the question of aircraft. We shall need a flight of helicopters – Whirlwinds, I suppose? – for quick ship to shore transportation. They could also provide some of the Air/Sea Rescue cover at Christmas as well, which would help the RAF a lot. Could we get six aircraft and double-bank the crews to cover periods of intense effort? Secondly, we need air transport between Christmas and the carrier when in the Malden area; so could we find a small flight – say, four aircraft – of something rugged and reliable – Avengers, for instance?'

'We ought to be able to arrange that' replied Gretton, himself an air enthusiast and knowledgeable in such matters.

'That's good' said the TFC. 'And speaking of choppers, I have to sweat all the way to Devizes on Thursday to see the army engineers. Would there be any chance of one of yours picking me up at Northolt and taking me to Erlestoke Camp and back? It would save me a lot of time and would help to inject the proper inter-service spirit into the army team.'

---

* The Controller of the Navy, the Third Sea Lord.

Commodore Gretton turned to his new secretary:

'Wallington-Smith, will you ask FOFT* if he could do that for us, please. Time, Wilf?'

'08.00, if that is convenient to them. Can we now look at other requirements for ships? The scientists will need a technical control ship off Malden before and during the test. This might be the carrier, perhaps, but I suspect it may be better to use HMS *Narvik* when she gets back from Monte Bello.

'We shall need weather-reporting over quite a long period before each test to give the forecasters a general picture as well as data for detailed forecasts on test days. I reckon we need at least two ships for that. Also we shall need surface ship back-up to the air search for shipping in the danger area. Perhaps these tasks can be combined; but we shall have to talk to the Met people at Bracknell before we can make up our minds about that.'

'We'll put that in our list of requirements' responded Gretton.

'I've just been thinking,' intervened Captain Western in his quiet way: 'Presumably the carrier will have to spend quite long periods at Christmas – she can't be under way for months on end. That raises the question of an anchorage. From a quick look at the chart, she can't anchor just off-shore because there isn't sufficient depth of water; and if she goes further out, it's suddenly too deep for anchoring. Looks as though we shall have to lay a deep mooring, which will require a mooring ship; and there we shall be in more trouble. This is a job for a boom defence vessel, but ours are all coal-fired and don't have the range to get to Christmas Island. I don't know what else might be made available, but shall I find out, sir?'

Gretton, with an interrogative glance at the TFC, who nodded assent, replied: 'Yes. See if there's something like a salvage vessel which we might get and we'll try to have the answer by next Monday.'

The brain-storming session went on for another hour and

---

* Flag Officer Flying Training.

then broke up with agreement to meet again a week later. In the meantime, the TFC and the Naval Task Group Commander would meet as often as possible.

8

Looking for a home

Making his way back to the Air Ministry building, it was quite a shock to the TFC to realise that it was some minutes less than a week since the bombshell of the new job had landed in his lap, as the saying goes. It felt more like a century! However, nothing would be gained by missing lunch again and possibly catching a cold in this chilly February weather. So he went down to the staff canteen at the sub-ground level and queued up unobtrusively with all the worker bees for a quick sandwich and a cup of coffee. He caught sight of Corporal Beall in animated conversation at a table with several other uniformed drivers. So that was good – Beall was settling in all right. Then back up to Mrs Harris's office to find two more new members of the team waiting for him. A tall, slim, elegant figure with a badly burnt face – the disfigurement curiously giving him an air of distinction – introduced himself.

'I'm Squadron Leader Helfer, sir. I understand I am to be your ADC and Personal Staff Officer.'

Behind the courteous and correct manner, the eyes and face were keen and intelligent. Maurice Heath would have picked out a first class chap for this job and it looked good.

After a hand shake and words of welcome, the TFC turned to the second man, a quiet, unobtrusive, neatly dressed type, medium build, well-brushed curly hair, gold-rimmed spectacles – looked like a leading barrister's clerk.

'Flight Sergeant Kitchingman, sir. I understand I am to be

49

your secretary and run your Orderly Room – if that is the right name for it here.'

'Very glad to have you here, Flight Sergeant. There's not much to do at the moment, but there surely will be in a few days' time. Unfortunately we don't have an office yet, other than a quite incredible temporary arrangement; but I hope to have that fixed soon. Meanwhile, Mrs Harris here will very kindly help us out, but we must try not to be an impossible burden on her. So let's all go up to our temporary office and I'll give you some idea of your new job.' Which he did during the next hour or so.

This office problem was very serious and something had to be done.

Acting on yet another hunch, he went down to the fourth floor to see Group Captain Menaul again.

'Paddy – can you spare a minute?'

'Hello, sir – yes, sure – but only a minute' – pausing in the process of packing books, papers, documents, into a large cardboard carton.

'Did you tell me that you are moving down to Weston Zoyland to take charge of your Air Task Group?'

'Yes, indeed. That's why I'm packing up all this stuff to take with me. In fact I'm off tomorrow.'

'Does that mean that your office will be empty for a while?'

'Yes, of course. I don't expect to be back for six months.'

'Could I borrow the office for a week or so until I get fixed up properly?'

'Sure thing, sir. Help yourself. I'm leaving a lot of stuff locked up in the filing cabinets, but the table, chairs and telephone are all yours.'

'Bless you, Paddy. That's an immense help. I'll move two of my chaps in tomorrow, after you've gone; and I hope to visit you before you leave for Australia.'

They chatted on for a few moments and then, as Menaul obviously had a lot to do, the TFC returned to the Air Council Room to discuss the immediate future programme with his new embryo staff. Having emphasised the importance of security and the need to keep a very low profile on their new jobs, he turned to his ADC:

'Now, Helfer, I want you to collect, as unobtrusively as possible, all the information you can lay hands on about Christmas Island and all the other islands within about eight hundred miles radius. The Navigation people can probably help and Mrs Harris can put you on to the best chap to start with – Squadron Leader Attlee or Wing Commander Clare. Also, since this will be the only time when the RAF can get some first-hand experience of these dreadful weapons which will be the core of our national defence policy for years to come, I want as full a record as possible of the whole operation. I think we should make a film of it. So see if you can find a service film unit to make a photographic record of everything we do, starting now. I believe there's an outfit called the Army Kinema Corporation – you could begin there.'

Thinking it was time to keep up the pressure for proper office accommodation, the TFC went along to see Deputy Secretary II again and told Humphries-Davies about the Menaul deal.

'I can add to that' responded Dep Sec II with a smile. 'I've been enquiring about who may be on leave or away for any other reason and there's another room close to Menaul's which you can have for a couple of weeks. Maybe one more at the end of this week. We're still looking to see what better arrangement we can make for you.'

This was good news indeed, even if only temporary, and he went back to fix appointments for visits to the scientists and the army; then to clear the Air Council Room of all evidence of unlawful occupation, ready for the morrow.

51

9

An introduction to Aldermaston

Promptly at eight o'clock the following morning, there was Corporal Beall outside the TFC's house with the shiny black staff car and a grin of satisfaction as he whipped the black leather covers off the front and rear air force blue plates, each with two shining silver stars, and – slipping off the protective sleeve – unfurled the Air Vice Marshal's pennant on the stubby little mast fixed on the front of the bonnet. It was hard not to feel a small thrill of satisfaction at such signs of VIP-dom, no matter how temporary.

'Good morning, Corporal Beall. I see you've been at work. Very nice too!'

'Good morning, sir. Thank you. I understand we're in a hurry about everything in this new job, so I – er – borrowed a few things to save time.'

'OK. Nice work. But make it legal as soon as you can. Meanwhile, we're off to Aldermaston, near Newbury. The A 404 at the top of the drive will take us nearly all the way, so let's get cracking.'

Soon after nine o'clock they pulled up at the entrance gate of the Atomic Weapons Research Establishment – an unimpressive collection of low red-brick buildings and workshops, surrounded by a high security fence. The barrier was down, blocking the further movement of the car, and a stern-faced security guard in police uniform came round to the passenger's window.

'Good morning, sir. Can I help you?'

'Good morning. I have an appointment with the Director at 9.15.'

'Yes, sir. Would you please come into the guardroom and sign the visitors' book?'

The TFC went into the sparsely furnished room, typical of its kind, signed the book and offered his RAF Form 1250 identification card for inspection by the sergeant behind the desk. The sergeant studied it carefully and made a telephone call, after which his severe demeanour changed to a smile of welcome.

'Yes, sir. Sir William is expecting you. Please go ahead to the main building over there – that's the main entrance at the front, facing this way. A guide will meet you there and your driver can go round to the MT section where someone will look after him.'

'Thank you, sergeant.'

The barrier was raised and Corporal Beall, looking very dignified for a change, drove at a sedate and stately speed to the head office entrance where he decanted his passenger.

A uniformed messenger was waiting and led the visitor up to the Director's office on the first floor, knocked and showed him in. A squarely built, homely figure, came across the room to meet him, extending a hand for a firm handshake and said:

'I'm Bill Penney. Glad to see you.'

'I'm Wilf Oulton, Sir William. Thank you for seeing me at such short notice and I'm sure you know why I've come.'

Sir William Penney, one of the finest brains in the world, and an original member of Oppenheimer's Manhatten Project team at Los Alamos, looked more like a prosperous tenant farmer than an eminent scientist and Fellow of the Royal Society. Very casually dressed, somewhat untidy in appearance, rather tousled hair, middle height but broad in the shoulder and beam, altogether a very amiable-looking chap with eyes twinkling cheerfully behind horn-rimmed glasses. But despite the friendly and informal welcome, the fledgling Task Force Commander felt himself unwontedly in considerable awe of this great man and all too much like a junior schoolboy being interviewed by the headmaster.

Penney turned to a third person in the room and made the introduction: 'This is Bill Cook, my deputy, who is going to be the scientific director for Grapple and I think it will be best if you deal entirely with him on that job. I'm going out to Australia soon to run the Mosaic and Buffalo tests myself – I expect you know all about them and that they are essential steps before Grapple – and I reckon we both have our hands pretty full.'

The TFC turned to Cook and shook hands.

'Hello, Bill. I'm Wilf to my friends, and I hope that will include you.'

'I'm sure it will, Wilf.'

Bill Cook, a brilliant mathematician but much more famous for his widely known reputation as a first class scientific administrator and former head of the Royal Navy Scientific Service, was in some ways quite the antithesis of the ebullient Bill Penney. Very neat and well-organised in his personal appearance, wearing a well-tailored light tweed suit, highly polished shoes, fresh-faced with sandy hair, slightly receding and firmly brushed back in a conventional 'short back and sides' style. He was of medium build, carrying himself with quiet and confident dignity and easily passing for much less than his fifty years. But his affable manner barely concealed a ruthless and determined character, normally only evidenced by the coolly appraising look in his eyes. He certainly looked like a sound colleague for this Christmas Island affair.

The TFC turned back to face the Director.

'Well, Sir William, I suppose I'd better go off into a huddle with Bill Cook; but could you first of all tell me, please, what you hope to achieve in the Grapple tests?'

'Yes. Sure. As you probably know, we've already established our own capability, without any help from the Americans, to utilise atomic fission to make a so-called kiloton weapon. We're going to take this further with the tests at Monte Bello and – later this year – at Maralinga, including the first air-drop of a device – you couldn't really call it a bomb, although it will be in a bomb-case. But the real thing is to produce a fusion device as the basis for a so-called megaton bomb and here we shall be exploring an area which is unknown as far as we are concerned. We *think* we've got the right ideas – several of them – but we won't know until we test them and see if they work at all, and, if so, how well. Hence Grapple, to prove our theories.'

'What sort of yield do you *think* you are going to get?'

'God knows! Might not work at all, although I obviously think it will. Might be a fizzle of a hundred kilotons or might be ten megatons or more. We're aiming for something about one megaton, but we'll just have to wait and see how it works out. Also, it's not enough just to make a big bang with a few pounds of plut*. We want to know exactly what happens in the process and that will need a lot of instrumentation, recording of results, collection of samples from the cloud and analysis back here at Aldermaston.

'By the way,' continued Penney, 'I know we have a naval chap running the Monte Bello operation and I'll be off there very soon. Are you going to run the Maralinga show and shall I see you there?'

'No. I haven't been asked to run Maralinga and I don't see how it would be possible anyway. I've got my hands more than full with the Christmas Island bit; but, yes, I would like to come to Maralinga to see the air drop at least.'

'Then who *will* be running it?' queried Penney.

'I don't know,' replied the TFC. 'But I suggest that a sensible idea would be to have Air Commodore Weir run it. He'll be in charge of all the RAF side of things at Christmas Island, using the same Canberra aircraft that you'll have at Maralinga and it would provide useful continuity.'

'Would that be "Ginger" Weir?' asked Penney.

'Yes. Do you know him? He's a very good chap.'

'Yes. I've met him before. That's fine by me. Can you fix it?'

So with that agreed upon and with thanks for the meeting and briefing, the TFC went off with Cook to his office along the

---

* Plutonium.

corridor, where they were cheered by a good cup of coffee. Cook lit up the pipe, which was seldom out of his hand or mouth, and they settled down to discuss things in more detail.

The scientific Director of the Grapple tests and the Task Force Commander took to one another immediately and it was obviously going to be a good working relationship.

'First of all, Bill,' began the TFC, 'Will you please tell me in more detail just what you want us to do to meet your scientific requirements?'

Cook relit his pipe and puffed composedly for a few moments.

'Sure! The main requirement is to deliver the bomb – that is to say, the experimental apparatus fitted up inside a ten-thousand pound bomb-case – to an exact point in space eight thousand feet off the south-east corner of Malden Island at a height of eight thousand feet above sea level and at a time within a few seconds of when we are expecting it. The eight thousand feet altitude we will manage ourselves, with the help of RAE, with a barometric fuse in the bomb. That should be OK for less than a couple of hundred feet either way. How about accuracy in plan?'

'What's your requirement?'

'We need it within three hundred yards of the designated point.'

The TFC thought for a moment before replying.

'Normally a good Bomber Command crew in practice would reckon to do that with some certainty. We'll back it up with radar monitoring and, I think, with Decca Navigator equipment in the aircraft. I reckon we shall be OK.'

'Next,' went on Cook, 'we shall need to know that each of several steps in the process of arming and releasing the bomb has been correctly effected. That means telemetry transmitters in the aircraft and bomb, and receivers in the scientific control – presumably in a ship.'

The TFC silently nodded 'his acknowledgement.

'Then we need banks of instrumentation equipment of various kinds installed in protected shelters on the ground at

Malden and focused on the point of burst. This will include very high speed photography, radiation meters and so on and we shall need to have access to these shortly before the drop and very soon after, and also to be able to switch them on by remote control just before the drop. We'd like to have these records back at Christmas Island very quickly. Similarly, we need to have observations made with special equipment at sites up to a thousand miles from the explosion in as many directions as may be practicable – whatever you have in the way of suitable islands. Next, we need samples of the composition of the cloud taken at various levels as soon as possible after the burst, presumably by the same – or similar – Canberras with filter and radiation monitoring equipment that we shall use at Monte Bello and Maralinga. But in this case we want to have those samples back here at Aldermaston not more than twenty-four hours after the burst.'

'Ouch!' murmured the TFC. 'That's a rough one! But we'll see what we can do.'

'To comply with the Government's mandatory safety requirement,' Cook went on, 'we need accurate upper air wind forecasts over a wide area so that we can estimate the pattern of possible fall-out, either from just the bomb itself if all goes well or from a lot more if things go wrong. Also there will have to be extensive measures to protect our own people from any possible radiation hazard, plus decontamination facilities for personnel and equipment which have necessarily been so exposed – such as the sampling Canberras and their crews. Will that do for a start?'

'Right!' replied the TFC, 'I've got all that. Now let's look at a few of the operational problems. What are the risks to the aircraft and crew who will drop the bomb?'

Cook knocked the dottle out of his pipe, refilled and relit it before answering:

'As far as radiation is concerned, there's no problem, since we assume the aircraft will be at a fairly high level – forty to forty-five thousand feet – and the significant radiation won't have any effect beyond eight thousand feet. But the heat flash and the overpressure from the blast may be serious.

'The heat flash could cause a significant rise in the temperature of the metal skin of the aircraft; and as we understand that the construction of the Valiant includes a lot of metal-to-metal bonding by the Redux process, this might come unstuck if the temperature rise were sufficient.

'Then, not knowing what the yield will be, we don't know what effect the blast will have on the structural integrity of the aircraft. To cope with these risks, we've asked F E Jones at Farnborough to compute the best escape manoeuvre to put the greatest possible distance between the aircraft and the bomb at the moment of burst.'

There were some seconds of silence while the TFC contemplated this unpleasant information, which he had in fact half expected.

'Could the effect of the heat flash be reduced by painting the aircraft with some reflective kind of paint – perhaps brilliant white – instead of the usual dull grey-blue-white camouflage?' he asked.

'Yes, indeed. That could make a significant difference. We'll look into it.'

'As to the escape manoeuvre, Bill – I like the phrase! – I'll go to see F E Jones and find out what ideas he has so far. We can't eliminate all risk, but we must keep it to an acceptable minimum. What else have we got?'

'Well, the bomb itself. There's a limit to what we can do in the very short time available and in no way can these devices which we are going to test be regarded as operational weapons. There will be no normal weaponry safety system and once they are assembled we don't want to have to dismantle them again.'

'Which to me,' responded the TFC, 'means that we don't want to land them back at Christmas in case of a malfunction in either the bomb or our operational procedure. So we'll have to be damn' sure that everything is OK before starting a live drop sortie.'

'Yes, indeed!' affirmed Cook emphatically.

'About how many people do you think you will have at Christmas and Malden and how long before a test will they need to be there?'

'There'll be about a hundred chaps in all, I would guess, organised into three main divisions – services groups, weapons groups and measurements groups – you'll meet the chief people later on at lunch. I would guess it will take about two to three months to get everything set up.'

'And will you require frequent access to Malden during that period?'

'Oh, yes. There'll have to be quite a lot of coming and going.'

'In that case,' decided TFC, 'we'll certainly need an airstrip on Malden and suitable aircraft for a shuttle service – Dakotas if we can get them. That brings me to the domestic point that living conditions at Christmas and particularly at Malden are going to be pretty rough. The troops, of course, are supposed to be used to it – which "ain't necessarily so" as the song has it; but it's certainly going to be hard on your chaps, who may always have worked in a fairly civilised environment. However, we'll do the best we can.'

Discussion ranged on for another hour and then Cook said:

'Let's go and have a drink before lunch and you can meet some of the leaders in my team.'

'Fine. But before we go, Bill, there's one thing I must have absolutely clear. There are some high risks in this operation and certainly if anything goes wrong, we must have instant decisions, accepted without argument. So it must be understood that I am in absolute command of everything and everybody in the Christmas Island area – including your chaps, but operating through you, of course. Is that acceptable and agreed?'

Cook puffed at his pipe and looked hard and appraisingly at the Task Force Commander for several seconds, then replied:

'Yes, Wilf. You're the boss. That's agreed.'

That's OK then,' he acknowledged composedly and with no sign of anxiety; but inwardly he breathed a sigh of relief at having got over that hurdle without any need to go back to the Minister of Supply or the Chiefs of Staff for support. Relations between scientific staff and service personnel had not always been happy and it was going to be essential to have good, harmonious teamwork throughout the Task Force to bring Operation Grapple to a successful conclusion. He went on to voice this thought to Cook.

'Bill, I deem it essential to have complete understanding and co-operation between your chaps and the uniformed people. Will it be OK with you if I come down to AWRE every week, bringing with me Commodore Peter Gretton – he is the head sailor and my deputy – plus a variety of the service planning staff, so that we can develop together our plans in detail as the problems unfold?'

'Of course, Wilf. That's a very good idea. When would you like to come?'

'I think Tuesdays would be very suitable for us. How about you?'

'Tuesdays will be fine. Starting next week?'

'Yes, please.'

'OK. So now let's go and have a noggin and meet some of the staff.'

Off they went then to the staff dining room, where a number of the scientific and administrative staff were assembled over a sherry, pink gin or beer before lunch. Introductions were effected. Retired Rear Admiral Pat Brooking, a tall, gaunt, immaculately turned-out man was the Administrator of the Establishment. Charles Adams, a big, heavily built amiable scientist, would be deputy to Cook. John Challens, tall, lean, saturnine of face with a sharp dry wit and a keen sense of humour, was to be in charge of the work on Christmas Island itself. Ken Bomford – so this was the Mr Bomford whom ACAS (Ops) had thought was to be in charge of Operation Grapple! – turned out to be a very pleasant and cordial youngish man, tall, lightly built, dark curly hair, pale features, very earnest about everything. He was to be in charge at Malden

Island and in control of scientific events in the forward area. There were several others too, but this was more than enough for the TFC to take in at this first meeting.

The conversation was kept on a fairly light level – it was sufficient at this stage just to make contact. So after a quick lunch, and confirming arrangements for a working meeting the following Tuesday, Corporal Beall was summoned and the TFC was on his way back to Whitehall.

10

The Sappers

At five minutes to eight on a drizzling, grey morning, the staff car – flaunting its pennant and two-star plates – pulled up at the barrier at the entrance to the Royal Air Force aerodrome at Northolt, on the western outskirts of London. After a quick check at the guard-room the RAF sentry raised the barrier, saluted, and waved them on to the VIP departure lounge.

Squadron Leader Helfer, wearing his gold aiguillettes on the shoulder of his uniform tunic for the first time, and accompanied by the Northolt duty officer, was waiting for the Task Force Commander.

'Good morning, sir. Your aircraft is ready,' and the Duty Officer led the way across a few yards of the tarmac apron to the Royal Navy 'Whirlwind' helicopter. The engine was running and the main rotor turning slowly, the pilot already strapped in his right hand seat in the cockpit.

The TFC and his aide climbed aboard into the very noisy interior of the cabin and the pilot turned and gestured interrogatively to the TFC, inviting him in aviation language to take the left hand co-pilot's seat. With a smile and a nod in acknowledgement and thanks, the TFC did so, fastening the seat-belt and donning the proffered headphones and microphone.

'Good morning, sir. OK?'

The TFC held up a thumb in the conventional signal.

'It's a bit murky, sir, and we have to go VFR* because these Whirlwinds are not yet cleared for IFR**, but I think we can make it. The weather should improve as we go westward. Are you ready for take-off sir?'

Once again the thumbs up sign and after a radio request for take-off clearance and approval by the control tower, the chopper took off at 08.00 on the dot and headed westward.

There was some neat contour flying in the reduced visibility in moderate rain squalls for a time, but as they passed a little north of Newbury, the low cloud broke up and the day became fair and clear, although still with a grey overcast. At nine o'clock, exactly on time, they touched down gently on the helicopter pad in the Army Erlestoke Camp, near Devizes.

A small reception party was waiting for them and the TFC, after words of thanks to the pilot – a cheerful young lieutenant, Royal Navy – put on his cap, moved quickly to the now open door and jumped to the ground. Bent double to keep well below the still rotating blades, and followed by his aide, he walked clear of the aircraft. To his delight he saw that the reception committee was headed by Brigadier Craddock, an old friend and fellow-student at the Imperial Defence College two years previously.

'Hello, Dick! How nice to see you again! Very good of you to come to meet me.'

'Hello, Wilf. Glad to see you too. Can't have you mixed-up types dropping in on a pure and innocent army unit without a careful check! So I thought I'd better come and keep an eye on things! Besides, I'm bursting with curiosity as to what you are up to! May I introduce Lieutenant-Colonel John Woollett, who is to be in command of the Sappers for this job of yours?'

Colonel Woollett stepped forward, a very correct military salute, a strong handshake and a warm smile of welcome for the TFC. A tall, strongly-built man, very erect bearing, ruddy faced

---

* VFR – in visual contact with the ground at all times
** IFR – flying by instruments without sight of the ground

with a heavy dark moustache, wearing working army uniform, he looked typical of that special breed of men in the British Army, the Royal Engineers, always referred to informally as 'the Sappers'.

'Good morning, sir. We're very pleased that you could come to see us so soon. Things are a bit rough and ready round here, but it suffices very well for the job. I'd like to take you first of all to our planning room where you can meet some of my officers and inspect the sand model. It's not very far to walk if you don't mind.'

'Thanks, John. That will suit me very well. I'll be glad to stretch my legs after that bone-shaker,' gesturing towards the helicopter.

'May I introduce my ADC – Squadron Leader Helfer – and could someone look after the helicopter pilot, please?'

As the little group walked some short distance to the clutch of war-time huts which served as Colonel Woollett's HQ, he explained that this was a temporary camp used by the US Army in World War II and which had been re-activated to house the 28th Field Engineer Regiment of the Royal Engineers on their return from Korea, where they had formed part of the British Commonwealth Division in the United Nations forces. They had temporarily left behind 55 Field Engineer Squadron, and a Field Park Squadron, to support the remaining British Army in Korea, whilst the main body of the regiment had settled into Erlestoke and the not very exciting job of providing the 'sapper' element of the First Division. Fifty-five Squadron were due to return and join them in a couple of months.

Meanwhile, in January, Woollett had been sent for by his ultimate boss, the Engineer-in-Chief in the War Office, and had been told that he and his regiment were to construct an airfield and provide all ancillary services on a Pacific island, as part of a top-secret operation. They had acquired sufficient information to start some planning and had just completed a sand model of Christmas Island, based on the RAF photographic survey, to enable them to study some of the problems involved. He carefully did not ask any questions, but was obviously bursting to know more.

Woollett led the way into what had been an underground operations room, the centre of which was now occupied by a large table, about ten feet square, on which rested a beautifully made model of Christmas Island, complete with clumps of green waving coconut palms, beige scrubby bush, glistening white coral sands, blue lagoons and all. But no child's plaything. The Sapper team must have moved very fast indeed to make this accurate and very detailed model in such a short time and this was to be typical of their speed and efficiency in the months to follow.

At a sign from the CO, a sergeant offered the TFC and others of the group large mugs of strong, steaming, sweet tea – an army speciality slangily known as 'gunfire' – very welcome on this raw morning and something one could always be sure of on visiting any sapper unit. Meanwhile Colonel Woollett introduced Major Tom Marquis, his second in command who also commanded one of the squadrons, and several other officers. He then turned and asked: 'Could you please give us an outline of the whole operation – or at any rate, as much as you are able to, sir, and tell us what you want us to do; then we could show you how far we've got in our planning.'

The TFC agreed and gave a summary of the Grapple operation as far as could be seen at that time. He then went on: 'The key date, I think, is that the new main runway and the technical support buildings and other facilities, such as the bulk fuel installation, must be ready for the RAF Valiants and the Canberra squadrons to move in and start operating on March 1st next year. They cannot use the existing coral airstrip, although the Shackletons and Hastings – and of course the Dakotas – can do so for the time being. Furthermore, this cannot be any makeshift runway. It must be to Class I standard, with an LCN of 35 and at least two thousand yards long. I expect you already have the detailed specification – if not, we'll get it for you – but for instance the surface level must be correct to within about one inch overall. You will understand the reason for this when I tell you that the devices which we are going to test will not have the normal safety arrangements incorporated in standard RAF weapons, because there just isn't the time available to develop them to that stage. So we simply cannot afford to neglect any detail which could possibly cause an accident on take-off, or even in taxiing to and from dispersals and the weapon assembly area. You can imagine the possible consequences of such an accident.

'Another key factor is that I'm pretty sure we must have an airstrip on Malden Island capable of taking Dakota aircraft or something similar. One thousand yards will do, of the type you have probably provided in Korea and elsewhere. We need to have that in use by February 1st, to provide for all the coming and going by the scientists and for the logistic support of your own men setting up a very large and complex instrument base.

'There are other vital requirements, of course, and I'm afraid more will turn up as we uncover unexpected problems. So we'll need to have regular planning meetings with your staff, the Navy, the Air Force and the scientists, to keep you up to date with requirements as they change. It would be a great help if I could have one of your officers resident at Grapple HQ in London as a day-to-day liaison officer.'

'Yes, sir. That seems a very sound idea. I'll fix that.' replied Woollett in his precise and emphatic manner.

'Good. Now, in view of what I've sketched, what's the position as far as you sappers are concerned?'

'Firstly, sir, the time-scale is very tight and I think we could save some time by sending 55 Field Squadron and some supporting units direct from Korea to Christmas Island – except possibly for a few compassionate cases. They could get cracking building a camp in the port area ready for the main force to move in and start work without delay. Of course, they have as yet no idea that they will not be coming home on leave and I think it would be sensible and prudent to go to Korea to break the news and sell them the idea that it would be fun to try out the charms of a coral island!'

'That sounds good; and I suppose, the sooner the better?'

'Yes, sir.'

'Helfer,' said the TFC turning to his aide, 'will you please see that the necessary air transportation arrangements are made immediately to suite Colonel Woollett?'

'Yes, sir.'

'Next,' continued the Colonel, 'the runway, taxiways and dispersals are going to need vast quantities of concrete of the right quality. To begin our detailed estimating we need to know the composition of the coral which we shall crush to use as aggregate. I had understood that samples had been picked up by a survey ship and flown back to UK; but we've seen no sign of them and we need them urgently.'

'We'll chase that,' said the TFC with a look at Helfer, who made another note.

'For the tasks which you have outlined, sir,' continued Woollett, 'I think we have enough manpower in the regiment once it is brought back up to full strength as planned; but we are going to need a great deal more heavy plant for runway construction, road building, excavation of footings and so on. We'll do our sums as quickly as possible and put in requisitions; but I doubt whether there is enough, and it would take months to get it out of industry. This could be a very difficult problem. Next point: from what we've learnt in the past few days, there is very little fresh water on Christmas Island. We shall have to build a large distillation plant to provide fresh water for domestic use and rather less than fresh for construction work. Incidentally, such a plant will consume enormous quantities of diesel oil. Until this water supply is working, we shall have to rely on the Navy to ship in fresh water or help with distillation facilities on board ship.

'Now as to the programme in general' – Woollett turned to point to the sand model with the cane which he habitually carried – 'our first job is to get the workforce ashore and established in a tented camp here at Port London, so called. As I'm sure you know, sir, that means not only sleeping accommodation but also cook-houses, feeding arrangements, sanitary and washing facilities and everything else necessary to enable the men to work a twelve hour day, six days a week. I expect you know that for some years there was a modest cultivation of copra by an Anglo-French company, which had a small jetty here for loading the copra, and a small establishment here at Paris on the other side of the lagoon for collecting the nuts. The Americans improved the jetty and dredged a channel during the war, not adequate for our use but it will have to do for a start. As soon as we have the troops reasonably settled in the Port Camp, we can improve the jetty and start the work on the airfield and the main camp. About how many people do you think we shall have ashore, sir?'

'We haven't got the RAF and scientific establishment figures yet,' replied the TFC, 'but at a rough guess I'd say about three thousand ashore plus about a thousand in ships who will need to come ashore sometimes.'

'Will tented accommodation be acceptable?'

'The scientists won't like it and some of our more tender chaps, perhaps, but it will have to do as far as sleeping and personal kit are concerned; but I hope we can have decent semi-permanent messes and recreation rooms and kitchens. Many people will be there for a year or more, working flat out, and we must make life tolerable for them. Where do you propose to put the main camp and the operations centre, admin offices and laboratories?'

'Well, sir, here's the existing airstrip – which we can improve a bit. Subject to checking on the ground when we get there, I think we should put the new runway and aircraft park about here – up-wind of the old strip, with the main camp in this fairly open area near the sea and a mile downwind of the old strip, and then the ops centre, offices and laboratories half-way between the main camp and the port area. So it will all be laid out along the north coast, which is the only decent stretch of firm and level land as far as we can see. But a factor that worries me, sir, is that all of that area is only a couple of feet above sea level. If we get one of those tsunami tidal waves from ocean-bed volcanic activity it could wash the whole lot away. It's a risk, and I don't know what the likelihood is of such an event; but I don't see what else we can do.'

'I've not heard of tsunami before,' responded the TFC, 'but of course I've heard of the submarine eruptions. I believe there's a research outfit in California working on this problem – I think it's called the Scripps Institute of Oceanology or something like that. We'll try to get an opinion from them.' Another look at Helfer, who acknowledged. 'Meanwhile, we must go ahead with the plan as you have outlined it. Now, back to the airfield. We must have regular communication by aircraft with Honolulu as quickly as possible after your arrival there; and while the Coastal Command Shackletons will cheerfully make their way into almost any airstrip, with or without facilities, Transport Command are very firm about having their minimum requirements met before they will allow a Hastings to go in. So would you please arrange to set up very early something which can be called an "Air Traffic Control Tower" – a twenty foot square wooden hut with windows all round to give 360 degrees of view and up on stilts, which will also provide covered storage for airfield equipment. They will also need telephone communication with the port area as soon as possible, so that will bring in your army Air Formation Signals people, I suppose? But all of this and many other points will firm up as the detailed planning proceeds. The AWRE scientists also will have some hefty requirements for construction work, both at Christmas and at Malden – and possibly on other islands within a thousand miles. I could make a guess at what these might be, but it would be better if you yourself could go and see them as soon as possible, John – before you go to Korea.'

'Yes, sir, I'll do that.'

The discussion then broadened out to include the other members of the group round the sand model and went on for another two hours, covering (but only in outline) the many requirements of the Sappers in getting going on their mammoth task and the interlocking needs of and demands on the Navy and Air Force in supporting them during the constructional phase of Operation Grapple.

Soon after one o'clock they broke up the meeting and walked round to the austere wooden building in which 28 Field Regiment now had their officers' mess. A quick sherry, a good but simple meal and then back to the helicopter. The pilot had been warned and was ready to start up. Quick thanks and goodbyes all round and a few minutes later the TFC and his aide were on their way back to Northolt. A clear cold grey February afternoon with no flying problems.

Corporal Beall wasted no time in getting them back to Whitehall. The homeward rush westward along Western Avenue from the city had begun, but eastbound traffic was still fairly light and they were back in their makeshift office by half-past four.

Good news was waiting from the office of the Air Ministry Deputy Secretary (II) that they had solved the accommodation problem, at least for some time ahead. During World War II the block of houses comprising Richmond Terrace in Whitehall Gardens had been requisitioned and served as part of the Air Ministry. Application for restitution now having been made by the owners of the property, it was soon to be de-requisitioned and was empty awaiting conclusion of negotiations. Meanwhile it could be used as headquarters for Task Force Grapple, at least for several months.

This was excellent and the tiny nucleus staff immediately began preparations to move in at the beginning of the following week. Rooms were allocated to the various sections of the Grapple staff, as far as could be estimated at that moment; furniture was requisitioned, scrounged or borrowed, an old friend in the Post Office was beguiled into laying on a special effort to get the telephones re-connected and Task Force Grapple was really underway at last. About time too, in view of

the problems which began to fly in like a never-ending shower of
brick-bats.

11

The Grapple Committee – or 'Too many cooks'

This Friday morning was to be the first full meeting of the Grapple Executive Committee, which had its origin in the deliberations over some years of the Defence Research Policy Committee, a body which reported directly to the Prime Minister of the day. The DRPC had recommended and had received the approval of successive Prime Ministers, that Britain should develop its own atomic weapons. They had later gone on to recommend and had received approval for the development of a 'Megaton' fusion bomb. In doing so, the DRPC had noted that 'a very large effort by the Royal Navy and the Royal Air Force would be required to mount this trial'.

Preliminary work on outline planning had been done during 1955 both at Government level and at AWRE. Then, in view of an imminent international ban on further testing of nuclear weapons, it had become necessary to accelerate the programme. So the Ministry of Supply, the Admiralty, the War Office and the Air Ministry had been told to get on with the job, now code-named 'Operation Grapple'.

In due course, a formal directive to the Task Force Commander was prepared and was approved, at their meeting on 21st February 1956, by the Chiefs of Staff Committee, comprising the Heads of the Navy, Army and Air Force under the chairmanship of Marshal of the Royal Air Force Sir William Dickson, himself interestingly enough a direct descendant of Admiral Horatio Nelson.

This directive laid down the chain of command for the

Grapple trial. It said:

'1. On the authority of the Prime Minister, responsibility for the planning and execution of Operation Grapple has been placed, at Ministerial level, with the Minister of Supply. This responsibility is discharged on his behalf by the Atomic Trials Executive, of which the chairman is the Controller of Atomic Weapons in the Ministry of Supply.
2. With the approval of the UK Chiefs of Staff, you have been appointed to command the Operation as a whole in accordance with the policy laid down by the Atomic Weapons Trials Executive.
3. You will be assisted in the discharge of your duties by a staff comprised of representatives of the three Services and of the Atomic Weapons Research Establishment.
4. You will be responsible to the Controller of Atomic Weapons for the planning and execution of the operation as a whole and for co-ordination of all agencies taking part.
5. The Chiefs of Staff have decided that you will be in operational command of all forces taking part in the operation.
6. Subject to your responsibilities as above, you will conduct the operation to meet the technical requirements of the Scientific Director.
7. You will plan the operation in as economical a manner as practicable and subject to financial authority by the Ministry of Supply. An administrative officer from the Ministry of Supply will be attached to your senior planning staff to assist you.'

Early in January the Admiralty had offered to provide a Task Force Commander, basing their suggestion on the Royal Navy's management of the previous ground-based test at Monte Bello

73

and on the preparations then in hand for the next 'Mosaic' test at the same location under the command of Commodore Hugh Martell RN. Rear Admiral Edden had been provisionally warned for the appointment. On further consideration, however, the Chiefs of Staff had recognised that as the bomb would be dropped from a Royal Air Force Valiant and the cloud-sampling and the massive reconnaissance and air transport programmes would be carried out by RAF aircraft, the critical test phase of Grapple would be primarily an air operation. It was therefore more appropriate that an Air Officer be appointed as Task Force Commander and this had now been done.

So now the Task Force Commander made his way to Castlewood House, the operating headquarters of the Ministry of Supply, located between St Giles' Circus and New Oxford Street, where the members of the Grapple Committee were assembling in one of the gloomy, dingy conference rooms. Promptly at one minute to eleven the chairman, accompanied by his secretary, marched in smartly to the head of the table where Eric Jackson and Frankie Lloyd were standing chatting. General Sir Frederick Morgan, now Controller of Atomic Weapons in the Ministry, had won a great reputation as a logistic planner and administrator during the invasion of Normandy twelve years previously and, from the cut of his jib, could be expected to keep this mob under control.

The Task Force Commander, entering unobtrusively, glanced round the crowd and quickly wended his way through to introduce himself to the chairman and then exchanged greetings with Jackson and Lloyd. The General looked at his wrist-watch and remarked: 'Time to start.' Three quick bangs on the table and then:

'Please be seated, ladies and gentlemen. Air Marshal, would you like to sit here next to Jackson, so that I can have my secretary to my left hand?'

As the shuffling subsided, he looked round the table and continued:

'We are here to see that all necessary resources and facilities

74

are provided – as far as is humanly possible – to support Operation Grapple. May I remind you all of the current Top Secret Atomic security classification of this project. Firstly, I would like to introduce the Task Force Commander, who has just been appointed. Air Vice Marshal Oulton. Secondly, so that he knows who you are and what you do, would you please state your names and departments, going round the table, starting with you' – pointing to a portly, ruddy-faced man on his left. 'Brigadier Jehu – Publicity and Public Relations for the Ministry of Supply.' 'Miss Brown – Foreign Office' – a pleasant looking quiet young woman in a brown woollen pullover and tweed skirt. 'Wright – Foreign Office' – a cheerful looking, slightly tousled extrovert, horn rimmed glasses, friendly smile. 'Allen – Commonwealth Office' . . . and so on round the table.

'Next,' continued the chairman, 'would you please tell us, Air Marshal, how far have you been able to get with your planning in the few days you've had so far and are there any immediate problems with which we can help?'

'Detailed planning has not started yet,' replied the TFC, 'because I don't get either staff or adequate office accommodation until Monday. But no time has been wasted and I am in working contact with the three Service ministries and AWRE. Broadly, we should be able to start construction at Christmas Island in June, likewise at Malden in September, move in the Valiant and Canberra aircraft to start the operational working-up phase on March 1st and, with a lot of good luck, make the first live drop early in May of next year. But that all depends on the Navy, Army and Air Force producing the equipment and forces for which I've asked. Only time will tell whether or not that happens.

'I would, however, be grateful, General, for help on two immediate matters. Firstly, I understand that some weeks ago a New Zealand survey ship collected samples of soil from the proposed new airfield site at Christmas. The Sappers need these samples urgently in order to calculate their requirements for cement, bitumen, etcetera and we have no idea where the samples are now. Could the Commonwealth Office and the Ministry of Supply Mission in Australia make enquiries and speed up delivery, please?'

'We'll have that looked into right away,' replied the chairman. 'Your second point?'

'It is quite clear to me,' continued the TFC, 'that it would be very difficult to support the intense operational air effort at Christmas going east-about via Singapore and Australia. Furthermore by that route it is quite impossible to meet AWRE's requirement to have samples and records back at Aldermaston within twenty-four hours of a test. So I need clearance to route my aircraft to and from Christmas Island via Canada, California, Hawaii, and to position ground handling parties at the several staging posts – probably Goose Bay in Labrador, Winnipeg or Edmonton, Vancouver, San Francisco and Hawaii. In the ordinary way, there is no difficulty in getting clearance for RAF aircraft to stage through such places; but in view of some of the special loads to be carried and the need to have handling parties resident for a year or more at the staging posts, perhaps it ought to be cleared on the Foreign Office/Commonwealth Office/State Department/Canadian External Affairs net. Could Mr Wright and Mr Allen advise us?'

The chairman looked at the Foreign and Commonwealth representatives and asked:

'What do you think?'

Willie Wright replied first.

'Yes, chairman, I certainly think we ought to get State Department clearance as well as US Air Force agreement to the use of US military bases. Shall I put in a formal request right away?'

'Yes, please; and how about Canada?'

'No difficulty foreseen,' replied the Commonwealth Office, 'but certainly we must observe protocol and ask their permission and approval. I'll put the request into the proper channels.'

'Anything else, Air Marshal?' queried the chairman.

'That's all for the moment. I expect there'll be more problems later on though.'

'Very well. Now are there any questions, or points of which we should be aware, from departmental representatives.'

Brigadier Jehu raised his hand and, on a nod from the chairman began: 'I would like to raise the question of publicity and press representation at the tests, sir. We shall want to get good and favourable press coverage and we shall also want to invite American and Commonwealth representatives to witness the tests. So would the Task Force Commander please make the necessary arrangements and we will liaise with his staff in due course?'

Immediately the TFC responded vigorously.

'I am absolutely against having any visitors or press at the first test. It is going to be fraught with many difficulties and uncertainties and we certainly don't want to look stupid and incompetent if anything goes wrong. But once the first test is successfully accomplished and we have confidence in our operational plans and equipment, I'll be glad to make arrangements for as many visitors as you wish to send. I assume Brigadier Jehu will let me know well in advance the various categories of people witnessing the second test and provide also some brief on what information can be given to them.'

'That seems reasonable,' commented the chairman. 'Does that satisfy you, Jehu?'

'Yes, sir: but the Press will be badgering me for weeks before the first test, after the Government has announced publicly that the tests are to take place. To help me hold them off, could it be agreed that there will be no release of publicity or photographs of any kind before the second test?'

'That suits me,' replied the TFC. 'We'll do that.'

The Ministry of Agriculture and Fisheries representative then raised the point that, in the light of some of the troubles which the Americans had had, could the Task Force Commander arrange some method of convincing world opinion that the tests will not have caused any radio-active pollution of pelagic fish?'

'Pelagic fish! What on earth does that mean?'

'Pelagic fish are those like tuna in particular and also salmon, which in their breeding and feeding habits, move considerable distances from one part of the ocean to another. There would be a great outcry if fish were to carry radio-active pollution to fishing areas.'

'I note the problem,' answered the TFC. 'We'll consult with our AWRE colleagues on how to deal with it. Then we'll let you know in due course what we've done and results of our efforts, so that you can satisfy the environmental enthusiasts. Barring a serious failure or accident, I can't see that there is any risk to fish or fish-eaters.'

Other minor questions came up and were discussed and then:

'Have you any idea what is your target date for the first test?'

'Well,' responded the TFC cautiously, 'It's obviously much too soon for more than a guess, but the bracket is pretty narrow. I'm quite sure we can't be ready before May 1st next year and the Prime Minister says it must be before June 1st. So if the end product of our detailed planning shows it to be possible, I'm going to aim for about May 8th.'

'Oh! You can't do that!' exclaimed someone. 'That's right in the middle of Holy Week.'

'No it isn't!' came another voice. 'Holy Week is the week before Easter.'

'Nonsense!' from the end of the table. 'Anyone knows that Holy Week is the week commencing Easter Sunday.'

'Not so!' from somewhere in the middle, and the argument raged.

For the first time, the meeting had really come alive. The chairman let the battle go on for a few seconds, then banged the table and restored order.

'Before we get worried about Holy Week, we had better wait and see how the Task Force planning works out and then adjust if necessary and possible.'

After dealing with a few further relatively minor points, the chairman brought the meeting to a close and arranged for the next one a month later.

As the meeting broke up and individuals and small groups began to disperse, the TFC took his leave of General Morgan and made his way over to the two Foreign Office representatives and shook hands.

'Hello, Miss Brown, I'm Wilf Oulton,' produced a rather shy but warm and friendly smile.

'I'm Willie Wright,' responded her colleague with a twinkle in his eye and with his hands raised in prayer — or possibly it was the eastern 'namasti' greeting?

'I'm so glad we got down to the really important problem — Holy Week, I mean!'

The TFC laughed and answered: 'Me too! I think we ought to discuss it further. Would you both care to come and talk about it over a glass of gin or something and then some lunch at the "Senior"?'

Miss Brown excused herself, having an appointment already, but Willie Wright accepted with alacrity and twenty minutes later over the aforesaid gin in the bar of the United Service Club in Pall Mall he and the TFC established a friendly under-standing and rapport which was to be of very great help in the execution of Operation Grapple.

12

Getting down to the job

The next Monday morning at 08.45, Headquarters Grapple began to take on substance and a corporate identity. The Task Force Commander, his aide Squadron Leader Terry Helfer and his secretary Flight Sergeant Kitchingman moved into the offices in the not-yet-derequistioned Richmond Terrace building. They went round sticking labels on doors to allocate rooms to specific activities and sorted out the jumble of scrounged office furniture to fix up some half dozen offices in reasonable shape for work to begin.

A few minutes later Group Captain Freddie Milligan arrived.

'Here at last, sir, and ready to get on with it. I handed over Bassingbourn on Saturday morning, with some regrets I must admit, but this is going to be much more exciting.'

'You don't know the half of it, Freddie, but you'll soon find out. Very glad you're here at last; we've a lot to do. And who is this?'

A burly, square figure presented himself, medium height, broad of build everywhere, with a face like a successful prize-fighter but keenly intelligent eyes.

'Wing Commander Surtees, sir. I'm posted to your staff.'

'Welcome aboard, Surtees. For the moment you are going to assist Group Captain Milligan here as Air Plans I, but eventually you'll be the senior RAF controller in a joint RAF/Navy operations room. We'll have a little meeting in a few minutes and give you an outline of the job.'

Surtees turned away and his rather serious face cracked into a broad smile as he saw Helfer. 'Hello, Terry!' 'Hello, Butch!' – having known one another in some previous set-up.

Waiting at the door was another recruit to the team, a fresh-faced youngish chap with an athletic open-air look about him – a rugby player, perhaps?

'Squadron Leader Longley, sir – Equipment Branch.' – a pleasant slight antipodean accent? – New Zealand?

'Hello, Longley, come on in. You're going to be the Supply planner on the Air side for the time being and to look after air movements as well.'

Douglas Longley looked mystified. Like others joining the team, he had had no briefing on what the job was going to be. Security was tight.

'Don't worry,' said the TFC, 'all will be explained in a few minutes.'

Corporal Beall knocked at the door and came in carrying a cardboard carton with an electric kettle, a large jar of instant coffee, a bottle of United Dairies milk, a bag of sugar and an assortment of earthenware mugs.

'Where shall I put these, sir?'

'Ask the Flight Sergeant to give you a corner of his office and set up a coffee swindle right away, please, Corporal Beall. I reckon that on this first day we can have a cup now instead of waiting until eleven o'clock.'

Turning to the little group, the TFC said: 'We've allocated room 217 for staff meetings, but I shall have quick impromptu discussions here in my office. Terry, can you please organise a six foot table and six chairs over in that corner right now, so that we can all write notes as we talk; and all of you please remember the security classification of anything you write down and make sure it is properly locked up in your filing cabinets when you leave your offices.'

Five minutes later, furnished with coffee and note-pads, the little team assembled round the table for the first Task Force staff meeting. The TFC summarised quickly the Government's intentions, the main task ahead and the intermediate steps leading up to it – initially the Navy to do the heavy transportation, the RAF to provide day-to-day transport support, the Sappers and other Army organisations to do the construction and installations. Later, AWRE to provide and assemble the devices to be tested, the RAF to carry out the various tasks of dropping the bomb, cloud sampling, courier service to and from UK, the Navy to assist in controlling the operation, weather reporting, and *Narvik* acting as technical control in the forward area.

'I want the complete programme for the next fifteen months drafted out as soon as possible, noting particularly the training schedules for the considerable variety of personnel involved on the Services side.

'Speed is essential, as you can see; so I want to keep the central staff as small as possible – little more than we have now. But as Air Commodore Weir can't join us for about another month, I want you, Freddie and Surtees, to get on with the outline of the Air Plan; then the Air Task Group can take over the more detailed planning later on and not be behind the rest of the team.

'The Naval planning team will move in here in the next day or so – and I want you, Freddie and Terry, to come with me over to the Admiralty for a meeting set up for ten-thirty.

'The Army staff here will, I think, be very small – probably just the Army Task Group Commander, his secretary and a liaison officer from the Sappers. I don't think we need a resident AWRE chap, but we'll see how it goes.

'Since we have all four Service elements in the Grapple team, let's try to use the new standardised staff paperwork system devised by the Joint Services Staff College. It might save time, trouble and misunderstandings in translating between Air Ministry files, Admiralty dockets and War Office papers of all kinds.

'Another thing about planning, which all too often tends to generate pomposity: I remember that during the War, the German forces suffered many unnecessary calamities as a result of their planning being carried out by the OKW, who had no responsibility for the execution of their plans. So here in Grapple, anyone who plans anything will execute that plan when the time comes. I think that will help to concentrate our minds on the job in hand.

'Also, this is a team job. Scientists, army and navy are just as essential as the RAF and I shall immediately discard anyone who causes inter-service friction. Vigorous views and arguments on which is the best way to do any particular job – OK! But once it's decided, then "all gentlemen will draw and haul with the sailors, all of one heart," as Francis Drake said, and we don't have any dark blue v light blue v khaki nonsense.

'That brings me to the next point, which will arise at our meeting in the Admiralty. The Valiant squadron is required to put the bomb within a couple of hundred yards of a fixed but invisible point one and a half miles off shore from the south-east corner of Malden. Bomber Command will say that they can do that without any help and I believe them. But there is just a chance – maybe only one in a hundred thousand? – that they might be in error and we can't accept that chance without trying to do something to eliminate it. So we must have the bombing-run track of the Valiant monitored by radar – which means an aircraft carrier and good interservice co-operation. Then the carrier herself will have a problem too, in knowing her own position within, say, one hundred yards. Likewise, in case we have to drop on a day with some cloud cover, the aircraft must have a check that it is on the correct bombing line, again to within about one hundred yards. So I want a Decca chain, and the Decca equipment in both the Valiant and the aircraft carrier.

'Lastly, since even quite a small change in the high level wind speed during the bombing run could cause under or overshoot errors, the Valiants must have Green Satin Doppler wind-finding radar, or something like it.

'Freddie and Butch, you take over that job now and keep me informed weekly.'

A lively discussion ensued as the staff got to grips with

realities and went on for another hour. Then the TFC and Milligan walked over to the Admiralty to the room where Commodore Gretton had arranged the second Naval Task Group meeting.

Guy Western, Geoffrey Thatcher and Tony Wallington-Smith were there and two others. One, a tall fair-haired athletic looking type, was Commander Paul Whitfield of the Fleet Air Arm, who was to be the Commander (Air) of the aircraft carrier. The other, of medium build, less extrovert in character but with sharp, intelligent features, was Lieutenant-Commander D A F Finlay, who was to plan and set up naval communications.

After introductions all round the meeting got to work. The TFC opened by saying that office accommodation was now available in Richmond Terrace and arranged with Peter Gretton for the Naval Task Group Staff to move over as soon as convenient. They then went on to review the request for naval ships.

'We've been fortunate enough,' began Gretton, 'to get *Warrior*, a light fleet carrier. She's in reserve at Devonport at the moment and will have to have a partial refit. It's going to be a hell of a rush, but work is starting immediately and we'll have her ready in time.'

Years later it came out that, on his return from a tour of duty in Washington, Gretton had been promised command of an aircraft carrier – *Warrior* herself, no less. But that, alas!, had been cancelled for lack of money and men. Now, thanks to Grapple, the Navy had got an extra carrier back in commission. No wonder Gretton and Western looked so pleased – not nearly so pleased as the Task Force Commander, however, who was very relieved to be assured that a carrier would be available.

'That's great!' he enthused. 'And now do you think you could lay hands on three or four Avenger aircraft? I'm sure they are the best for this particular job.'

Commander Whitfield agreed warmly and added: 'I think we have a few left in store. I'll make enquiries.'

'We shall also need helicopters – Whirlwinds? – but we won't

84

know how many until the operational plans are worked out in some detail. What next, Peter?'

'Next,' went on Commodore Gretton, 'about an LST* to deliver heavy equipment and stores to Malden and other islands. They're scarcer than hens' teeth and not in very good condition. But we've located one in Malta – the *Messina* – and she'll be coming home immediately to Chatham for a re-fit and some substantial improvements to living conditions on board. We've had serious criticism of the living conditions in LSTs in the tropics even for short periods. For a year or more at Christmas we must have a big improvement.'

'During the re-fit, she'll be modified in several ways: to carry six LCMs** – so that she can discharge heavy equipment in places unsuitable for beaching the LST herself – plus a couple of DUKWs†.

Also, she'll be fitted with extra water-distillation plant to produce about a hundred tons of fresh water a day, which should keep the Sappers going until they can build the shore-based distillation plant.

There will be a greatly improved wireless and voice radio fit, so that she can act as the headquarters ship of the Grapple squadron and the main communication link between Christmas and UK. Finlay here has planned all that and I'm sure that will be OK.

The other LST, *Narvik*, will leave soon to act as headquarters and control ship for Operation Mosaic at Monte Bello and will then return to Chatham for re-fit and all the modifications she'll need to act as Technical Control at Malden. That's going to be a big rush job too.'

At this point Captain Western came into the discussion.

'*Narvik* will have to spend long periods at Malden and she can't go steaming up and down the whole time; nor can she anchor off shore because of the very steeply shelving bottom. So

---

* Landing Ships for Tanks.
** Landing Craft for Mechanised Vehicles.
† Amphibious vehicle.

we need a deep mooring. At Christmas Island, too, we need a deep mooring for *Warrior* and it will save a great deal of time and wear and tear of launches and LCMs if we can put all the supply ships on moorings with ship-to-shore telephone. Trouble is that such moorings are usually laid by boom defence vessels, but all of ours are coal burners and none has the range to get to Christmas. So we're trying to get hold of an ocean-going salvage ship, *Salvictor*, and have her modified to carry and launch the moorings. We'll also try to get her to carry a DUKW on her quarterdeck, which would make her very useful for supply and ferry tasks.'

Turning to the Commodore, Western went on: 'Can I say a few more words about Malden, sir?'

'Yes, of course.'

'We've dug up quite a lot of information about Malden from reports of various ships which have visited there in the last fifty years and from the records of a London company which ran a guano exporting operation there until 1927 when they ran out of guano and abandoned the place.

'There is a reef right round the island, except for a gap about two hundred feet wide on the north side and there is usually a strong tidal current between the reef and the shoreline. There's another hazard too! In the case of one visiting ship which put a landing party ashore, some of the oars of the boat were bitten off by sharks!

'At the gap in the reef, there are the remains of a jetty and a few derelict buildings and part of a light railway used for the guano export, but nothing of any use to us. Clearly, getting equipment and personnel ashore is going to be difficult much of the time and sometimes impossible.'

'That confirms my view that we must have an airstrip on Malden and regular air transport between Christmas and Malden,' interjected the TFC.

'Yes, sir,' agreed Western. 'But since the guano company *did* manage to get ships into their jetty often enough to export fourteen thousand tons a year at their peak there must be occasions when we can get stuff ashore by LCM or DUKW.'

'Thank you, Guy,' acknowledged the TFC. 'We need to have belt and braces. Now, how about other ships?'

'We have allocated to us,' replies Western, 'Royal Fleet Auxiliary ships *Fort Beauharnois* and *Fort Constantine* as supply ships, *Fort Rosalie* for ammunition and explosives, and four tankers for bulk fuel. We're shopping in the Baltic Exchange for merchant ships for carrying stuff like cement and bitumen and heavy equipment.'

'What about unloading heavy equipment at Christmas? Have you had any luck with the pontoon idea?'

'Yes, sir,' broke in Commander Thatcher. 'The Army does have a number of the hollow cube elements to make the pontoons at Marchwood, on Southampton Water, and they are going to make up four. Two will be fitted with diesel outboards to be used as ferries, two will serve as piers in the port area. The problem is going to be to get a cargo ship which can carry them and unload them over the side at Christmas – they weigh eighty tons each, so we need a heavy lift ship.'

The discussion ranged on for another two hours, considering various aspects of moving the vast quantities of materiel and several thousand men some nine thousand miles to the central Pacific Ocean and getting both ashore rapidly in all the required places.

'What about other operational ships, Peter?' asked the TFC. 'We're going to need weather reporting ships and maybe even the capability of escorting intruding vessels out of the danger area.'

'We've had a bit of luck there,' replied Gretton. 'The New Zealanders have offered to help and they are going to let us have two 'Loch' class frigates – *Pukaki* and *Rotoiti* – which will be just right for that job.'

'That's great! Well, I think that's enough for today. We'll have another session on our naval problems next Monday in our new offices. Thank you all.' Turning to Gretton, 'Tomorrow, Peter, could you come with me to Aldermaston to the first of our regular weekly meetings with the AWRE chaps?'

'Of course,' replied Commodore Gretton. 'Could we travel together and use the journey time for discussion?'

After a brief consideration of the best way to do this, it was agreed to meet at Ealing Broadway railway station and to travel in a reserved compartment, where they could talk freely, as far as Reading, where Corporal Beall would be waiting for them with the staff car. This turned out to be an excellent arrangement and was in fact, in the weeks that followed, the only time when the TFC and his Deputy could have quiet discussion without interruption.

Back in the discreetly anonymous offices in Richmond Terrace, another key member of the team was waiting for the Task Force Commander – Colonel J E S Stone, OBE, appointed to be Army Task Group Commander. Jack Stone was a cheerful, solid, professional soldier, medium height, stocky build, heavy moustache. He was calm in temperament, diplomatic, knowledgeable and with a keen sense of humour lurking only just beneath the surface of his slightly solemn exterior. He very soon easily and quietly fitted into the team and became a valued colleague and partner.

He, too, didn't know much about his new appointment until after a quick outline briefing by the TFC. Whereupon, in silence, he took his pipe from his pocket, politely waved it interrogatively, filled and lit it, pulled on it and remarked: 'Well! Quite a job, isn't it! I think I'd better go and see Woollett before he dashes off to Korea; and there'll be the other army activities to be co-ordinated with the Sappers – Air Formation Signals to provide telephone and other communications on the island, RASC for unloading and stockpiling stores and feeding the whole force, living facilities, a large POL depot for handling fuel of all kinds, some provision for guards and security I suppose? – and a postal service? Good Lord! I'd better start getting some outlines down on paper. May I use your Flight Sergeant until I get some staff of my own?'

'Of course, Jack. We're all one team. No racial discrimination here! – although we may have a staff language problem sometimes.'

13

The weekly meeting at AWRE

Tuesday morning, the first of the regular weekly meetings between the Task Force Commander or his staff and the scientists at the Atomic Weapons Research Establishment went smoothly. The TFC and his deputy, Commodore Gretton, met as agreed on the platform at Ealing Broadway railway station at eight o'clock and had a reserved compartment to themselves for the 50 minute journey to Reading. They took the opportunity to talk over several matters arising from the meeting in the Admiralty the previous day. Among which:

'You know, Peter,' remarked the TFC, '*Warrior* is going to have to control closely quite a lot of RAF aircraft on five different jobs immediately before, during and immediately after the bombing run; and this will apply in the working-up practices, in the dress rehearsal and in the live drop. I'd like to have an RAF liaison officer resident in the ship and present in the air control room at those times. Would that be agreeable to you?'

'Yes, of course, Wilf. I think that's a very good idea. He could also team up with Whitfield in planning the operational procedures to be followed.'

'Right! We'll do that. Another thing, although we hope and intend to ensure that our planning and provisioning is going to be right, if there are any serious problems your ships are going to be a hell of a long way from any RN base facilities. It would be comforting to think you could fall back on Pearl Harbour if necessary. Wouldn't it be a good idea for you to nip across to Washington, contact your USN chums and see if you can get it set up that we can call on CINCPAC for informal help if necessary?'

'I agree. That's been in my mind too,' replied Gretton. 'But if I'm to do that, then the sooner the better; because as the navy plans and preparations go ahead here, it will become more and more necessary for me to be available here from day to day.'

'Right. Then I suggest you go as soon as you can set up the visit, but don't be away a day longer than is necessary. By the way, we now have an RAF supply officer – Squadron Leader Longley – who will also act as Air Movements Officer. He's a very good chap and will fix up tickets and reservations for you.'

The train pulled into Reading station at nine o'clock and Corporal Beall was waiting for them with the staff car. No time was wasted and twenty minutes later they were in the Deputy Director's office at the AWRE.

'Morning, Bill,' said the TFC as they entered. 'May I introduce Commodore Peter Gretton, who is my deputy and Commander of the Naval Task Group for Grapple?' Turning to Gretton – 'This is Bill Cook, deputy to Penney and, as you know, Scientific Director for Grapple.'

Cook welcomed them both in his usual urbane and affable manner and then led the way to a conference room in which the first of these regular meetings was to take place.

About a dozen of the AWRE staff designated for Grapple were waiting there already – John Challens and Ken Bomford whom the TFC had met the previous week, Mr Hicks the Theoretical Predictions expert whose job it would be to evaluate on the day the extent and intensity of any radio-active fall-out, Wing Commander Ambrose Eyre, an armament specialist, who was the RAF liaison officer at AWRE and several others. After introductions all round, Cook said:

'I don't think you need me at this particular meeting so I'll leave you to discuss outline plans with Challens and Bomford, who are the key people at this stage.'

The meeting immediately got down to work on the many problems of sea and air transport requirements for the elements of the bombs, technical and building requirements for assembly, instrumentation, the sequence of checks that everything was in order at each stage and – among many other points – the degree of risk that would have to be accepted to get the test carried out by the date required by the Government. It was emphasised that there was no merit in delaying the programme by refusing to accept a risk of disaster in one area of say, one in a million, when in another potentially equally disastrous area a risk of one in a hundred thousand had already been accepted.

'For instance,' asked Challens, 'what is the risk of the Valiant crashing on take-off, leading possibly to a very undesirable consequence?'

'I suppose,' mused the TFC, 'we could establish some kind of a figure from air accident statistics. That would have to be modified by guesswork as to the effect of the exceptionally high state of training of the select aircrew for the job and the much above average technical maintenance of the aircraft. Silly to say that there is no such risk. It may be equally silly for me to say so, but I would put the odds at one in a million. Just to cheer you up, we may have the same degree of risk of the lot of us being swept off Christmas by a 'tsunami' tidal wave!'

'All right then,' said Challens, 'for the time being let's work on us accepting the risks of the order of one in a million for everything.'

'But there must be some factors for which there is no risk at all,' protested the TFC. 'For instance, there's no risk at all of that light switch on the wall suddenly turning itself on!'

'Not so!' objected one of the staff. 'If a meteorite or an aircraft crashed into the building, or an earthquake occurred, the switch could be broken and the wires short-circuited. It may be extremely small, but there is a risk – there's some degree of risk in everything.'

This was a new concept to the TFC and his deputy; but in military life, only one in a million was virtually fire-proof.

The author – Air Vice Marshal W E Oulton CB CBE DSO DFC – Task Force Commander.

Sir William Penney KBE FRS – Director, Atomic Weapons Research Establishment, Aldermaston.

Mr W R J Cook CB – Scientific Director of 'Operation Grapple'.

Commodore P W Gretton DSO OBE DSC – Deputy Task Force Commander and Commodore Grapple Squadron.

Colonel J E S Stone OBE – Commander, Army Task Group

Air Commodore C T Weir DFC, Commander, Air Task Group.

Captain J G T Western RN,
Chief Naval Planner.

Colonel J C Woollett OBE
MC RE, Christmas Island
Garrison Commander, and
Commander Royal Engi-
neers.

Mr Percy Roberts, the civil
administrator, examining a
frigate or bos'un bird.

Mr Douglas Lovelock –
Ministry of Supply adviser.

Royal Fleet Auxiliary *Fort Beauharnois*, a supply ship.

SS *Ben Wyvis*, a heavy lift ship.

The talk moved on to the programme of events prior to a live drop. The carcase and electronics of the bomb would have been transported to Christmas by sea some time ahead; but it was desirable that the radioactive core and the explosive sphere surrounding it should arrive, separately, as briefly as possible before final assembly began. This meant delivery by air, of course. Furthermore, once the bomb was assembled, there should be no delay in carrying out the live drop.

'And how long is the process of assembly and checking going to take?' asked the TFC.

'We guess something between twelve and twenty four hours.'

'So we are going to have to make a decision to go ahead with the drop twenty four hours previously and it will be difficult – or at least hazardous – to change that if conditions turn out to be not quite right?'

'Yes. That's the situation.'

This certainly was a pretty serious factor to be taken into consideration in the operational planning, but only one of so many.

'What about modifications to *Narvik* when she gets back?' asked Commodore Gretton. 'What extra facilities do you need?'

Ken Bomford spoke up. 'That will be in my area of responsibility. We shall need a quite extensive telemetry receiving system for a start. As each step in arming the bomb in flight in the Valiant is taken, and as each sequential action such as opening the bomb doors and selecting the appropriate bomb release switch is taken, the telemetry senders in the aircraft will transmit a signal, which will indicate that everything has happened correctly and in the right sequence before we OK the release and trigger off our recording instrumentation. We shall of course need good voice communication with the pilot and with other ships in the area and also command telemetry to switch on the instrumentation on Malden. We have our rough plans for all this, which we need to discuss with your signals staff – Lieutenant – Commander Finlay, isn't it?'

The morning passed quickly, with problems being outlined

and solutions suggested, establishing a sound base for good co-operation between the AWRE team and the Grapple staff in London. Then a quick lunch and back to Whitehall where the naval staff were already moving into the new Grapple offices in Richmond Terrace.

Arrangements were quickly made for Commodore Gretton to go to Washington and for Colonel Woollett to go to Korea to fetch 55 Field Squadron of the Royal Engineers into the Grapple team.

An urgent request was put in to the very co-operative Air Ministry personnel branch for a suitably qualified and well experienced navigator to be the RAF liaison officer in the aircraft carrier *Warrior* and a few days later Squadron Leader 'Roly' Duck arrived, a very sharp and worldly-wise operator as well as being professionally highly qualified. It was a very suitable choice, as not only had he previously worked with 'Butch' Surtees in the Directorate of Bomber Operations, but had in fact drafted the staff paper on consideration of which the Chiefs of Staff had decided to appoint an Air Officer to command Grapple. He was to turn out to be a valuable and many-skilled member of the team.

14

The Royal Aircraft Establishment, Farnborough

Just past the 'Tumbledown-Dick' public house, well known to generations of aviators, the staff car turned off the main road through Farnborough (Hampshire, not Kent) and down the hill to the main entrance of the Royal Aircraft Establishment. Since the very early days of flying, when Samuel Cody and many others had bounced their primitive and fragile stick-and-string aeroplanes into the air above Laffan's Plain, as it was then called, the Establishment had grown through two world wars and the associated fantastic advance of aviation to be now a vast conglomeration of hangars, buildings, laboratories and test centres of every kind to do with aircraft and the business of flying them.

Many were the inventions and discoveries which had helped the march of aviation progress, unremembered and taken for granted even by the aviation fraternity. How many, one wonders, know for instance of the brilliant woman mathematician who calculated the small change in the propeller gearing ratio of the Spitfire engine which restored the vital margin of superiority which that famous fighter aircraft had temporarily lost to the then current Me109? Or, in later years, the painstaking detective work by Arnold Hall and his team which traced the cause of the first 'Comet' aircraft disaster to a small crack in the too-sharp corner of a small overhead window? Now RAE was to make another valuable contribution – this time to the success of Operation Grapple.

The Task Force Commander was familiar with the geography of Farnborough and its maze of buildings. After being cleared by the Security guard at the gate, he directed Corporal Beall to the block where Dr F E Jones had his office.

'Good morning, Frank.'

'Hello, Wilf. Haven't seen you for years! How goes it? I suppose you've come to talk about the Valiant problem?'

'Yes, Frank. At AWRE they told me you hope to work out a solution.'

Dr Jones concisely reviewed the problem of ensuring the survival of the Valiant after dropping the first British megaton bomb. Direct radiation – alpha, beta and gamma rays – were no serious threat, since in the atmosphere the worst of these would not effectively travel more than about eight thousand feet. The damage, if any, would be caused by heat and/or blast.

The first defence was to ensure the maximum separation between the aircraft and the explosion; and since the bomb would be exploded at eight thousand feet above sea level, the bombing run would be made at the maximum height at which the Valiant provided a stable enough bombing platform to permit the necessary accuracy. This had been calculated to be about forty-five thousand feet and this would be verified by tests on the bombing range at Orfordness on the Suffolk coast. This would be a task for the Valiant squadron, supported by an expert evaluation team from the Aeroplane and Armament Experimental Establishment at Boscombe Down.

The next step would be to move the aircraft in the horizontal plane as far away as possible from the rapidly ascending atomic cloud, by executing the maximum rate of turn to head the Valiant directly away from the bomb burst without causing a high speed stall. On first calculations this would be a turn at about 1.7g and 60 degrees of bank on to a heading at 135 degrees away from the bombing run. This too, would have to be verified by experimental flying with the aircraft at the same all-up weight that it would have at that moment of the operational sortie. After the experimental verification – or slight amendment if necessary – of these figures, some additional means should be provided to enable the aircrew to fly extremely accurately at these parameters, the most important being the 1.7g. RAE would therefore produce a special and very sensitive g-meter for this purpose and one would be fitted to each Valiant scheduled to make a live drop.

Having achieved the maximum possible separation in space and with the aircraft moving rapidly away from the cloud, something had to be done to reduce the effect of the heat flash. The whole airframe would therefore be painted with a brilliant white highly reflective cellulose paint, which on the day would have to be washed spotlessly clean. This would reflect most of the heat before it could cause a temperature rise in the skin of the airframe and hence any structural damage.

The paint however, would not protect the aerodynamic seals between the moving and non-moving parts of the control surfaces – rudder, elevators, ailerons, since the standard seals were of rubber which could not tolerate the special paint. Steps were in hand to produce a flexible silicone material which would be immune to the heat but would function correctly in the aerodynamic sense. All controls would have to be fitted with these new seals – a very considerable task when the time came.

It would be most important to ensure that the extremely bright flash from the explosion did not enter the cockpit and flight deck of the Valiant. During the bombing run, all windows would have to be fitted with special light-tight screens, and that would include the bomb-aimer's window as soon as the bomb was released. There would be adequate time to do this, since it would take the bomb some fifty-three seconds to fall from release height to burst height. RAE and Vickers – the makers of the aircraft – would co-operate in the design, manufacture and testing of these shutters, but already time was getting short if adequate time was to be available for the aircrew to practise.

As far as the blast effect was concerned, calculations showed that given the separation and aspect described, the blast overpressure wave from a one megaton explosion should produce shock no worse than that often experienced in clear air turbulence. No special measures would be necessary to cope with that problem.

The discussion then ranged on over the details of these proposals and their implementation, and it looked as though the safety of the aircraft and crew could be assured within the degree of risk accepted in other areas of Operation Grapple. A great relief to the TFC.

'Good Lord! It's 12.30 already!' exclaimed F E Jones. 'How about some lunch?'

'Fine! And many thanks for all your help, Frank. Is it OK with you if I ask Group Captain Milligan – and later on Ginger Weir – to keep in touch with you over the progress of these mods – as I have one or two other things to look after?'

'Yes, sure!' and they made their way up to the old Officers' Mess.

Back in the Grapple HQ office, there were messages waiting.

Returning Willie Wright's call from the Foreign Office, the good news first was that the Americans had agreed to the west-about route and to accommodate servicing crews at Travis Air Force Base near Sacramento, California and at Hickam Air Force Base, Honolulu, Hawaii. The bad news was that an airline company called South Pacific Airlines, (SPAL for short) had applied to the FAA and the Department of Transportation to run a new air service by flying boat through Hawaii and Christmas Island (!) to Tahiti and had started work on facilities. On the face of it, there was no valid reason to with-hold approval and it was going to take some delicate 'fixing' to hold up the approval until after the Grapple trials. State Department would do their best but in such a politically sensitive situation, there could be no guarantee. We could only wait and see. Maybe handsome financial compensation would do the trick.

Then the Commonwealth Office. They had at last located the missing soil samples. The New Zealand survey ship, HMNZS *Lachlan*, was in Sydney where the Australian Customs authorities adamantly refused permission for the soil samples to be brought ashore, which would have been a serious breach of Department of Agriculture regulations. Hampered by the security restrictions on anything to do with Grapple, the Ministry of Supply mission in Melbourne had so far been unable to solve the problem, but they were working on it jointly with the High Commission.

Lastly, a message from the office of the Ministry of Supply. Would it be convenient for the Task Force Commander to call on the Minister that afternoon at four o'clock? He reckoned he could just about make it – and that would be one more job done.

At four o'clock, slightly out of breath, the TFC was shown into the Minister's office. The Right Honourable Reggie Maudling, PC, appeared to be a bluff, friendly, somewhat rustic type, comfortably built and wearing an old loudly checked tweed jacket in which he did not look at all like a senior politician. A friendly welcome – 'Ah! Yes. Grapple. Tell me all about it.'

The TFC began a succinct outline of the operation, of the problems to be encountered and of the proposed ways of tackling these problems; but in two or three minutes he noted that the eyes which, behind their horn-rimmed glasses had sparkled so intelligently at first, were now glazing over. Ministerial responsibility evidently didn't mean getting down to nuts and bolts.

So the meeting was switched back smartly to a friendly protocol visit and fifteen minutes later the TFC took his leave, laden with the Minister's good wishes. However, he was soon to find out that the Minister – although quite uninterested in operational problems, was – like the Bishop of Chichester in the famous limerick – certainly no fool and intended to keep a firm grip on the financial side of Operation Grapple.

Early next morning, Squadron Leader Helfer tapped on the door.

'Mr Lovelock, from the Minstry of Supply, to see you, sir.'

Through the door of the TFC's office came a tall, gangling

young man, dark curly hair, heavy spectacles, a jutting jaw and a ruddy countenance, with the aggressive air of a truculent schoolboy determined not to be imposed upon. But Mr Lovelock proved to be no schoolboy. 'Good morning, Air Marshal. I've been appointed by the Minister of Supply to be your adviser on matters concerning the Ministry, which means in effect that I approve any expenditure you need to incur and see that the bills get paid. I know that you are required to do this operation as economically as possible, but my brief is to see that you get all the help you need from Ministry of Supply to get it done.'

'That's splendid, Mr Lovelock. I'm very pleased to have you in the team and we'll find an office for you right away. Come and meet the other members of the Grapple HQ staff. Ah! – beginning with Colonel Stone here, the Army Task Group Commander,' – as Jack Stone appeared in the doorway.

After the introduction, Stone asked: 'Can you spare me five minutes, sir? We have a real problem. The Sappers can't get hold of nearly enough heavy plant – scrapers, graders, bulldozers, wobbly-wheel rollers and other machines for the construction of the runway. We can order from industry, but there is no way it could be delivered in time for our latest shipping date. The only thing I can think of is that a prudent Quarter-Master General always keeps a hidden reserve up his sleeve for a war emergency, which he would not normally admit to having. It might be worth trying to winkle out the particular items which we need.'

'Right, Mr Lovelock, here's your first job. If we can place the orders on industry immediately for the plant required and go to the Quarter-Master General with those orders in our hand, so to speak, he might let us have his hidden reserves in a swop for the new stuff when it can be delivered. Let's get the orders placed now and I'll tackle the QMG – or rather his deputy, who is an old friend of mine. Will you get on with that immediately, please?'

Lovelock nodded and went off into a huddle with Stone.

After a quick check to ensure that the Deputy QMG could see him, the TFC walked smartly up Whitehall to the War Office.

'Hello, Adrian. Nice to see you again and good of you to spare the time at such short notice.'

'Hello, Wilf. Always nice to see you. What can I do?'

If you've heard of it, OK. If not, please take my word for it that I have a directive from the PM with authority to have anything I want for a hot job. We urgently need these items of heavy engineer plant' – putting a list on the desk – 'and you may have some of them in your hidden reserve. If so, can we have them please? New stuff is on order and will replace whatever we borrow in a few months time.'

'Good Lord! Are you talking about Grapple? I've just heard about it.'

'Yes, Adrian. Can you help?'

There was no hesitation on the part of the Deputy QMG. The two had served together on the staff of the Joint Services Staff College years earlier and later had been fellow students and good friends at the Imperial Defence College. Such contacts were immensely valuable in that they gave immediate confidence and trust in situations which could only have developed very slowly – if at all – along the formal lines of interservice cooperation.

'Well, Wilf, you're welcome to anything we've got. I'll have someone look into it right away; but I'm afraid it will be in poor condition and will have to be overhauled before it's of any use; and the civilian maintenance men have been very difficult lately. How long have we got?'

'We need to have the plant in about eight weeks to have time to prepare it for shipment.'

'That's going to be far from easy,' pondered DQMG, 'but we'll do our best.'

'Thanks a lot, Adrian. Perhaps someone could ring my Colonel Stone – on this number – to let us know what you can find?'

'Yes, of course; and if I may make a suggestion, it might help if you put on your sky-blue uniform and went down to Liphook to give the civilian maintenance chaps a pep-talk and make them feel they are part of something big.'

'Splendid idea, Adrian. I'll do that. Thanks for the suggestion – and for any help you can give us.'

Two days later Colonel Stone got word that the Quarter-Master General could supply all the needs in repairable state, except for two Barber-Greene macadam laying machines; but these were absolutely vital. What to do? With Lovelock's agreement, it was decided to try to buy a couple of used but serviceable machines for cash from one of the major road construction companies who might be lightly loaded for work and glad of some help with cash flow. This ploy was eventually successful.

The excellent Mr Lovelock soon came back with the good news that he had fixed approval of the orders to manufacturers for the plant.

'While I'm here, Air Marshal, can I raise another point? What are you going to use for money at Christmas Island? I mean, what currency are you going to use?'

'Can't we just use Sterling?'

'No, I'm afraid not – or at least not without some special concession from the Treasury. Christmas is outside the Sterling area and very large sums will be involved. You might try Australian dollars, but they would have a similar objection. Maybe New Zealand would help, but I think it would be difficult for them.'

'Oh, Lord!' moaned the TFC. 'What next! I can see all kinds of problems. Could you try to persuade the Treasury to make Christmas a temporary enclave of the Sterling area? Wouldn't that be the least difficult course?' Lovelock agreed to try.

15

Making friends and influencing people

Commodore Gretton came into the TFC's office.

'Wilf, the naval team is pretty well settled in now, so I'm off to Washington tomorrow, as you suggested. Longley has fixed up the travel arrangements and I've advised the naval staff in the BDS* that I'm coming informally to clear up a few points hanging over from my last appointment there. That hasn't excited any curiosity – so far, anyway. But it means that I'll miss your naval staff meeting on Monday, so I want to let you know that we have a problem with coxswains and crews for the landing craft to do the unloading at Christmas and Malden. This job is traditionally done by Royal Marines, but because of the post-war rundown of skilled personnel, we're desperately short of them. So we've arranged to send a course of raw National Service recruits to the Amphibious Warfare school at Fremington to be trained. Unfortunately it's a fifteen week course to qualify as a coxswain and we don't have fifteen weeks. We'll just have to push them along as fast as we can – plus the deck-hands for the landing craft, who don't need so long. I'll go and see them as soon as I get back and pressurise them a little.'

'OK Peter. I note the coxswain situation. As for Washington, you'll call on the ambassador, won't you? He's bound to be in the picture on Grapple by now, because of our request through the Foreign Office for facilities. The same goes for the Head of

---

* British Defence Staff, Washington.

the Defence Staff – Mark Selway. Was he there before you left your last job? But otherwise better keep your visit within the navy net, not to risk crossing wires. Have a good trip and I'll see you next week when you've caught up on your sleep.'

Two days later, after a wearying journey by BOAC through a snow-bound Gander and a chilly Idlewild (New York), Gretton disembarked from the Eastern Airlines shuttle into the balmier air of Washington's National airport. One of his erstwhile junior colleagues was waiting for him with a staff car and, since he had only hand baggage, they were soon bowling along the George Washington Parkway, over the 14th Street Bridge across the Potomac river, up to Pennsylvania Avenue, past the White House and up 17th street and to the Army and Navy Club.

'Thank you for meeting me, but don't wait any longer. As soon as I've had a shower and changed clothes, I'll get a cab up to the Embassy – in about an hour. Perhaps you could check that it will be convenient for me to call on the ambassador and Head of Defence Staff this afternoon.'

He turned into the club foyer and immediately got a warm welcome from the dignified, elderly Filipino commissionaire – a retired Chief Steward of the US Navy.

'Welcome back, Commodore! Nice to have you back with us again. There is a room reserved for you, if you'd just sign in at the desk, please.'

Gretton returned the greeting, signed in, went up to his room, showered and changed. Forty minutes later, refreshed, he made his way down to the Farragut Square entrance of the club, to defeat the delays of the one-way traffic circulation and hailed a Yellow Cab cruising north on 17th street. A minute later they were heading up Connecticut Avenue, Dupont Circle, Massachusetts Avenue – all very nostalgic – and he directed the cabbie to turn into the British Embassy – not to the handsome portico of the Lutyens-designed residence, but round the back to the 'tradesmen's entrance', the offices of the British Defence Staff, Washington.

New faces at the reception desk, so the full nausea of security procedures before he was allowed in and was shown up to the office of the Head of Defence Staff. A warm welcome – it was only a couple of months since he had been working in the building in his previous assignment – and then a quick rundown on the Grapple situation. The request for facilities had already been processed with State Department and the Pentagon and there appeared to be no difficulties.

Meanwhile the ambassador was in and could probably see him right away, if he wished. Grab the chance? Yes! A quick telephone call confirmed that it would be convenient in ten minutes.

'Dinner tonight?' invited the Head of Defence Staff. 'Just us?'

'Yes, please. I would like that. Thanks very much. Could I now call Admiral Burke's office for an appointment tomorrow morning?'

'Of course, help yourself,' waving at the telephone on the desk.

Gretton walked over to the residence and was immediately shown up to the ambassador's study. Sir Harold Caccia, a famous rugby football player in his youth, still retained a breezy open-air manner and welcomed his visitor warmly.

'Nice to see you again, Gretton. I hear you have an exciting new job?'

'Yes, sir; and thank you for seeing me so quickly. The main object of my visit is to see Arleigh Burke in the Navy Department and arrange for some informal help at Pearl Harbour, if that should prove necessary.'

'I don't think you'll have any difficulty,' replied the ambassador. 'We passed on the request from the Foreign Office regarding aircraft movements and positioning ground crews and that seems to be quite in order. I'm sure the Navy will be equally helpful and you know Admiral Burke well, don't you?'

They chatted on for a few minutes, the ambassador being keenly interested and wishing to help in any way possible. Then

Gretton took his leave. A staff car took him back to the club for a couple of hours' sleep and then he went on to a quiet and pleasant meal with the Head of Defence Staff and his charming wife in their residence overlooking Rock Creek Park.

Early next morning the Embassy staff car picked up Commodore Gretton at the I-street entrance of the club and, against the inbound flood of commuter traffic, took him fairly swiftly across the Potomac to Arlington and on to the Pentagon, the Department of Defense. A messenger was waiting for him and he was conducted immediately to the office of the Chief of Naval Operations. The admiral's aide, an old acquaintance, welcomed him, knocked twice on the interior door and showed him in.

'Commodore Gretton to see you, sir.'

Admiral Arleigh Burke looked up from his desk, put on a ferocious scowl, waved a hand in the general direction of the chart of the Pacific Ocean covering one wall and demanded:

'What the hell are you doing with *our* island, Peter?'

Then a great laugh and the scowl turned to a smile of welcome. No argument today about the gently disputed sovereignty of Christmas Island.

Over a cup of coffee, Gretton outlined the logistics of the Grapple operation, of which the main plot was evidently already known to Admiral Burke, and tactfully broached the idea of calling on the US Navy establishments in Hawaii for assistance, if ever this should be necessary. No problem at all; and since the Chief of Staff to the US Commander-in-Chief, Pacific Fleet, one Rear Admiral George Anderson, was an old friend and fellow student at the National War College, an informal 'old boy' net was already available. This was good news indeed.

After a brief chat about mutual friends and naval affairs, Gretton took his leave, not wishing to impose on the courteous hospitality of a very busy man, albeit an old friend.

Back in the offices of the BDSW, he reported his successful discussion with the Chief of Naval Operations and was told that the US Air Force were being similarly very co-operative. In addition to agreeing to the transitting of the continental United States by relays of RAF aircraft – some of them carrying 'special loads', meaning radio-active or explosive contents – they would arrange accommodation for RAF ground servicing teams to be located at Travis Air Force Base, between San Francisco and Sacramento, and at Hickam Air Force Base, the military side of Honolulu international airport. This generous agreement, although confidently expected, was of the greatest importance and was a great relief.

Having achieved what he had set out to do, Commodore Gretton wasted no time. He thanked all round for help received, picked up his bag from the Army and Navy Club, and made his way back to the airport and the long slog back to London.

While Commodore Gretton had been rushing westward to renew old and useful naval contacts in Washington, Lieutenant Colonel John Woollett left London on March 4th and flew eastward to his former stamping ground in Korea to seek help in meeting the apparently impossible time scale for the construction of the Christmas Island base. It was a long and wearying journey and it was four days later when he arrived at the Royal Engineers Kohima Camp, near Kamak San and that vital bridge over the Imjin river.

He was warmly greeted by Major Laurie Young, the CO of 55 Field Squadron, which had been left behind temporarily in Korea to support the British Commonwealth Division when 28 Regiment returned to England. Young and his troops had been confidently expecting to return home in the fairly near future for some well earned leave, before rejoining the regiment.

When Woollett explained – in great secrecy – that the regiment had been given a new highly secret job and that because of desperate shortage of time 55 Squadron, instead of returning home, would go directly to the Pacific to build an air base on a tropical island, Major Young burst into quite uncontrollable laughter. When he had recovered sufficiently to share the joke, he explained that only the previous day the troops had been given the opportunity to purchase at attractive prices their

Korean heavy cold weather clothing. Most had accepted the offer and the paper work was at that moment going through the Pay Office! John Woollett joined the laughter and then added – a little more seriously – that he hoped the men would be equally amused. In any case, he hoped the tropical island project could be made to sound interesting and would generate some enthusiasm. This indeed turned out to be the case, except for a very few compassionate cases such as when young fathers had not yet seen their offspring.

It was agreed that 55 Squadron would be the first sapper unit to arrive at Christmas Island in June and that the first task would be to establish and equip a camp in the port area, ready for the arrival of the main force. These latter could then start work immediately on the construction programme. To that end, Young's troops would utilise the time before sailing to pre-fabricate as much as possible of the structures for the domestic accommodation. Details were worked out over the next few days and then Woollett and Young went over to the main base in Kure, Japan, to explain the situation to HQ British Common-wealth Forces Korea and to enlist their help. Most fortunately the CRE, the senior sapper in BCFK, was a most cooperative Australian officer, Lieutenant Colonel Sam Fletcher, who had much experience of military operations in the Pacific. He both gave valuable advice on what stores to take and provided from his local resources much of what was needed.

Well pleased with the results of his visit, Woollett left for the UK and arrived back at Erlestoke on March 21st to start a period of intense activity. Not only had he to organise all the supplies for his force and have them ready to commence loading in about six weeks; he had also to design and provide the very considerable and quite unusual requirements of AWRE. He had made one visit to Aldermaston in February and went again on April 17th to elaborate the detailed list of works to be done for the scientists, who would need laboratories with clean air, a high standard of air conditioning and temperature control, com-pressed gases, stabilised power and other special services. A

108

special building would be necessary for the assembly of the nuclear devices, blast-proof heavy sheet steel bunkers welded on site on Malden to provide the right accommodation for sensitive instrumentation and many other facilities for recording the effects of the detonation; and all this material had to be taken nine thousand miles, where there would be no quick re-supply if anything was forgotten. For the moment he could only set up close working level contacts between his sapper staff at Erlestoke and Bill Cook's team at Aldermaston and leave it to them to get the details right. It was a formidable task.

None of it would be of any use, however, unless the airfield were ready more or less on time. Later that day he joined the TFC at No 2 Engineer Supplies Depot at Liphook, where the mass of plant released by the War Office was being refurbished – too slowly. So the TFC had the civilian work force assembled and he talked to them very frankly of the great national importance of this project which was agreed by, and which had the full support of governments of both political persuasions. He asked for their whole-hearted cooperation to meet the time scale. The men responded magnificently and agreed to work overtime and weekends to get the job done. It was.

Chatting about it afterwards, the TFC went on: 'And while we're here, John, are you doing anything to see that the maintenance tool kits actually arrive with the plant?'

'Ah! We have that fixed,' replied the sapper with a broad smile. 'All tool boxes are being welded closed and then welded to the machine to which they belong. Without an oxy-acetylene cutter and time, no one can pinch them!'

A week later the TFC and his deputy paid another visit to the sapper HQ at Erlestoke. They were taken aback to see how – as the planning progressed – the volume of stores and equipment to be shipped steadily increased, with an inevitable extension of the time needed for unloading; and now that the RAF figures were coming in – something like 20,000 tons of equipment and fuel – the total to be landed at Christmas by December was approaching 100,000 tons. With only thirty feet of broken-down jetty on a shallow channel to start with and the nearest cargo ship anchored or moored more than a mile off-shore, the chances of working quickly up to an unloading rate of a thousand tons a day looked pretty poor. But it had to be done. If only they could get the big pontoons unloaded from *Ben Wyvis* at an early stage and the channel dredged enough so that fuel could be brought ashore in bulk instead of in barrels, maybe it would all work out.

It was obviously necessary not to take anything not absolutely essential and to keep to a minimum the amount of stores to be put ashore in the early stages; and similarly to keep down the number of men to be supported in the camp. This meant they would be very short of labour for unskilled chores yet there would be a premium on sapper tradesmen for skilled jobs. Any airmen, sailors or Royal Marines not immediately needed for their proper specialist work would have to be employed in erecting tents and other domestic chores.

This question raised the point that most army, navy, air force and civilian personnel would be meeting one another for the first time on shore and many might be totally confused. Personal contact between at least some of the officers would be a great help. So Colonel Woollett set up a two day study period to take place in the middle of May, shortly before the first sailing, to which Major Young would come from Korea plus other Task Force personnel from the RN, RM, RAF, so that at least a nucleus of people would know what it was all about when they landed.

The TFC then took the opportunity to raise the question of health hazards. Many of the younger men would have had no experience of tropical conditions and could easily find themselves unfit for work unless precautions were observed. For the first four or five days, everyone ashore should be careful not to expose himself too much to the sun. Officers should exercise control over their men in this respect. Secondly, in a hot and very humid climate to which they were unaccustomed, there would be a risk of skin infections. Clean clothing was

110

essential. What was going to be done about adequate laundry facilities?

This last point caused some dismay, not having been included in the plan as yet. Normally the sappers would have expected to use local facilities, which were obviously non-existent in this case.

'We may have to buy a mobile laundry,' said the TFC. 'I'll get Colonel Stone and Mr Lovelock to look into it.'

Meanwhile at Marchwood the stevedores of No 51 Port Detachment were getting on with their training, prodded frequently by Commodore Gretton, and the vast pontoons had been assembled and tested, two of them with great outboard diesel engines. They performed well, which news gave great satisfaction and comfort in the Grapple HQ. Now they went for loading in the *Ben Wyvis*.

All in all, the Army plan was proceeding fairly well, but with no safety margins. It was going to be a 'damned near-run thing'.

16

Wind and weather worries

Milligan and Surtees, the Air-side planners, came into the TFC's office.

'Can we have half an hour, sir?'

'Yes, Freddie. At the table. Shoot.'

'We have here the first rough draft of the operation order for a live drop and it brings out one point which you ought to know now. With everything ready and on the top line, from the moment you give the order "Go" it takes forty-eight hours to release of the bomb; and if you stop the programme halfway – say, after twenty four hours – it will take about a week to recover and get everything ready to start again; and we shall have used up a lot of our resources. Do that a few times and the whole programme could be set back a month. So when you give the order "Go" it has to be right. Of course, as we refine the plan and prune the details, we can probably cut down the forty eight hours a bit, but not all that much. Another consequence is that there will have to be a lot of night flying and some of it may be during pretty lousy weather; so the airfield night flying facilities need to be first class – not just a scratch arrangement. That's it, sir.'

The TFC looked at them thoughtfully for a moment.

'Thank you both. Good work, getting so far so soon. I'm dismayed, but not really surprised and we have a similar situation on the AWRE side, except that they only need twenty four hours decision before a drop.

'We'd better have the Navy in on this. Butch, would you please see if Captain Western is free and ask him to come in?'

Moments later, Guy Western joined the group and was quickly put in the picture. How long before a drop would the naval team have to start their count-down procedures?

The problem was not quite the same as for the air elements. Starting from scratch, they would probably need 72 hours to get into position and properly lined up; but once there, a delay of two or three days wouldn't matter much, as long as it was not more than about seven days.

'Thank you, Guy. That's not so difficult. Now the main factor in giving a "Go" decision is clearly going to be the weather and wind forecast at various levels and the resultant fall-out prediction. So the sooner we get to grips with the Meteorological organisation and requirements the better. This is going to impose a massive task on both aircraft and ships, as well as on island reporting stations and communications. I think you, Freddie, and you, Guy, had better go together to Bracknell, see the Director of the Met Office, meet the senior forecaster who will be in charge of Met at Christmas and get out a detailed Met plan as soon as possible. Could you go tomorrow? OK. I'll look after the shop while you're away. So I suggest, Freddie, that I pick you up in the staff car at Gloucester Terrace at 8am, you drop me off at Whitehall, go on to Waterloo to collect Guy off his train and go on to Bracknell by road. Better ring up now and make the appointment. All agreed? Thank you.'

The next morning, after their courtesy call on the Director, Milligan and Western went into conference with Mr M H Freeman, who was to be in charge of the Met organisation in the Grapple area. He was a quiet, unassuming and pleasant man, but very direct and calmly confident in his manner and in expressing his professional views. Despite his aura of great technical competence, he was clearly a little concerned about the magnitude of the task facing him and the responsibility which he would carry. Being a very practical and down-to-earth character however, he wasted no time but took the two visitors

113

off to his office, spread a chart of the Central Pacific on his desk and launched into an outline of his problems and his requirements to overcome them.

The task of the Grapple Met organisation would be to give the Task Force Commander forecasts of two conditions in the Malden Island area and out to about a thousand miles downwind, namely:-

1. cloud cover, visibility, wind speed and direction from ground level up to 45,000 feet to enable him to decide whether conditions were suitable for visual bombing and photography

2. wind speed and direction, temperature, humidity, and precipitation up to 100,000 feet to enable him, on the advice of the Scientific Director and the AWRE Theoretical Predictions Group, to be assured that any radio-active fall-out from the vaporisation of the bomb itself in the case of the planned air burst, or from surface vaporisation in the case of a malfunction of the barometric fuze, would not cause any radio-active contamination in excess of the agreed safety level in any inhabited area down-wind of the explosion.

To a query as to why it was necessary to forecast these conditions up to such a great height, the explanation was given that a nuclear explosion produces, in a tiny fraction of a second, local temperatures of many millions of degrees of Celsius. This causes the surrounding air to become so hot as to be incandescent and very buoyant, whereupon it rises at great speed, carrying with it the particles of the vaporised bomb and forming the mushroom cloud as it ascends. In ascending, the cloud cools and slows down and that from a nominal kiloton bomb might not reach the tropopause at about 50,000 feet and would certainly not pass through it. But theoretical calculation, supported by some of the evidence from American tests,

114

indicated that the cloud from an explosion of a megaton or more would probably go right through the tropopause and on up to possibly 100,000 feet. So every precaution must be taken.

To produce these forecasts, the central Met office at Christmas would need to accumulate a background knowledge, as well as frequent measurements immediately prior to a test of barometric pressure, temperature, humidity, wind speed and direction from sea-level up to 100,000 feet over an area of some one thousand miles radius from Christmas.

As yet there was virtually no record of such information. They would have to start from scratch to build up the

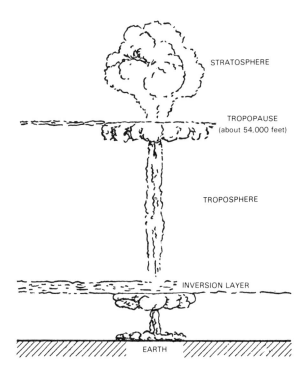

STRATOSPHERE

TROPOPAUSE
(about 54,000 feet)

TROPOSPHERE

INVERSION LAYER

EARTH

Cloud penetrating the
tropopause

background knowledge of the weather pattern and this meant starting to collect and collate such data at least three months before the date of the first planned drop.

The meeting then set to planning how to meet these requirements. Firstly, by aircraft. Shackleton aircraft crews had a standard role of weather observation and a squadron based on Christmas could collect and transmit to base the necessary data at sea level, 10,000 feet and 18,000 feet. Canberra PR7 aircraft equipped with 'Green Satin' doppler radar and the necessary Met instrumentation could make the observations from 20,000 feet at 50 millibar intervals up to 45,000 feet or higher – maybe even 50,000 feet.

Ships of the Naval Task Group, at least HMS *Warrior*, *Narvik*, and HMNZS *Pukaki* and *Rotoiti* all had height-finding radar and could be equipped for high altitude wind finding as well as surface observations.

Under the standard international arrangements for the collection and dissemination of meteorological information, data would be received from Honolulu, Fiji, Samoa and a full scale weather-reporting station would be established on Penrhyn Island, some 600 miles south of Christmas.

All of that, however, did not deal with the levels above 50,000 feet. Resort would therefore be made to a new device – the radio-sonde, an ingenious instrument which measures temperature, pressure and humidity and then transmits these parameters in turn by means of a small battery-powered radio set. The radio-sonde is carried aloft by a hydrogen-filled balloon, which also carries a radar-reflector, by means of which the sonde can be tracked by radar and its position plotted, and the wind calculated.

The balloon at launch is about seven feet diameter and swells as it rises until it bursts at about 100,000 feet, by which time it is larger than the average four-bedroom house.

The radio-sonde results, plotted on a 'Te-phi'-gram form, then provide the data on which can be forecast both the height to which the cloud will ascend and the 'foot-print' of any

116

consequential fall-out. Armed with this information, the planners returned to Whitehall to draft an outline of the necessary logistic support for the Met organisation.

17

Daily problems – or 'the nitty gritty'

By the middle of March 1956 the planning for the British nuclear tests was beginning to be translated into action. Group Captain Menaul had organised and assembled his Air Task Group for the Monte Bello Operation Mosaic and this was of great interest to the Grapple Task Force Commander, since it included the same 76 (Canberra) Squadron which would later go on to do the same atomic cloud sampling tasks at Christmas Island.

On March 15th, after a press briefing, the entire Mosaic Air Task Group left Weston Zoyland for Western Australia, where the Canberras would have to operate from the Royal Australian Air Force base at Pearce Field, near Perth – over 700 miles from Monte Bello; but the Varsity general transport aircraft and a flight of helicopters would operate from small local airstrips, lacking every facility, to carry out their tasks both of fetching and carrying and of tracking the radio-active clouds as they drifted slowly eastward, fading to a harmless level as they went. Accordingly, each Varsity was crammed full of tables, chairs, desks, filing cabinets, servicing equipment, aircraft spares and all the impedimenta essential to operating intensively from a bull-dozed strip in the desert. No kitchen sinks, but everything else.

The Air Task Group proceeded via Idris (Libya), Habbaniya (Iraq), Mauripur (India), Negombo (Ceylon), Changi (Singapore), Darwin (Northern Australia) and then westward along the coastal route to Perth. The helicopters had been shipped and ground crews had gone by civil air or the regular Hastings shuttle. All had arrived on time by 26th March.

HMS *Narvik*, Commodore Martell's flagship, was already at Monte Bello, as were the Royal Engineers and the AWRE scientific staff, busy erecting the test towers and installing the ground equipment. The first test – a tower burst – took place successfully on 16th May. This was, of course, an essential preliminary step to Operation Grapple, as was the second Monte Bello shot on 19th June.

Meanwhile, back in London at the Grapple HQ, planning procurement and preparations were proceeding apace. The LST HMS *Messina* had arrived at Chatham and dockyard work was started immediately on the many and extensive modifications which had to be made to have her ready to sail for Christmas Island early in June. The much greater task of re-fitting HMS *Warrior* was urgently proceeding at Devonport. *Salvictor*, an ocean going salvage vessel, was in dock at Chatham having her stem hacked about and fitted with launching ramps for mooring chains and buoys, and her quarterdeck modified to carry a DUKW. Personnel, too, were being modified as the Landing Craft crews were being trained at Fremington and the stevedores at Southampton. The pontoons were being assembled at Marchwood and the Grapple naval staff were busy in the Baltic Exchange chartering ships for the transport of personnel, stores and equipment.

The preparation of the vast vocabularies of stores, transport, specialist vehicles and plant of all kinds, many different types of fuel and lubricants and so on was handled largely in the individual Ministries, but required the constant co-operation of and monitoring by Grapple staff. If anything were to be forgotten or omitted, other than a relatively small amount which could be supplied by air transport, it would take two months to rectify the error after it had been detected. Such a mistake could easily wash out the entire operation.

Inevitably the HQ Grapple staff had grown in numbers

beyond the closely-knit little team which the TFC had originally envisaged and towards the end of March he realised that he was beginning to lose touch with what was going on under his feet. That wouldn't do at all.

He called Freddie Milligan into his office.

'Freddie, there are so many of us in the team now that I'm losing touch and I'll bet you are too. From now on, I want each working day to begin with a five minute meeting of everybody not away on some trip, just to mention the highlights of what each chap is worrying about and to develop a family atmosphere. Let's start on Monday.'

'Good idea, sir. I feel the same; and while we're on about it, this new Latimer Joint Services staff system is a great handicap and no help. The several ministry departments we work with are just confused by it. Can we drop it?'

'OK, Freddie. We tried. It's too soon to use the new system, so let each team – Navy, Army, Air, scientists – do its staff work in its own traditional way. After all, each of them has derived a way of working that best suits its own needs. A few of us in the centre of Grapple will just have to speak all four languages and I reckon we can do that.'

The next Monday morning, at nine o'clock, about twenty of the staff of all colours assembled in the conference room and the TFC outlined the idea.

'I hope this need only take five minutes – absolutely not more than ten – and will help to promote good team work. So, round the table quickly. You first, Guy,' nodding to Captain Western – 'anything on your mind?'

'I hope it doesn't sound frivolous, but I think we ought to have a Grapple tie and not just for fun. Working in plain clothes as we do most of the time, and with new people coming in, we don't know who is in the team and who not. Also, it would help to promote the team spirit.'

'Good idea. I like it. Does everyone agree we should have a Grapple tie?' Murmurs of approval all round, so that was that. Next point:

'Freddie?'

'We're not progressing fast enough with the Signals plan. I know that Finlay has a good organisation planned for communication between Christmas and the UK, and between ships; but that won't do for en route control of air movements and for general air control in the operational area. I think we should get RAF 90 (Signals) Group into the act without delay.'

'Agree. Do it.'

Squadron Leader Dobbs, a tall dignified engineer officer of quiet unassuming manner, a recent arrival in the HQ, spoke up quite firmly. 'I understand, sir, that we have to change the aerodynamic seals between control surfaces and non-moving surfaces of the Valiants before a live drop. I also understand that there is a pretty steady 15-20 knot wind on the ground. It's just not possible to change controls in the open in such conditions and I don't suppose there's any possibility of a Bessoneaux type hangar big enough to take the tail of a Valiant. So what do we do?'

'Thank you, Dobbs. We'll have an Airside meeting later to discuss that.'

After going round the table quickly and collecting a number of other points, the TFC concluded: 'Now I have a small point. For the sake of the film we are making to record this unique operation – probably unique, anyway – I want to have a shot of a staff meeting to start the story. So will you all please turn up in uniform on Wednesday of next week — and I'd like everyone here – and will you, Terry please have the film people lined up? Not more than fifteen minutes, in this room, let's say at 2.15. That's all for today.'

These quick morning meetings then continued throughout the planning stage of Grapple and worked very well in keeping the members of the team closely in touch with one another. It was interesting also to watch firm friendships springing up between individuals of different uniform but 'on the same wave length', all adding to the cohesiveness of the team.

The Monday nine o'clock was, of course, followed by the

naval staff briefing; and on this occasion, in the absence of Commodore Gretton, Western and Thatcher produced the good news that they had found and chartered – after some considerable 'arm twisting' – a heavy lift ship to carry the pontoons, lighters, the small dredger and the Landing Craft, which could not be handled by a normal cargo ship. This was the *Ben Wyvis*, one of the Ben Line ships, which were the only ones in the world with derricks capable of lifting 120 tons at a time. They had been built in America to a British design during the second World War and were in great demand all over the world. It had been very difficult to procure *Ben Wyvis* to meet the time scale for Grapple and the news was a great relief. At a later and less critical stage, the sister ships *Ben Rinnes* and *Ben Nevis* also gave very valuable support in the build-up of the main base.

While his naval staff were coping so heroically and efficiently with the mass of detail, Peter Gretton was employing all his tremendous drive and determination to push all the various programmes along faster than was theoretically possible. On this day he had flown up to Scotland in a naval Vampire aircraft to visit a weather ship – an old Flower class corvette – to investigate the techniques and equipment for weather reporting which would have to be used in *Warrior, Narvik* and the two New Zealand frigates. Later in the week he hustled round the training going on at Fremington and Southampton to try to save a day or two of time here or there and to impress on everyone a sense of urgency to which not all were accustomed.

On that particular day, another piece of the jig-saw puzzle was placed in position on the air side.

'Wing Commander Bower to see you, sir,' announced Helfer.

At the door of the TFC's office was a tall, lean, stern-looking character, very erect and stiff as a ram-rod, bristling moustache, looking more like a prototype guardsman than an ace air navigator with numerous long-range pioneering flights to his credit, including one of the earliest flights over the North Pole and the first non-stop transatlantic flight in a jet aircraft, a Canberra.

'Come and sit down, Bower. Glad to have you with us at last. Coffee? Flight Sergeant! Two coffees, please...

'Now, Bower, have you any idea what we are about, here?'

'No, sir. I'm just told that I am posted to your staff.'

'Well, let's begin with your immediate job. I want you to take a Shackleton and a small team to a deserted coral island in the Pacific where there is a derelict airstrip, which may or may not be usable when you first arrive, and set up a staging post. You'll have to take with you everything you need to get started, until reinforcements arrive by sea a few days later. Target place – Christmas Island, 1100 miles south of Hawaii. Target date – mid June.'

'Yes, sir.' No sign of perturbation or surprise. Just complete calm and a slight smile. Good!

'You may have guessed that this is in preparation for an atomic test. We are going to be very short of time to get the base established and your initial task is to organise regular air support and communication in the form of a Hastings shuttle service between Honolulu and Christmas Island as quickly as possible and to keep it going like clockwork. You'll get plenty of help from the Royal Engineers, and standard equipment will be unloaded from the ships, once they have set up their own base: but I want the Hastings service sooner than that. So you must take mobile VHF and H/F radio, a homing beacon and anything else you need to meet Transport Command's minima criteria to enable the service to start. Also based on my own experience in the war, I want you to take in your team a first class NCO carpenter, complete with his tool kit. Although in theory you'll be able to ask the Sappers to do any necessary job for you, you would always find that it could only be done at the expense of disrupting some equally vital work schedule. They just don't have spare hands waiting. So it's much better to have your own man, particularly as you may well find the odd derelict hut which can be improved to be something better than the tent in which you will probably start operating.

'Initially you will have no transport; so I want you to take a couple of those parachute regiment folding motor-cycles – I think they are made by the James two-stroke motor-cycle people – to give you some mobility in the first few days.

'All this is very broad brush. I want you to get out your own detailed plan, clear it with Group Captain Milligan and Surtees and then execute it in June. One last point, the old airstrip may well be serviceable enough; but even if not, you *must* put down and establish the staging post, even if it means damaging the aircraft. OK?'

'Yes, sir. That's all quite clear. Sounds interesting!' – and Dougie Bower went off calmly to join the air planners.

Later that day, the TFC was ruminating about the problem of changing Valiant control surfaces in the windy conditions on Christmas Island, when a flash of memory came back to him of walking in the frequent spring gales along the edge of the high and precipitous cliff tops on the south-west coast of Malta. He had served there as a very junior and impecunious officer; and when the weather was too bad for swimming in off-duty hours, frequently walked from Hal Far aerodrome to the cliff top and along the edge to Wied Zurrieq. On the very edge one got the full force of the onshore gale. About fifty yards back, the wind came from behind; and in between there was a zone of relative calm. Could a wind deflector be constructed to deflect the air flow over the top of the Valiant, leaving the rudder or aileron or whatever in air calm enough to allow work to proceed?

He called in Dobbs, Duck and Milligan and outlined the idea. They all thought it worth trying; so Milligan was to contact the aerodynamics department at RAE Farnborough and set up a working level contact. In due course RAE quickly produced the design, tested it in the wind tunnel. Vickers then manufactured the deflector, which was eventually shipped to Christmas, installed and worked just fine. Another problem solved.

So, if this was a good day for solving problems, what about the one which Guy Western had brought up – a Grapple tie?

Being an enthusiastic supporter of the Joint Services Staff College, the TFC wondered if the emblem of that establish-

HMS *Messina*, a Landing Ship (Tank).

Commander H De Vere (front row in the centre) and officers of
HMS *Messina*.

The port area ('Port London') of
Christmas Island where everything
had to be landed. *(Photo: R Townsend)*

Construction work on the runway. A dumper laying down the cement.

The Commander, Royal Engineers, in formal working dress! *(Photo: J C Woollett)*

Major Tom Marquis, Second in Command, 28 Regiment RE and Regimental Sergeant Major Jones.

Major Laurie Young, OC 55 Field Squadron RE.

ment, a Cormorant, could be the basis of a motif. Next, 'Grapple' was a centuries-old name for a grapnel, a several-pronged anchor-like device used in boarding enemy ships. A four pronged, or should it be four fluked (?) grapnel would indicate the four services involved in the operation and would be a nice pun on the name. So how about a cormorant carrying a four point grapnel as the emblem for Task Force Grapple and as the motif, against a plain background, for the club tie? He called in the three senior planners, apologised for disrupting their work and put the suggestion to them. They were quite taken with the idea.

'You started this, Guy, so what do you think we should use for colours?'

Western pondered for a moment.

'We want to get away from the usual run of colours used in single service ties, so how about silver for the motif? And wouldn't that look good against a black background — indicative of the black magic we're playing with?'

There was general agreement to try it out and Helfer - who turned out to be a surprisingly good artist - offered to do a sketch in water colours. In due course this looked so good that not only was the idea adopted for the tie, but the Cormorant-and-Grapple design was adopted as the insignia of the Task Force and was used to identify all Grapple documentation. When the tie design was shown to Peter Gretton a day or so later, he too liked it but suggested the addition of a thin silver diagonal stripe at intervals, and this too was adopted. Lewin's, the tie specialists in Panton Street, produced the material and the ties very quickly, and there was soon considerable speculation in Whitehall as to what this strange phenomenon might signify. But no hint was forthcoming from the tightly buttoned lips of the Grapple team.

A little diversion like this serviced to lighten the spirits, but it was time to get back to serious business.

18

'Ginger' Weir

Early in April a most welcome recruit appeared in the Grapple HQ – Air Commodore C T Weir – universally known as 'Ginger' — who was to be the Air Task Group Commander. Lean in face and figure, sardonic in manner, with a very keen dry and whimsical sense of humour, he was professionally extremely competent but always hid it under a cloak of levity, sparking off a light hearted atmosphere even when dealing with desperately difficult problems. He was still limping badly from injuries suffered in a car accident and was impatiently using a walking stick as little as possible. However, for the moment that didn't matter. The immediate need was for his organising ability to create and operate a highly efficient Air Task Group of considerable complexity.

Weir and the TFC greeted one another as old friends who hadn't met for about six years and who were both delighted to be working together again. Over a cup of coffee and after catching up on personal histories since they last met, the TFC gave a quick summary of the task ahead.

'I know, Ginger, that you've been on the fringe of the atomic business for some time, so forgive me if I go over stuff with which you are already familiar. Your main job now is to get the Air Task Group organised, manned and operating as quickly as possible. But at the same time, I've agreed with Bill Penney and have fixed with Air Ministry Personnel that you will be the Task Force Commander for 'Buffalo' at Maralinga in September/

October. As that will involve the same Valiant and Canberra B6 squadrons as for Grapple, it seemed a logical progression. I hope that's all right with you?'

'I'm delighted, Wilf, and it does seem very sensible too.'

'You'll obviously need to build up your own small personal staff as quickly as possible, but for the time being Milligan and his team must continue with the air side planning and you can take over gradually as and when you are ready; but I must stress that we are all one team here and there must be no barrier of any kind between Task Group and Task Force staffs.

'There is a hell of a programme of aircraft modifications, aircrew training and much else; so I suggest we have all the air staff round the table and go briefly through the whole thing. So let's wander across the road to the Cabinet Office mess – if you're OK to walk that far – for a bite of lunch and we'll set up the full meeting for 2.15.'

At the risk of some boring repetition of information already well known, it was sensible to review the aircraft tasks to bring the new Air Task Group Commander fully up to date, and no bad thing to remind all the Air Force staff seated round the table of the overall picture. It was all too easy to become so immersed in some particular set of problems as to lose sight of the whole picture.

In order of appearance on the scene, the Task Force would require the following aircraft from the Air Task Group:

Shackletons to deliver the initial staging post party to
    Christmas.
Hastings to run the shuttle service to Honolulu, and some-
    times Australia.
Dakotas for the Malden and inter-island airlift.
Shackletons for low and medium level meteorological
    flights, sea searches and photography, starting February
    1957.
PR7 Canberras for high level wind finding, photography
    and rapid transport of the cloud samples back to UK.

Valiants for the weapon drop and instrumentation of the explosion.

B6 Canberras for cloud sampling.

Whirlwind helicopters for Air Sea Rescue and local air taxi work.

In addition, there would be close integration with the Navy, requiring Naval Whirlwind helicopters for airlift between Malden and *Warrior/Narvik* in the forward area.

Naval Avengers for bringing instrumentation records back from Malden via *Warrior* to Christmas and thence by Canberra to UK. Also for rapid communication between Christmas and *Warrior* in the Malden area.

All of these aircraft, except possibly the Navy ones, were going to require considerable modification, ranging from only a little for the Hastings to a vast programme of about two thousand mods for the Valiants. Detailed lists for each type of aircraft were being prepared by the technical staff in conjunction with the relevant Command and Air Ministry staffs, with the aircraft manufacturers and – in the case of the Valiants and B6s – with RAE Farnborough and AWRE Aldermaston.

Touching briefly on each type, the Shackletons, Hastings and Dakotas would need additional radio navigation and communication fits to cope with the very different en route and terminal facilities in Canada and America. The Shackletons would also need additional meteorological equipment, installation of special cameras for taking low level photographs of the explosion and of the cloud, up-dating of their search radar, installation of Decca and Loran, and improvements to their 'sniffing' gear to enable them to assist in tracking fall-out from an accidental low level burst.

The PR7 Canberras would need periscopic sextants, 'Green Satin' doppler radar, Loran and an improved radio fit, including 'Rebecca', to help in the long range over-water flights and return to Christmas where there was no diversion airfield available. They would also need to be fitted with the bomb-bay modification to carry a massive beam – nick-named 'the Forth Bridge' – on which would be mounted heavy lead cannisters containing the samples of the radio-active cloud for rapid transport to Aldermaston. This was necessary to protect the aircrew from excessive radiation during the long flights.

The numerous changes to the standard Valiant bomber aircraft fell into five main groups.

1. Those to ensure as far as possible the safety of the Aircrew.
2. Those to ensure accuracy in the delivery of the weapon to the designated point, 8000 feet altitude, $1\frac{1}{2}$ nautical miles on a bearing of 200 degrees from the marker on the south-east corner of Malden Island.
3. Those to give the AWRE scientists a second-by-second check of the weapon system up to the moment of release from the aircraft.
4. Those to provide the maximum amount of information on the performance of the weapon and its effect on the aircraft.
5. The additional radio-navigation and communications fit to ensure the safe and timely transit of the aircraft through Canadian and American airspace and staging posts.

Eight special Valiants were to come off the Vickers production line, incorporating during manufacture all modifications so far agreed. Inevitably there would be last minute additions and alterations, but it would be clearly advantageous to build in as many as possible on the production line; so the technical planning should be completed quickly and urgently.

Many of the requirements were already clear; for instance, a brilliant white reflective paint for the exterior of the airframe,

129

flash shields for all windows and apertures, a specially modified bomb-sight with associated computer and control gear for the overshoot bombing technique, special camera mountings in the tail cone and elsewhere, Decca, Loran, simultaneous transmission from the pilot's microphone on both VHF and H/F, the special-to-task weapon arming system, aircraft to ground telemetry, the sensitive g-meter, airframe stress gauges, blast overpressure gauges and hundreds of other items. A meeting would be held at RAE on April 16th to review all the modifications and bring the list to as near completion as possible.

Moving on to the B6 Canberras, the TFC observed that the 76 Squadron aircraft would already have had most of the necessary modifications fitted for Mosaic and Buffalo; but in view of the possibly much greater risk to the aircrew in Grapple, there must be better radiation monitoring, improved pressurisation, and a 'demand' oxygen system to avoid the intake of cabin air which might be contaminated after passing through the cloud.

If feasible, sampling should be carried out at much higher altitudes than for operation Buffalo – 56,000 feet or more; but at that height the current aircraft would be on the edge of the stall. Napiers were therefore producing for RAE some experimental 'Scorpion' auxiliary jet motors which might improve the high-altitude performance of the B6.

Long range over-sea navigation on the stages between Australia and Christmas Island would require the fitting of periscopic sextants, as for the PR7s and some extra crew training in astro-navigation.

Other changes might also be required and this should be studied by the Air Task Group as a matter of urgency. It was also necessary to bear in mind that some of the aircraft used for Mosaic and Buffalo might still be too 'hot' to use safely in Grapple – or even to stage through international airports such as Nandi. Likewise, some of the crews, both air and ground, might have reached or be near to their safe limit of exposure to radiation. So as a matter of prudence, there must be some further provision of B6s with all modifications incorporated and of reserve crews trained for the task.

Whilst on the subject of radiation, he noted that he had not yet seen any outline plan for the decontamination centre. Short of a serious accident there could be no risk of significant radiation effect on any member of the Task Force, other than the air and ground crews of the B6 sampling aircraft. Every step had to be taken to ensure that none of these received more than the agreed limit of radiation, that decontamination procedures were effective and rigorously applied and that follow-up checks were made as necessary.

Lastly, the helicopters. One might have thought that here at least there was no need for troublesome modifications; but when Westlands had heard that their aircraft were to go to an environment with heavy sea-salt and coral corrosion, high humidity and high temperatures, they had immediately sounded the alarm. Corrosion was already causing serious trouble even in the mild conditions of the UK. Special measures would have to be taken with the aircraft going to Christmas or they would very soon cease to be airworthy.

That was enough to be going on with as regarded the aircraft programme. The meeting then turned to organisation matters.

The Air Task Group would be established as Number 160 Wing, RAF, and would form at RAF Station Hornchurch, an old RAF fighter airfield on the eastern outskirts of London, on April 16th. The wing would have an initial establishment of 10 officers and 94 specialist tradesmen of various trades and would begin to move to Christmas Island in June. There it would gradually build up to an overall strength of about a thousand – subject to any changes Air Commodore Weir might wish to make.

The operational squadrons would be supplied by Bomber, Coastal and Transport Commands and would come under command of 160 Wing on reaching the operational area at Honolulu. 160 Wing would be fully responsible for operations and first-line servicing. Servicing might have to be more flexible in the light of events.

Bomber Command would furnish No 76 (B6) Canberra Squadron, No 100 (PR7) Canberra Squadron from RAF Wyton and a Valiant Squadron, understood at that time to be No 138 at RAF Station Wittering. Coastal Command would furnish Nos 206 and 240 Shackleton Squadrons, both from RAF Station Ballykelly and a flight of No 22 (Helicopter Air/Sea Rescue) Squadron from RAF Station St Mawgan.

Transport Command would not allocate a fixed Hastings Squadron, but would provide continuously an agreed number of aircraft in the area to meet the Task Force requirements. They would also provide No 1325 Flight with three Dakotas and four crews, which would form at RAF Station Dishforth later in the year. The Dakotas had just been unearthed in some Maintenance Unit and were about to be completely overhauled for Grapple. This was particularly good news, as so much would depend on regular daily access between Christmas and Malden Islands.

By now the afternoon was gone and the new Air Task Group Commander had plenty to think about for the next few days. So the TFC ended the meeting and took his newest recruit round for cordial introductions to the Navy and Army members of the team. With his easy and affable manner, Ginger was immediately at home with them and the team went on from strength to strength.

Detailed planning now went on apace during April. As more organisations and departments became involved in providing the necessary resources for the operation, it became increasingly difficult to maintain complete secrecy and eventually the gaff was blown.

The press had been briefed on the departure of the 'Mosaic' Air Task Group in March and since then had been monitoring closely the progress of the atomic weapons programme announced by the Government in 1955. Having received the information from the Government's chief defence scientist, Sir

Frederick Brundrett, the distinguished *Daily Express* Defence Correspondent Chapman Pincher broke the news that the H-bomb tests would take place near Christmas Island. A few days later, on May 2nd, he gave the further news that a Task Force Commander had been appointed.

This was followed a month later by a statement in the House of Commons by the Prime Minister on June 7th. In this Sir Anthony Eden said: 'Her Majesty's Government has decided to carry out a limited number of nuclear explosions in the megaton range. The tests will be high air bursts and will not involve heavy fall-out. All safety precautions will be taken in the light of our knowledge and the experience gained from the tests of other countries.'

Despite these disclosures, the Task Force continued to maintain the maximum security possible.

After jumping in at the deep end of the planning for Operation Grapple, one of the may pre-occupations of Air Commodore Weir was that of meeting the Task Force Commander's insistence on the provision of Decca Navigator facilities as an important aid to both bombing and navigation in the uncertain weather conditions of the central Pacific Ocean. Other manufacturers, including notably Vickers and Marconi, were providing whole-hearted and vital assistance to the Task Force; but the Decca equipment played such a key role that it deserves a special mention.

There are other excellent radio aids to bombing and navigation: but by reasons of the geography and other conditions at Christmas Island, at least as foreseen in the planning stage, Decca seemed the most appropriate. For the benefit of the lay reader, the system enables an operator to fix his geographical position very accurately by reference to the mutual interference between transmissions from two radio stations. Readings from the Decometer 'black box' in ship or aircraft are plotted on a special Decca chart and the intersection between two sets of hyperbolic curves gives the position of the observer – subject to errors creeping in!

Unfortunately, the coverage required over Malden Island was very much further from any possible ground station sites than that used in existing installations and, even worse, the angular relationship was wrong. The available islands were just not in the right places.

The best that could be done was to put the Master transmitter station on Jarvis Island and the 'slaves' on Christmas and Penrhyn – over 600 miles away. This presented severe technical problems and there were many in the Decca Company who thought it impossible. However, the enthusiastic originator of the system – Harvey Schwartz – and his chief assistant Bill White, inured to vehement opposition over many years, were convinced and determined that it would be made to succeed. They had, after all, had the same kind of opposition in so successfully providing coverage for the Allied landings in Normandy in 1944.

Wing Commander Danny Clare of the Directorate of Navigation in the Air Ministry was already working with Decca technicians on the provision of a chain of stations for operational use in Europe and the Task Force air planners enlisted his aid to put pressure on Schwartz and White – not that much pressure was necessary. Before long, meetings between Task Force and Decca planners were taking place far into the night in Bill White's pleasant flat in Dolphin Square.

Another problem was to get some of the equipment manufactured in time to be shipped out to Christmas Island. It looked hopeless, but was eventually solved by recovering ground stations from North Borneo, where they had been used in survey for oil exploration. That brought the Task Force naval staff into the deal at an early stage and later on they would deliver equipment and personnel to Penrhyn and Jarvis and support them there.

In due course all went as planned, as will be told later; and despite many difficulties – some of them novel, because of the great height at which the Valiant aircraft would be operating – it eventually worked out well.

19

The Valiant squadron

March and April 1956 had for the most part been devoted to the problems of establishing the base on Christmas Island and the delivery of supplies and equipment. By early May it was more than time to consider air operations in more detail, since all the massive logistic effort was useless unless it ensured that one of the special new Valiant bombers could deliver the nuclear device to an exact spot at a fairly exact time and in perfect technical condition. So on May 7th the Task Force Commander and his ADC borrowed an Anson aircraft from Hendon and flew up to RAF Station Wittering, where No. 138 (Valiant) Squadron – the first of the new V-bombers – had formed.

After a protocol call on the Station Commander, who discreetly did not enquire about the purpose of the visit, they were escorted to the office of Wing Commander Oakley, the CO of 138, where they could talk in privacy. On broaching the subject of a forthcoming nuclear test, Oakley interrupted with the astonishing news that he was not involved in this plan, which was to be handled entirely by a special flight, No 1321 Flight, commanded by Squadron Leader David Roberts.

So Roberts, a tall and very personable young officer of modest demeanour but obviously of keen intelligence, was wheeled in. After being introduced, he took his visitors away to his own flight office in a separate building.

There he related efficiently and concisely how he had for eighteen months been the Valiant Project Officer at Vickers factory at Weybridge, working as a member of George Edwards' team, until 2 months previously. Then, under the usual restrictions of 'need-to-know' secrecy, he had been instructed to form 1321 Flight at Wittering, initially with only one standard Valiant and his own crew, for the purpose of carrying out the first British air drop of a kiloton atomic weapon at Maralinga later in the year. This was to be Operation 'Buffalo'.

Since then he had acquired two more standard Valiant aircraft and two more crews from the output of the Valiant Operational Training Unit at Gaydon. At the moment, all their effort was going into visual bombing training and the so-called F-series 'fly-over' bombing trials at Orfordness, these latter to determine, inter alia, the best standard bomb-case to contain the nuclear device and to establish the ballistic data necessary to ensure the required accuracy of delivery.

They were also trying to get the bugs out of the bombing system. The only attempt so far to drop a dummy 'Blue Danube' 10,000 pound bomb – the preferred profile at that time – had resulted in the bomb refusing to release from the bomb-rack on the dropping run. Then, when the bomb-doors had been closed and the aircraft was returning to base, the bomb had fallen off the rack into the bomb-bay. After landing and returning to dispersal, the bomb doors had been opened for inspection and the bomb had fallen to the ground. So evidently all was not well with the system. The thought of this happening with a megaton weapon instead of a load of concrete in the Blue Danube case was sobering, to say the least. He made a mental note that there would be no question whatever of a Valiant returning to Christmas Island with a bomb hang-up. Meanwhile back to Roberts. Representatives from Vickers, Farnborough and Boscombe Down were working on the hang-up problem, as also on the ballistics of Blue Danube and adjustments to the bombsight. But what with technical snags and the infrequency of weather suitable for high level visual bombing, the programme was not going very well and they would soon be due to move the Flight to Australia in preparation for Operation

Buffalo at Maralinga. To complicate matters further, there was now a rumour that 1321 Flight, which for some weeks had been attached to 138 Squadron as 'C' Flight to give it some technical and administrative support, was to be separated again and to be built up as a full squadron.

There was nothing for it but to give David Roberts the whole story, that Buffalo was merely the prelude to the much bigger Operation Grapple. Specially modified aircraft would be needed and at a meeting held at Farnborough on April 26th some two thousand modifications to the standard Valiant had already been agreed and would be incorporated into the production line of eight special aircraft. More would doubtless follow. It was clear that Roberts himself would not be able to go to Australia for Buffalo. He would have to concentrate on building up the new squadron for Grapple. Obviously disappointed, Roberts took the news stoically and at once threw himself whole-heartedly into his greatly expanded task, to bring Squadron Leader Flavell and Flight Lieutenant Bates up to scratch for Maralinga and in preparing a plan for Christmas Island.

The TFC spent several hours looking over the aircraft, meeting air and ground crews and discussing the problems sure to arise. He then hastened back to Hendon and Whitehall, where he summoned the air planners to examine this lastest snag of the bomb hang-up.

Ginger Weir, Freddie Milligan, Butch Surtees, Paul Whit-field and Roly Duck sat round the table with the TFC, discussing the implications of a hang-up on the 'live' bombing run. It was hoped, of course, that the experts would have solved the problem before such a thing could happen; but there would always remain a risk and there had to be a clear drill to be followed in such an event.

'If it doesn't come off after repeating the 'live' bombing run to the limit of the endurance of the aircraft, we have to save the crew and ditch the Valiant in a place where, if it detonates, it will not create a serious problem,' said the TFC and threw the subject open for discussion.

Eventually a plan emerged. In such a dire emergency, the Valiant would fly over HMS *Warrior* at 5000 feet and the three rear crew members would bale out, to be picked up by naval helicopters. The Valiant would be flown by the two pilots to a point 50 miles south of Malden Island, engaging the auto-pilot. The captain would then switch on an automatic fuel cut-off (yet another modification!) which would operate two hundred miles further on, the canopy would be blown off and the two pilots would eject. There would be a Shackleton aircraft, diverted from a photographic duty, standing by to mark their position until HMS *Warrior* arrived at full speed, preceded by her helicopters to pick them up. Meanwhile, 30 minutes after ejection, the Valiant would have dived into the sea in a position where, even if there were fall-out from a low yield detonation, the fall-out could do no serious damage.

This plan was accepted, but Air Commodore Weir added: 'I think we ought to know how the aircraft handles without the canopy. We'd better see what Trubshaw (the Vickers test pilot) says about that.'

'While we're talking about the live drop,' said the TFC, 'I'd like to make two other points. Firstly we must get as much practical experience as possible out of each test. Would you please look into the idea of a second aircraft flying below and behind the one doing the drop, to give the second crew at least some experience of the flash and the blast over-pressure. We could call it the 'Grandstand' aircraft.

'Secondly, while I'm forward in the control room in *Narvik* off Malden, you lot — Ginger, Freddie and Butch - will be in the Joint Operations Centre ops room at Christmas and I want you to hear everything that goes on. Now I *know* that we've arranged to have the running commentary from the captain of the *Valiant* transmitted simultaneously on both VHF and H/F and you should hear the H/F all right, except in the radio black-out just after the burst; but just to make sure, I want you to hear the VHF as well. So I want a relay aircraft – a Canberra – at 40,000 feet midway between Malden and Christmas, fixed up radio-wise to receive and re-transmit the *Valiant's* VHF running commentary. OK?'

The meeting then went on to review the whole programme of air operations prior to and on the day of a drop. In essence this boiled down to:

Shackletons on low level met and shipping search on D-2, D-1.

Canberra PR7 on high level met, D-2, D-1.

Dakotas to and from Malden and instrumentation island, frequently.

Shacketons, line abreast parallel search, 30 mile spacing, 300 miles down-wind from Malden, H-8 hours.

Valiant, one plus 'Grandstand'.

Canberra, relay for communication.

Helicopters, naval, for transport between Malden, *Narvik* and *Warrior*.

Helicopters, RAF, for air/sea rescue at Christmas.

Canberras, B6, for cloud sampling.

Avenger, naval, for flying instrumentation records from *Warrior* to Christmas.

Shackletons and Canberra PR7 for low and high level photography.

Canberra, PR7, with 'Forth Bridge' fitment, for flying cloud samples back to UK. Slip crews at each staging post en route.

This list of aircraft and their tasks then defined the technical maintenance programme for 160 Wing and hence the number of trained personnel of many grades and specialties who had to be available and their requirements in stores and equipment; and so back we come to shipping and air transport requirements. All this was recorded in due course in yet another volume of orders, bearing on its cover the Cormorant and Grapnel emblem of the task force.

139

Here another worry presented itself. It was one thing to send these orders to Commands, but quite another to be sure that they were being studied by the squadrons and arrangements made for implementation. After all, the Commands had heavy work loads – often beyond their capacity – other than supporting Operation Grapple. Would it not be prudent to have a Grapple Liaison Officer at Bomber Command, for instance, to check that all necessary action was being taken in time? So another request to the ever-helpful Personnel branch and another recruit arrived – Wing Commander Johny Ayshford, a most congenial character but sound and knowledgeable withal. After indoctrination, he went off to High Wycombe to safeguard Grapple interests.

Now what about the Valiant squadron and who was going to command it? A vital appointment, that one, and the TFC would have been very happy to see David Roberts in that job; but it wasn't for him to say and Roberts was perhaps rather young for the extra rank. After some delicate probing, it was eventually revealed that a famous old squadron number plate was to be resurrected and No 49 Squadron would be the sharp end of Grapple; and the Director General of Personnel told the TFC.

'We have an absolutely first class chap to command your Valiant squadron, Wing Commander Ken Hubbard. He's just about to do the OCU course at Gaydon and will be posted to the squadron on September 1st. I'm sure you'll find him a good man for the job.' And in due course this turned out to be very true; but it didn't leave much time for the squadron to work up before going out to Christmas.

20

Rations

All the high technology and first class logistic support in the world were not going to achieve the aim of Operation Grapple unless the working force – the troops of all ranks and colours and the scientists – were in good heart, reasonably well-fed and enthusiastic about their individual tasks. Once the initial excitement of seeing a tropical coral island for the first time had worn off, most of the personnel on Christmas and other islands would feel that they were in an unpleasant environment – hot, humid, gritty and uncomfortable much of the time, with primitive living conditions for the most part and very long working hours for month after month. The greatest help to morale would be reasonably good food.

Unsatisfactory food, on the other hand, would result in low morale amongst many of those who were not old campaigners, to the serious detriment of the whole programme; and whilst 'old hands' would 'moan' about it, put up with it and get on with the job, the civilians and inexperienced service personnel working on highly technical tasks would inevitably be adversely affected.

The army – the Royal Army Service Corps – was to be responsible for the scale of rations, which were to be drawn from the navy's Royal Fleet Auxiliary issuing ships such as the *Fort Beauharnois*, and all food would be prepared and cooked by army cooks. But even eleven years after the end of the war, austerity was still the rule in Britain and the TFC was concerned

141

that the army rations were far from adequate or suitable for personnel working twelve or more hours a day, six days a week, in the conditions obtaining on Christmas Island.

Most of the naval personnel would be on board ship, where the standard of messing was usually good; so the Admiralty weren't able to help much. Appeals to the War Office and Air Ministry for extra catering allowances came up against 'Standard Practice' and a firm negative. So how to defeat the system? What about the helpful Mr Lovelock?

Lovelock went through all the regulations looking for legal loopholes and came up with a plan to draw part of the ration in cash, which could be used for 'local purchases'. This would enable the Task Force to purchase salads and fresh vegetables in Hawaii, which ought to help a lot. The idea was also examined of growing vegetables on the island, but this turned out to be a flop – there was no soil suitable for growing them.

There were other social problems to be considered and one of these was contact between the Task Force personnel and the families of the imported Gilbertese natives, of whom quite a large number would be employed as labourers. Some of the servicemen might well have romantic ideas of friendly dusky maidens lightly clad in little more than a grass skirt. The reality might be very different and careful discipline would have to be exercised to ensure that no trouble arose.

In discussing this problem with the TFC, Colonel Stone dropped a bombshell. The War Office had insisted that two ladies of Lady Reading's Women's Voluntary Service should accompany the Army Task Group to act as motherly guides and counsellors to the younger soldiers. The TFC was aghast.

'That's quite impossible! Motherly types they may be, but after months of no female companionship, I'm afraid the troops will see these ladies getting younger and more attractive every day; and soon we'll have trouble. There's also the constant thought that one day we might have a really hairy emergency on our hands. Do we really have to have them?'

'Sorry, sir, the answer is yes. The War Office insists and Lady

Reading has two suitable volunteers ready to go. It's not as bad as you think – this has been done before and has been a great success. I'm sure there'll be no trouble and our experience is that they are very helpful with men who have family problems.'

The TFC had to accept this, albeit unhappily; but in the event the WVS ladies were a great asset to the force and there was never any hint of trouble. Peter Gretton, coming in at that moment on some other matter, heard the tail end of the discussion and raised another point on living conditions.

'I understand we're going to have about three hundred officers and civilians of equivalent status in the officers mess. Quite a collection of very varied types. What are you going to do, Wilf, about your own mess?'

'My own mess, Peter? I assumed we'd all muck in together. This is no place for formality or distinctions of rank and we all share the hardships equally.'

'Yes, sir, I agree. But there are other important angles. The younger and more junior chaps will want to let off a bit of steam now and again and how can they do that if you and the other senior officers are on top of them all the time, making them watch their step? Also, after going about our own jobs all day, you and the Task Group Commanders and senior staff will often need to discuss problems without being overheard. Wouldn't it be better to have a separate little mess set up for, say, four stripes and above plus your ADC and my Secretary? That would make about ten of us. It needn't be any more luxurious than the main mess – just a small hut as a lounge bar plus a small marquee for dining and another to house the cookery – but off to one side fifty yards from the main mess.'

The TFC reflected on this for a moment, not having given the matter any previous thought. The suggestion was, after all, in line with Navy practice. The Commodore commanding Grapple Squadron, no less the captain of a ship of any size, would not share the ward-room with his officers. Also, come to think of it, there might well be a few VIP visitors during the trials.

'What do you think, Jack?' – to Colonel Stone.

'I agree with Commodore Gretton, sir, and we have in fact provisionally planned it that way, although I hadn't got round to telling you yet.'

'OK,' conceded the TFC. 'We'll have an "A" mess for us and a "B" mess for the real workers.'

'Then what about evening rig in "A" mess?' – continued Gretton.

'Having been in khaki drill all day, we'll want to freshen up and maintain some standard of dress in the evening.'

'I agree with you, Peter. We could use the navy pattern short sleeve, open neck, white tropical shirts with light-weight uniform trousers; but as we shall have Bill Cook and maybe another scientist there, it would be more considerate not to use anything like uniform. How about a white long sleeved shirt and light-weight slacks? We can easily change if it turns out to be unsuitable.' This was agreed.

The next problem to come up was some relaxation for all ranks. There had to be something for everyone to do other than work, at least on Sundays. For a start, could there be a church – interdenominational – and taken in turns? Stone revealed that a small CofE chapel, and likewise an RC one were already included in the sappers' planning; just plain small wooden huts, in fact; but there would undoubtedly be keen volunteers to dress them up nicely to look like places of worship.

For evenings, the Army Kinema Corporation would provide an outdoor movie theatre and a steady supply of films. Nothing very grand, just a screen and a decent projector. The sappers would fix up bench seating. Fishing should be good and tackle would be provided. It looked as though reasonable football and hockey pitches could be scraped on patches of lagoon mud. Swimming should be excellent but they would have to guard against sharks and the dangerously sharp coral of the reef would require care. All this would be looked into as soon as time could be spared after the initial landing.

'One last thing from me,' said the TFC finally. 'I don't know where we'll get them from, the NAAFI perhaps, but I would like four pianos, one each in the NAAFI canteen, the sergeants' mess and the officers' "B" mess – and one to be mobile in case we can raise a concert party to go round outlying detachments. There's nothing better than a good old sing-song on a Saturday night to raise morale.'

21

In the steps of Captain Cook

In May 1956 the tempo of Operation Grapple began to increase rapidly. Whilst the planning of the air task and the preparation of aircraft proceeded apace, the carefully organised movement to Christmas Island began with the sailing from the UK of the Royal Fleet Auxiliary ship *Fort Beauharnois* carrying food supplies and consumable stores, and the heavy lift ship SS *Ben Wyvis* fully loaded with engineer plant, the pontoons, the dredger, motor transport and several LCM landing craft.

On 22nd May the 28th Field Engineer Regiment (RE) was joined at Erlestoke by 51 Port Detachment (stevedores), No 2 Special Air Formation Signals troop of the Royal Signals (who were to provide all the internal communications) and a special Royal Army Service Corps Unit, (a DUKW amphibious vehicle platoon together with Supply and POL detachments).

A week later the bulk of this force moved to Southampton to embark in a chartered Greek passenger ship, the SS *Charlton Star*. Major Marquis, the 2 i/c of 28 Regiment, was in command and the TFC and Colonel Woollett went to the docks to see them off. To their astonishment and shock, they found an angry Tom Marquis ordering the immediate dis-embarkation of those troops who had already boarded.

'I'm not sending my men in that filthy ship!' declared Marquis roundly. 'It's absolutely disgraceful!'

This was a serious blow which could disrupt the very critical timetable and there could be no possibility of getting another

146

ship at short notice. Arrangements were made to house the troops overnight, whilst the Ministry of Sea Transport representative vigorously made it clear to the shipping line that if the ship was not cleaned up and ready for inspection in 24 hours, the contract would be cancelled – and some others as well!

There was immediately a fine flurry of activity and the following day a steely-eyed Major Marquis agreed that it would do. The embarkation proceeded and the ship sailed with orders to the Master to make up the lost time.

Meanwhile, a few days later and half way round the world, 55 Field Engineer Squadron moved from Korea down to Singapore. All their vehicles and plant and the prefabricated structures which they had prepared were loaded into an old Landing Ship which had been converted to commercial use and now sailed as the SS *Reginald Kerr*. Some of the technician troops also sailed in her to work on the vehicles during the rather miserable and uncomfortable voyage.

At Singapore the main sapper contingent from Korea was rejoined by its CO, Major Young, just returned by civil air from the Erlestoke briefing and together with half of the Royal Marines detachment which had been training as LCM crews at Poole.

This party was to embark in the troop transport ship HT *Devonshire* which was taking home to Suva the Fijian Regiment after its years of gallant service in Malaya. She would then go on to Christmas Island with the Grapple contingent. But when it came to boarding, there was insufficient accommodation for the sappers and it was decreed that sixty of the Fijians would have to be off-loaded.

The Fijians were naturally unhappy about this and Major Young thought it quite wrong. So, with a little unofficial co-operation, sixty sappers were flown to Fiji instead and the Fijian Regiment continued intact, generating a great deal of goodwill.

A week later, on entering Suva harbour, *Devonshire* was met and given a royal escort by a wonderfully picturesque fleet of

Fijian war canoes, manned by crews in traditional battle dress and heavily adorned with sharks teeth, all coming out to greet their returning heroes. As soon as the ship was secured alongside the dock, the reception party clambered aboard, assembled on the fore-deck and performed a traditional dance of welcome, chanting in their deep melodious voices as they did so. For the Britons this was a memorable spectacle.

Young, as Senior British Officer, was invited formally to attend a Civic Reception for the returning Regiment, to be held on the city rugby field the following day and to bring all his force with him. Some spit and polish was clearly called for, without too much grumbling, and the British Force marched smartly down Suva's 'Sapper Street', so called after a long association between the Royal Engineers and Suva in the nineteenth century. All were seated with a good view of the festivities. Several hundred husky Fijian men in their traditional war dress gave a fine demonstration of national dances; and in the ensuing formalities, Major Young was garlanded and drank kava from the mandatory half coconut shell.

Whilst still in Suva, the *Devonshire* party was joined by a small RAF medical team, the nucleus of the RAF Field Hospital which was to care for the health of and for repairs to the whole Task Force at Christmas Island. In the early planning stage, the TFC had spoken to his friend, the RAF's senior surgeon, and explained the importance and isolation of the field hospital. Peter Dixon had selected an outstandingly good young surgeon to head it and now Squadron Leader Jack Bradley, with a sergeant and three medical orderlies, had arrived at Suva by the west-about route through San Francisco and Honolulu to Nandi, the international airport of Fiji. Then by airport coach through the hundred miles of lush jungle and sugar plantations to Suva. Their main equipment had gone by sea and the rest of the staff would arrive in due course by the air shuttle.

Their journey had been enlivened by an incident in New York. The party had carried with them as personal baggage everything needed to set up a first aid post, including the surgeon's 'little black bag'. On declaring the contents, including a lot of opiates, to the US Customs, these latter had fairly gone up in smoke. Quite impossible to allow the entry of these drugs! After hours of argument, the Customs had relented but had anxiously urged Dr Bradley not to lose it until he was out of US territory! Now they were all on board *Devonshire* and the little black bag was safe.

After another two days of recreation in Suva – which was at least a token recompense for the leave which the sappers were going to miss – the *Devonshire* resumed her voyage to Christmas Island, which she reached on June 24th.

Whilst all this ship-borne activity was going on, Wing Commander Bower was fulfilling his task of establishing a first foothold on Christmas Island. He had wisely decided to use two aircraft and on June 5th two Shackletons of 206 Squadron, WG836, captained by Squadron Leader R J Church and WG 529 by Flight Lieutenant AT Legresley, left Ballykelly and flew eastabout via Idris, Mauripur, Negombo, Changi, Darwin, Townsville, Nandi (Fiji) to Canton Island in the Phoenix Group, which they reached on June 18th. There they were most hospitably received by the resident QANTAS staff and immediately prepared for the final leg.

Meanwhile, on June 15th, the nucleus of the Grapple HQ staff for the initial phase assembled at Heathrow and departed by BOAC for San Francisco. The party was led by the Deputy Task Force Commander, Commodore Peter Gretton and included Lieutenant Colonel John Woollett, the CRE, Wing Commander Douglas Bower who would initially be the CO of the Christmas Island Staging Post, Lieutenant Commander Paton a first-class naval surveyor, Major Sales RE and fourteen others, including an RAF Sergeant carpenter and his tool box. There was a great deal of passenger-accompanied freight, items which would be needed immediately.

At the same time, but leaving by a different service, was a group of about twenty, led by Squadron Leader John Claridge. These were to establish the RAF 160 Wing staging post at

Honolulu International airport, or rather on the western side of the airport where the United States Air Force had its Hickam Air Force Base. There they were to be allotted living accommodation, office space and other facilities if needed and would handle British aircraft and personnel passing to and from Christmas Island. This detachment also included part of the Army's No 504 Postal Unit, RE, who would handle all the mail to and from Christmas and provide the connection with the United States Postal Service.

Flying by piston-engined aircraft of that period, Strato-cruisers and Constellations, the journey was long and wearying. All were glad to have a 24 hour stopover in San Francisco, where the NCOs and men were hospitably accommodated at a nearby USAF base, whilst most of the officers preferred to stay in a hotel and see something of the life of that great and attractive city. To at least one, however, it offered an unusual and mortifying surprise. On retiring at night, he put his shoes outside his bedroom door to be cleaned, as he would in England. When he looked out next morning, they had of course vanished. Poor chap!

On June 18th, the HQ party led by Commodore Gretton went on by the QANTAS trans-pacific service to Honolulu; thence after only a refuelling stop, on to Canton Island, where they arrived in the dark early hours of the 19th to be picked up by the Shackleton aircraft. Without any fuel at Christmas, these latter could not do the 1100 mile return trip from Honolulu, but could do so from Canton. The Shackleton air and ground crews, with some friendly assistance from the Australians, transferred all baggage and freight either to the capacious bomb-bay panniers of the Shackletons – which for the forthcoming fairly short sortie had been unloaded of most of the servicing gear which they had carried on their journey round the world – or to the interior of the fuselages. All except one item, a massive chest, which could not go in the now full panniers and was too big to go in through the door. It was marked as of high priority, so in desperation they opened it, to find a set of engine-fitter's servicing tools beautifully set out in recesses. The tools were extracted and put in a couple of shopping bags and the chest was left for another day.

One very unhappy man, the carpenter, wailed that he couldn't find his precious tool kit, which had been checked through from London. Frantic search, including of the QANTAS Constellation as it was about to continue on its way, yielded nothing. It must have gone adrift in San Francisco. Calamity, but it couldn't be helped now.

Two hours later, with the first faint streaks of dawn in the east, they were all aboard the Shackletons, Wing Commander Bower, in command of this phase of the operation, in the lead aircraft with Squadron Leader Church and with Flight Lieutenant Morgan-Smith the Air Traffic Control Officer designate plus technical personnel; Commodore Gretton with Woollett, Richie, Sales and the remaining ground servicing team in Legresley's aircraft. Fifteen minutes later, both aircraft were on course for Christmas Island, eight hundred miles and five hours away.

As the sun rose and the Shackletons cruised along at a mere three thousand feet altitude, the Pacific Ocean displayed to the eager travellers its fantastic variety of colours, ranging from deepest emerald through turquoise and amethyst to an ethereal blue. Stately columns of cumulus clouds, brilliantly white on the sunny side and ominously grey on the other, marched westward in line ahead, each one poised above its neighbour's dark shadow on the glittering, white-cap splashed surface of the sea. Tedium set in and was relieved by the occasional mug of coffee, and four and a half hours later the captain of WG529 turned round and beckoned to Peter Gretton. He pointed ahead and at first Gretton saw only the towering cloud mass of the Inter Tropical Front some fifty miles to the north. Then he focused on a smudge – just a different kind of green tinged with grey and brown – on the horizon ahead.

'Christmas Island?' he bellowed.

Legresley nodded and shouted back – 'Another fifteen minutes, sir.'

The smudge rapidly took on shape and became first of all a great sweep of shining white foam and spume, as the heavy ocean swell crashed rhythmically over the coral reef some two hundred yards off the dazzling white shore line. Beyond the beach, a great stretch of dull grey-green scrubby vegetation, broken by clumps of tall coconut palms swaying in a stiff breeze. Over to the right, it looked like desert – a brown sandy waste disappearing into the distance.

Then the lagoon appeared and the shape of the island became apparent, something like a lobster claw, with the arms of the claw enclosing a vast area of gleaming water and dun coloured mud flats, with a broad brown tail vanishing off to the south-east. At the opening of the 'claws' there was evidently a wide gap in the reef and a fairly broad channel – with a small island in the middle of it – leading into the lagoon. On the point on the left, signs of human activity – Port London. On the right, a vast coconut plantation stretched towards the south-west corner of the lagoon. Ahead, a stretch of land two to three miles wide, running north-west to south-east between the lagoon and the ocean. Dull grey scrub, clumps of large shrubs, out-crops of rock and occasional stands of palms. Legresley turned again to Commodore Gretton and pointed:

'There's the other aircraft, sir – four miles ahead. He's having a good look at the runway and we'll just stooge around while he makes his landing.'

In WG836, Wing Commander Bower and Squadron Leader Church were conferring, while the co-pilot circled the old coral mud airstrip. They made a low pass at 100 feet to have a good look at the surface. It seemed fine – no serious overgrowth of scrub, no pools of water or obvious large pot-holes; so back up to circuit height. Church took over control on the down-wind leg, lined up with the runway and brought her in, touching down as sweetly and gently as though he were back at Ballykelly. No sweat! He turned the great aircraft slowly and taxied back carefully down the runway, watching for any dangerous fault in the surface. Satisfied, he pulled off the runway at the downwind end and called Legresley on VHF radio.

'Come on in – the water's fine!'

The second aircraft made a more dignified approach, landed, taxied back and parked alongside the leader, whose signaller then called Canton on both single-sideband H/F voice and on W/T to say simply 'Both aircraft landed safely'. The Griffon engines were shut down and a peaceful silence returned, broken only by the murmuring of the Trade Wind and the cries of innumerable birds of many different species.

Bomb doors opened, as also the fuselage entry doors, ladders were fixed in position and passengers and ground crew stepped out into a very different climate. Although only nine o'clock in the morning, it was hot and humid, not to be compared with Jeddah of course, but still quite a physical shock for men who only the previous day, had been in the very temperate air of San Francisco.

However, there was work to be done and Wing Commander Bower, as Commanding Officer of this new RAF airfield, promptly took charge. Unloading began, personal baggage to start with, so that everyone could change into khaki shorts and shirts – tropical working rig.

A few minutes later, what must have been the oldest and most decrepit jeep in the world appeared on the scene, driven by a sturdy figure in Sunday-best smart, dazzling, white tropical shirt, shorts, stockings, polished shoes and a floppy straw hat. Percy Roberts, the genial, hospitable and very competent New Zealand administrator of Christmas Island. He introduced himself to Commodore Gretton and his team and suggested that everyone should move to the port area, where he could accommodate Commodore Gretton and Colonel Woollett in his house and could at least give everyone else shelter from the quite unpredictable weather. He had with him a one-ton open truck, one of four used in the plantation work of collecting copra (dried coconut 'flesh') and driven by his excellent Fijian mechanic who ran the little transport 'pool'. The vehicle Roberts very generously put at the disposal of the new arrivals for the time being. It would mean two trips to collect everybody, the round trip taking about half an hour; but that was the best he could do.

Roberts then turned to Wing Commander Bower and asked if the runway was satisfactory. He had been informed, about a week previously, in a cyphered wireless message from Wellington via the the Colony Government Wireless Department HQ at Tarawa, that a British force would soon arrive and advised of the planned arrival of the aircraft; so for the past seven days he had his entire Gilbertese work-force pulling out bushes and shrubs and filling in the worst of the pot-holes. Bower and the two captains thanked him warmly and assured him they had found the runway quite good enough for Shackletons.

It was agreed that the Navy and Army personnel should go first, as the RAF team had plenty to be getting on with, including servicing the aircraft ready to return to Canton on the morrow.

Gretton, Woollett, Paton, Sales and their gear were piled into the jeep and set off for Percy Roberts' habitation and office. The road made by US Army engineers fifteen years previously had deteriorated into little more than a picturesque track, running alongside the main lagoon. After driving for some fifteen minutes through the low bushy vegetation with the occasional half-hearted stands of dispirited-looking coconut palms, they emerged on to the point between lagoon and ocean, where an open area was backed by a palm plantation. On the left the small jetty fronted on the channel to the bay and on the right stood a low, long, bungalow-type building with a red (or rusty?) corrugated iron roof and bearing in large white lettering the magnificent announcement:

DISTRICT OFFICER
CUSTOMS AND EXCISE
AGRICULTURAL ADVISER
PLANTATION OFFICE
POST OFFICE.

'That's me,' said Percy Roberts modestly. 'I'm sorry I can't put you all up, but just back there under the palms are a couple of not-quite-so-derelict wartime US Quonset huts and the former plantation manager's disused native-style dwelling. I hope you can manage there until your first ship arrives.'

'Indeed we can,' agreed Major Sales. 'That's luxury compared with what we'd been expecting. Thank you very much. We'll hump our gear over there and set up our camp kit while you make your next trip.'

Meanwhile, at the airfield, Bower got all hands to unloading the baggage and freight. The ground crews then got on with checking the aircraft while the Staging Post team started to create some kind of organisation. Bower had spotted a couple of old US army huts, discreetly hidden under the palm trees some way back from the airstrip. As soon as the two paratrooper 'James' motor cycles had been unloaded, he sent Morgan-Smith over to see if they were usable. They were indeed. The roof of one was intact and the doors and windows could be patched up. It would make a temporary Air Traffic Control and airfield office. So when Percy Roberts and his jeep arrived back, they were commandeered for ten minutes to carry over the mobile VHF radio, the Eureka homing beacon, signal lights, flares and other minimum essential stores. The Christmas Island Staging Post was in business.

Next day, June 20th, the two Shackletons returned to Canton Island, refuelled and then flew up to Honolulu on the 21st, to be welcomed by John Claridge and his RAF staging post crew. Claridge was a fine young man of attractive personality and good professional competence. He had rapidly established cordial relations with his American hosts and soon had the staging post working smoothly. There were traumas from time to time, but in general it ran very well.

More RAF personnel, supplies and equipment had arrived at Hickam, including the missing carpenter's tool box which had gone to Los Angeles, having been wrongly loaded in London. On the 25th, the two Shackletons flew all this lot directly back to

Christmas, including the main part of the Army 504 Postal Unit. The aircraft then remained on stand-by until July 2nd when they returned to UK via Canton and the route by which they had come.

On June 23rd, the RFA *Fort Beauharnois* arrived and dropped anchor about a mile off shore from Port London. Peter Gretton immediately collected all his gear and asked Percy Roberts to take him in the District Officer's launch, out to the ship, where he hoisted his Broad Pennant as Commodore Grapple Squadron, the first time such a thing had been done in a Royal Fleet Auxiliary ship. He established his office in a dark and poky little cabin, but it served well enough for the time being and at least he was now in immediate communication with the Grapple HQ in London. He sent off a situation report by wireless and then set to with Captain Gausden, the pleasant and competent master of the 'Fort Bo', to oversee the unloading of stores and supplies – a slow business, using only the ship's Naval Stores Tenders.

A day later, the 24th, the HT *Devonshire* arrived with the 55 Field Squadron sappers, the Royal Marine LCM crews and RAF personnel. She was closely followed by the SS *Reginald Kerr* carrying the engineers' heavy plant and transport. Lieutenant Colonel Woollett went out to the *Devonshire*, had all the troops assembled on the fore-deck and addressed them from the bridge. Emphasising his points one by one with sharp raps on the bridge deck with his inseparable walking stick, he outlined the task ahead and the immediate programme, made it quite clear that life would be pretty uncomfortable until they were properly established ashore in the port camp, stressed the national importance of the job and told them to get on with it quickly.

The men were eager to get ashore and with well-ordered rapidity they began to set up the port tented camp. In a fine strike of initiative, in one of the first launches to reach the little jetty was the very enterprising NAAFI manager. By mid-morning he had a row of large, coloured beach umbrellas set up

Captain P S Wadsworth, in charge of the Sapper construction team on Malden Island. *(Photo: K Bomford)*

S *Messina* at Malden unloading stores by LCM and DUKW (in foreground).
(Photo: AWRE)

A Landing Craft (LCM) on the beach at Malden Island.

Malden 'City' – the living quarters of the scientists and Sappers working in isolation. *(Photo: AWRE)*

(Right): A Hastings aircraft for a scheduled service from Christmas Island to Honolulu and Australia.

(above): Another of Transport Command's aircraft, the Dakota, brought back into RAF service for Grapple.

A Christmas party for the Gilbertese children on Christmas Island in 1956. Commander Harry De Vere and pipe were present. *(Photo: H De Vere)*

The Vickers Valiant bomber, modified to 'Grapple' standard, before flying to Christmas Island. *(Photo: Author's collection)*

along the little strip of sand just beyond the jetty and provided very welcome mugs of 'char' for the men at their 'elevenses'.

A close second to the NAAFI was Squadron Leader Bradley and his medical team, who soon had their first aid post set up. It continued to operate until the hospital was ready at the main camp.

While one sapper crew speedily set up the mess-tents and domestic facilities, another was laying out the six man IP tents with mathematical precision on the open stretch of ground and erecting them at great speed. The Sergeant-Major in charge was interrupted by the civilian director of the film crew, who complained bitterly that he had been promised first class accommodation and petulantly demanded it to be provided immediately. The SM flung one of the tents into a space a little apart from the rest and said shortly:

'There's your .... tent. You can sleep in it or on it. It's up to you.' He slept in it eventually – after a little help!

Commodore Gretton was everywhere, driving the work along at top speed and physically lending a helping hand from time to time. A most urgent job was to get the jetty strengthened and some vehicles ashore. For this task a mobile crane had been planned and should have been top-loaded in the *Reginald Kerr*. Some genius had put it in the bottom of a hold with a great deal of heavy gear on top of it. All seemed lost for a while and then Gretton, remembering his training as a midshipman, showed the sappers how to rig up sheer legs as a temporary crane. It worked splendidly.

The work ashore was going well, but the movement of stores from ship to shore was unsatisfactorily slow. Gretton noted particularly the poor performance of the Fort Bo's store lighters and realised that their crews were pretty useless. The ship's master – Gausden – and Chief Officer Dobbie and the Chief Engineer were good professionals, but the rest of the ship's company were a poor lot, having been taken on indiscriminately and in a great hurry. So the unloading of stores from Fort Bo was suspended, while Gretton personally ran an intensive course of training for the boats' crews. After that things went much better.

On June 28th the heavy lift ship *Ben Wyvis* and the RFA tanker *Gold Ranger* arrived; so did a heavy swell, making it impossible for the moment to unload major items. But soon after midnight on the second night, the swell died away and the ever-watchful captain of *Ben Wyvis* snatched the opportunity to hoist out the four great 100 ton pontoons – a highly professional performance meriting great praise. This was the key to the unloading programme; the two dumb pontoons were secured ashore as landing jetties while the two powered pontoons with their powerful diesel outboards ferried vast loads with ease. Particularly impressive was the hoisting out and delivery ashore of the ninety ton dredger and the 120 ton water boat.

That day all personnel from *Devonshire* moved permanently ashore, having been sleeping on board for the first three nights, and *Devonshire* and *Reginald Kerr* sailed, their tasks completed. The port camp was now in full operation with over a hundred tents and marquees, together with 7000 square feet of buildings and a start had been made on laying out the main camp, some five miles away near the airstrip. At first it had been planned to put the tents under strands of palms, to give them some shade; but it tended to be stuffy and oppressive under the trees and Colonel Woollett decided it would be better to site the camp in the open, near the beach, where at least sleepers in tents would have the benefit of the fresh breeze. There the hundreds of accommodation tents, mess tents, cook house facilities, and all required for a well-ordered military camp began to go up at a most impressive speed. The troops, who had taken the sun cautiously at first, were now berry-brown and accustomed to the climate and the men were cheerfully working right through a twelve hour day. Oddly enough, the Gilbertese native labourers so helpfully supplied by Percy Roberts couldn't take the mid-day sun – they got sunburnt! Nevertheless, they were a great help.

As the RAF motor transports came off the *Ben Wyvis*, they

were brought into use immediately. An RAF M/T mechanic had travelled in the ship, continually servicing the vehicles and keeping the batteries topped up. This had paid off handsomely, as they were able to drive off from the jetty without help and some of them were used to supplement the army transport initially. Co-operation between the two services was excellent but for the most part the RAF M/T was employed in moving a steady stream of fuel, stores and equipment to the airfield, where much of it was accommodated in marquee tents provided by the sappers.

The vast quantities of stores created another problem for 160 Wing, in identifying and sorting so many different items. Documentation had deliberately been kept to a minimum to ease the administrative burden; but this had gone too far and too often urgently needed items could not be found without a long and exasperating search. One particular such item was the crate of Zwickey hand-operated wobble pumps for refuelling aircraft from the forty-gallon drums, indispensable until bulk fuel arrived much later.

Morale was high everywhere, despite the rough living conditions. The tented accommodation was fine although spartan; the food was pretty bad but understandably so in the early days before cold storage became available; but the flies were appalling. There were innumerable dead land crabs everywhere, which supported a large fly population; and any gash left lying around from the cookhouse or mess tents immediately brought a great increase in the nuisance. The CRE decreed that every scrap of rubbish was to be buried without delay and Commodore Gretton reported the problem to London.

The Task Force Commander was seriously alarmed by this report, having had some unhappy past experience of insect-borne epidemics. He immediately called in Milligan and Lovelock.

'I want an Auster aircraft with full agricultural pesticide spraying equipment purchased instantly – I don't care where you get it or how much it costs, and I want it flown out to Christmas in a Hastings with as much liquid DDT insecticide as you can get on board. Jump to it! NOW!'

Next, the Air Task Group Commander.

'Ginger, it seems that Christmas is thick with flies. If we get an epidemic of even just dysentery, let alone something worse, it will wreck the whole programme. I'm sending out an Auster for spraying the camps and I want you, within the next week, to send a good steady Auster-qualified pilot to drive it; and I want it to be made absolutely clear that no one' – with a very hard look at the Air Task Group Commander, a very enthusiastic pilot – 'absolutely no one other than the designated pilot is to fly it. Any risk of putting it U/S by using it for an air taxi or diversion for itchy aviators is out. Too much depends on keeping this fly menace under control. OK?'

'Yes, sir,' acknowledged Weir, not accustomed to such vehemence from his boss.

Within two weeks, the Auster – nicknamed 'Captain Flit' by the troops, was droning up and down spraying the Christmas Island camp and airfield areas every morning with DDT. The fly menace was kept down to a tolerable level and there were no epidemics, thank the Lord!

Meanwhile, having got the unloading activity improving day by day, although still a long way short of the necessary target of 1,000 tons a day which could not be achieved until *Messina* arrived with more LCMs and crews, the Deputy Task Force Commander turned his attention to the airfield.

'Where is the Hastings service?' he demanded of Wing Commander Bower, 'Shouldn't it have started by now?'

'Yes, sir. The first aircraft is already at Hickam, waiting to come. But we don't want to accept it until we can refuel it and send it back; and at this moment we're stuck because we can't find the Zwickey pumps in this mountain of equipment.'

'What are they? What do they do?'

Bower explained and added – 'Something like a sailing dinghy's bilge pump.'

'Well for Heaven's sake! There are hundreds of ruddy pumps all over the Fort Bo! Go and find anything that will do the job, unscrew it, test it and let's get that shuttle working!'

They did just that. Found and removed from the ship a suitable hand-operated pump, the carpenter fixed up a rig for it and Bower called in the first Hastings aircraft of No 24 (Commonwealth) Squadron on July 9th. It arrived with a full load of more personnel, stores, equipment and *mail*! The Army Postal Unit was delighted to be in operation at last and so were the first troops to receive letters addressed to British Forces Post Office 170. Regular mail from home was the most important single factor in maintaining morale and keeping the Task Force working to programme. The arrival of the weekly Hastings was from then on something to look forward to.

Taking advantage of the presence of this first Hastings, Wing Commander Bower next day – July 10th – arranged a reconnaissance flight to Malden, the target island 400 miles away. This gave Commodore Gretton and Colonel Woollett their first view of it, including a sobering inspection of the reef and the narrow channel through it on the north side of the island. Within three months there would have to be a sizeable force of sappers ashore there, constructing the airstrip and the vast instrumentation base, ready for use by January.

To catch the homeward mail, Peter Gretton wrote a long letter to the TFC, retailing all that had happened, good and bad. Woollett and Bower were first class and were doing great things, as was Paton the naval surveyor who had already buoyed the channel to the jetty and the anchorage and had set up all necessary navigation marks. The work overall was more or less up to programme. The film unit wasn't doing very well – it often failed to be on the spot for the most interesting incidents. The food was unnecessarily bad. But in general the letter was redolent of enthusiasm and a wonderful job being well done; and thank goodness! The inter-service co-operation was just terrific.

A few days later the SS *Charlton Star* arrived with the main body of 28 Field Engineer Regiment RE and its supporting services. The troops were rapidly disembarked and were transported directly to Main Camp, where their neatly laid-out tented accommodation awaited them. 55 Field Squadron had done a splendid job.

All their plant, barring the Barber-Greene machines, was laid out in an orderly fashion, together with sufficient supplies of material of all kinds for them to start work immediately on the main construction programme beginning most urgently with the new runway which had to be ready by early November. This task alone entailed the clearing of some seven hundred thousand square yards of scrub and bush for airfield approach zones; the clearing, compacting, grading, levelling and surfacing with asphalt of a runway 2150 yards by 60 yards to an accuracy of about one inch overall, together with eight inch concrete paving for runway ends, taxiways and the main hard stand apron for the mass of operational aircraft required for the nuclear tests.

But of course that was only half of the job. They had to provide all the facilities of a small industrial town as well.

On September 13th, the final army echelon arrived in the HT *Cheshire* and the Army Task Group was then up to its full strength of over 1200 all ranks, housed for the most part at Main Camp in a township of 700 tents and marquees, with some 40,000 square feet of hutted accommodation under construction (including two churches).

They had over 300 major items of engineering plant, over 200 vehicles and such facilities as a tented RASC bakery eventually producing 6000 pounds of fresh bread a day and a field laundry, run by the RAOC, dealing with 8000 bed-sheets and a mountain of personal clothing each week. This last had a most ingenious system for purifying and re-circulating the water, to economise in use of fresh water from distillation. To add to the home comforts, even the two ladies of the Women's Voluntary Services, the Misses Billie and Mary Burgess, had arrived and had been provided with suitable quarters. They were often to be seen cycling round the main camp, organising recreation for off-duty hours and were very highly regarded and appreciated by the men.

By the time the second Hastings shuttle arrived on July 16th, Commodore Gretton felt that good progress was being made and he could safely leave affairs in the capable hands of Colonel Woollett (now promoted to full Colonel rank and designated Garrison Commander), Wing Commander Bower and Lieutenant Commander Paton. He therefore returned to Honolulu and made a round of official calls on Admiral Stump, the CinC Pacific at Pearl Harbour, on his old friend Rear Admiral George Anderson, now Chief of Staff to the CINCPAC and on Major General Sory Smith who commanded the US Air Force in Hawaii. All received him most cordially and for several days he stayed comfortably with the British consul, a former naval officer with whom he had served in 1931. Commander Beale, the British exchange officer at CINCPAC was also very helpful. What a blessing it is to have friends!

A week later he was back in London and reported to the Task Force Commander on the great success of the initial landing on Christmas Island and useful lessons learnt. He then threw his energy into the follow-up naval programme, of which the next key event at home was to be the departure of the salvage vessel, HMS *Salvictor* with all the gear to lay the deep moorings at Christmas and Malden. She was to sail immediately the dockyard had finished the refit and alterations and, on the day before her departure, the Naval Task Group Commander went down to Chatham to carry out a detailed inspection. Unhappily the captain was obviously an ill man and not really fit enough for this onerous and vital task. The Number One, Lieutenant Commander Walliker - a first class and highly competent seaman - unobtrusively tried to steer the inspection smoothly, but there was no chance of defeating Commodore Gretton's eagle eye. He weighed up the situation, sent the captain ashore to hospital, appointed Walliker to command on the spot and ordered him to sail next day at the planned time. Then before leaving Chatham, Gretton telephoned Grapple HQ and told

Western to get on to the Second Sea Lord's office right away and have them appoint Walliker to command *Salvictor* forthwith; and no bloody argument! Such was the powerful combination of Grapple and Gretton that this unprecedented thing was done without a murmur. It is nice to report that Walliker did a splendid job throughout the operation.

22

Naval problems of re-fits and loading

While the establishment of the advance force on Christmas Island was proceeding so rapidly, events were moving fast in London as well. Amongst many anxieties, one of the foremost was the sailing of the LST *Messina* before the end of June, to be on station in time for her critical part in the build-up programme. Chatham dockyard worked wonders and had her ready for sea trials by June 20th. Captain Western and the TFC conferred and thought she should do a practice beaching operation, something which her captain, Commander Harry De Vere, had not done before; and they thought they ought to see it.

So on the 21st they made their way to Deal – to the Royal Marines barracks – and were taken out to join *Messina* as she sailed round from Chatham. The beaching operation at Deal went well, but only just in time; for immediately afterwards a strong on-shore wind sprang up, with a nasty short sea, which would have made the practice inadvisable. As it was, the visitors, on being put ashore by boat to catch a train at Ramsgate, had a rough ride. Not nearly so rough as their arrival, however, for the inexperienced coxswain was caught out by an exceptionally big wave from astern and rammed the pier at a rate of knots. Western saw it coming and murmured a word of advice to the TFC and they stepped off on to the pier as though leaving an Underground escalator, leaving the unhappy coxswain to retire discomfitted. No great disaster and *Messina* sped on to

Portsmouth to take on her cargo of LCMs, DUKWs, fresh water and a wide range of stores plus the remaining half of the Royal Marines contingent of LCM crews.

The day before she was due to sail from Portsmouth, however, a worried Commander De Vere rang Grapple HQ to say he appeared to be considerably overloaded and was he to sail like that. Captain Western immediately got hold of a representative of the Directorate of Naval Construction and they rushed down to Portsmouth. LSTs were very critical on overloading and the DNC expert ordered 400 tons of fresh water to be offloaded. A problem for the Garrison Commander at Christmas, but it couldn't be helped. *Messina* sailed next day – June 29th – and arrived in August. With six more LCMs and crews plus some DUKWs the rate of unloading increased dramatically and with her evaporators producing a hundred tons of fresh water a day, and with her large cold storage providing more fresh food, life ashore improved greatly.

Still on naval problems, it was time to see how the aircraft carrier HMS *Warrior* was getting on with her refit at Devonport. Early in July the TFC, his aide and Captain Western again borrowed an Anson from helpful Hendon and flew down to Roborough, Plymouth's tiny airport, where they were met by a dockyard car and taken to *Warrior*. They were received punctiliously by the Executive Officer presently in command of the ship – Commander Robin Begg, a great Viking of a man of genial manner but of very tough professional capability, and made a tour of all the work in progress, particularly the Air Control Room and Action Information Centre.

'We have a problem, sir,' said Begg to Western, 'in that according to the programme and the progress of the refit, we shall not have time to go round Cape Horn to Christmas Island, so we must go through Panama; but she's too wide for the locks. However, if we cut off the gun sponsons at the sides, she could just make it.'

Captain Western reflected for a moment and then agreed this

should be done. He would clear it with DNC* and have the instruction issued to the dockyard.

It was very useful to talk in some detail with the ship's Exec (Executive Officer), who would virtually be running *Warrior's* part in the forthcoming operations, and to review some of the problems on the TFC's mind. Was the accuracy of the ship's air guard radar really all that was claimed and would it, with the assistance of the Decca equipment to be fitted, be able to monitor and – if necessary – correct the track of the Valiant to the required accuracy? These and many other questions were discussed and the time passed all too quickly. The visitors then made their way back to Roborough and – it being now late Friday afternoon – put Guy Western down at RAF Thorney Island, next door to his home; and so on back to Hendon. All very satisfactory.

Sunday morning, the telephone rang impatiently in the TFC's house.

'Jack Stone here, sir. Would you believe it! They've dropped the bloody Barber-Greene in the river!'

Just count to ten – slowly!

'What happened, Jack?'

'One of the cargo ships loading bitumen and cement in London docks was to take the two Barber-Greene machines as deck cargo – they've only just finished being overhauled, as you know. A sling wasn't fixed properly by the stevedores and the machine just fell over the side into the water. Probably not damaged much, but what do we do now, sir?'

'Ring Guy Western right away. Ask him to have two Navy divers on the job first thing tomorrow morning. Get it hoisted out and dumped on deck. Sail the ship and get two manufacturer's technical maintenance men and a good REME engine man – and their tool kits – to sail in her to strip down and overhaul on the voyage to Panama. Then fly them back; and could you get a REME NCO to supervise the hoisting out and

---

* The Director of Naval Construction.

re-loading this time? We don't want it bent.'

'Right, sir. I'll let you know when I've got all that fixed.'

The TFC just prayed that this plan would work. Without the two Barber-Greenes there was no chance of having the runway ready for the first charter aircraft in November.

At the Monday navy meeting, Captain Western reported that the divers were working on the recovery of the Barber-Greene and it should be up that day. Also, the enquiries about the *Warrior's* radar had stirred up some interest at the Admiralty Signals Research Establishment and the Underwater Development Establishment at Portland. Apparently they had jointly under development a new mine-spotting radar – code named Avocado – which could track very accurately the flight of the bomb and might be useful in monitoring the aircraft itself. At the same time, after an initial lack of enthusiasm, ASRE had now warmed to the idea of having Decca equipment installed in *Warrior*. They had not previously contemplated any need to position the ship to within one hundred yards and were now interested. So the TFC and Western went to Portland to see Avocado in operation. It was a good and useful equipment; one was fitted in *Warrior* and performed well 'on the day'.

For every point gained, there was one lost – or so it seemed. Group Captain Milligan came into the TFC's office with a gloomy face.

'They've lost both the Canberras with the experimental "Scorpion" motors. The crews are safe, but there's no chance now of having them for Grapple. We shan't get any cloud sampling above 55,000 feet at very best.'

'Pity; but maybe it's all to the good. We can do without uncertain equipment. But here's something to cheer you up – Peter Gretton's first letter from Christmas. Things seem to be going quite well – except for the film unit. Please tell the Marcus Cooper people we must have a better man on it – and I'd like to see him before he goes.'

Two days later a robust and cheerful fellow, Harvey

Harrison, turned up for vetting as film director and was soon on his way. The filming went much better from then on.

The unhappy but not unexpected word came that the Grapple HQ would soon have to vacate their pleasant offices in Richmond Terrace; and the TFC was turning this over in his mind, staring gloomily at the back of the half-built Air Ministry building opposite his window, when he noticed a workman – or at least a man in overalls – open a narrow gap in the fencing round the building site and vanish inside. Curious! The new Air Ministry building, fronting on to Horse Guards Avenue, was only half built when work had to stop for the 1939 war. Since then the second half, fronting the other way on to Whitehall Gardens, had been no more than concrete foundations surrounded by a high fence. What went on?

At lunch time he wandered over to the fence, looked round quickly to see that he was not observed and slipped through the same gap. Just a dead building site with dirty concrete footings: but over in that corner, it looked like steps, damp and dirty, leading down. So down he went and to his astonishment, came into a well lit long corridor, with office after office leading off it. All clean and tidy. All absolutely empty! Discreet enquiries revealed that this was part of the planned bomb-proof 'citadel', brought into temporary use during the latter part of the war and then apparently forgotten. No point wasting time wondering why the administrators hadn't thought of it and too bad about there being no daylight – it would be bound to be called 'the dungeon!' – but it would do admirably to house HQ Grapple when they were eventually kicked out of Richmond Terrace. This was arranged with the Deputy Secretary and in the event the move took place at the end of August.

Meanwhile, Commodore Gretton had arrived back fit and full of enthusiasm at the end of July, bearing film clips of the landing at Christmas. These were quickly processed and were shown in the splendid little cinema in the Admiralty. It was good for the staff to see results of all their hard work and all were delighted at the success of the operation so far.

169

At this time, the two standard Valiant aircraft, commanded by Squadron Leader Flavell and Flight Lieutenant Bates, departed for Edinburgh Field, the RAAF base just outside Adelaide, Australia. The ground crews had gone by charter aircraft and after a period of training under the control of Group Captain Menaul the whole team would move to Maralinga to play their part in Operation Buffalo and to do the first air drop of a British atomic weapon.

Air Commodore Weir was to go early in August to be the Task Force Commander for Buffalo and – as he would be away for three months – it was essential that all Air Task Group preparations for Grapple should be well in hand. He had chosen a good team – including a future Chief of the Air Staff as his personal assistant, which seemed to indicate good judgement! – and the Air Task Group team were well integrated with the Grapple Task Force Commander's staff. Under Group Captain Milligan's capable and determined direction, the air plan was emerging in comprehensive and elegant detail – volumes of it; and now Group Captain Richard Brousson was brought in to be head of the technical planning, with an exceptionally good Wing Commander 'Ron' Boardman to be the Chief Technical Officer (CTO) of 160 Wing on Christmas Island.

On the air side, the main preoccupation was the preparation of the Valiant squadron and on August 17th the TFC again visited Wittering and flew a sortie with Squadron Leader Roberts on one of the F-series trials. The crew drill was working very smoothly and it looked as though the bomb hang-up problem had been cured by substantially increasing the heating of the bomb bay. The new CO and four more crews would join at the end of the month, but in the meantime Roberts was doing an excellent job on planning and training.

Wing Commander KG Hubbard took command of No 49 Valiant Squadron on 1st September 1956, having done a full refresher flying training course on Meteor and Canberra, followed by the full Operational Conversion Unit course on the Valiant at Gaydon. On September 5th, he reported to the Task

Force Commander at the Grapple HQ in the new Citadel accommodation in the Air Ministry. He had a full and detailed briefing on the whole of Operation Grapple and on the principal role which his squadron, with its new and special aircraft, would play in it. He had just six months to have his aircraft and crews in position on Christmas Island. The TFC had never met him before, but found himself at first sight in full agreement with the strong recommendation given by Maurice Heath. With Dave Roberts to back him up, there should be no anxiety about the competence of the Valiant squadron. Attention could for the time being be turned to other problems.

Then there was another important visit to the new Grapple offices. The progress of the British preparations for the nuclear test series was evidently of great interest to the Americans, who for some years past had been very co-operative and helpful over British monitoring of their tests, even to accepting RAF sampling and tracking of their atomic clouds. Now evidently they hoped, reasonably enough, for reciprocal co-operation and word came from the Ministry of Supply Controller of Atomic Weapons to the Task Force Commander that a Doctor Allen Crocker would like to pay a social call on him. Doctor Crocker was Technical Director for Geophysical Studies in the monitoring organisation which the US Government had set up to develop scientific means of monitoring A-bomb tests. He 'happened' to be in London on vacation.

The visit was fixed up immediately and next day Dr Crocker was shown into the TFC's office. He was a fine impressive man, tall and well built, modest and courteous in manner, well spoken and – as emerged little by little – of outstanding intelligence and professional capability as a scientist and engineer. Much later it transpired that he had played a key role under Oppenheimer in the Manhattan Project and in the first successful tests at Los Alamos. The visit was very cordial and was the beginning of a warm and enduring friendship. Afterwards, the two men collected Mrs Crocker from her hotel and took her off to lunch. She, too, was a remarkable person and, like her husband, a direct descendant of one of the original Pilgrim Fathers of *Mayflower* fame.

Such friendly relationships were not only a great help during Operation Grapple, but continue to be of inestimable value in the development of defence and security policy of the West.

23

Works in progress

On September 4th, Captain Western and Colonel Stone left for their first visit to Christmas Island. With a view to possible future requests for facilities, they stayed over at Honolulu for two days to make courtesy calls on the US Army and Navy headquarters, where they were received most cordially. Then after making good contact with the RAF Staging Post staff, they went on the weekly Hastings shuttle to Christmas, where the main purpose of their visit was to oversee the first landing and establishment of the work force on Malden Island.

The place was a hive of activity from early morning until nightfall and even later. The anchorage and the marked channel to the Port London jetty seemed to be full of Landing Craft, stores tenders, powered pontoons and ship's boats of every description, bustling to and fro, empty outbound, loaded to the limit on the return. The management of the port area was becoming a major task and the rate of unloading was now edging up above seven hundred tons a day. The dredger was busy improving the channel to enable small tankers to come alongside to discharge fuel in bulk, as would be essential once the major flying programme began.

There was a steady stream of both Army and RAF vehicles on the five miles of road between the port and Main Camp and the Trade Wind breezes carried clouds of coral dust blown downwind from the immense rock-crushing plant east of the new airfield site, where twenty tons of coral rock every hour was being pulverised into aggregate for the construction work.

The main camp was the size of a small town, with all its very basic infrastructure, all tented in orderly rows. Large prefabricated huts were being erected to provide more substantial accommodation for messes and recreation, but these would not be ready for another two months. Telephone and electric power cables were being laid at high speed and the large sea-water distillation plant, looking very like London's Battersea power station, was being set up on the shore line west of Main Camp, to provide an adequate supply of fresh water.

Work on the new runway was proceeding at a tremendous pace and necessarily under very careful technical control. The quality and composition of the crushed coral aggregate varied constantly and enormously and almost every truck-load required individual analysis and treatment to ensure consistency in the quality of the concrete produced. Because of the November deadline to accept the first charter aircraft, the major effort was being concentrated on the runway itself; turn-offs, taxiways, hardstands and the technical areas would come later.

The wear and tear on machinery was very severe and the Special Engineer Regiment Workshop of the Royal Electrical and Mechanical Engineers was doing a heroic job of taking in a constant stream of broken down vehicles and plant of every variety, repairing and refurbishing them and restoring them to full use. There were some miracles of improvisation and 'cannibalisation' when standard replacement parts were not available.

The unit doing this valuable work included fitters, turners, welders, blacksmiths, sheet-metal workers, telecommunications mechanics, electricians and other allied tradesmen; and although it gave great assistance to the Royal Navy and RAF elements, the work was controlled to give the priority to the plant and vehicles required for the runway. One happy note was that the two Barber-Greene macadam spreading machines had arrived and were now in good shape ready to start their race against time.

It was worth noting that this immense and important task was only made possible by the close integration of the Royal Army Ordnance Corps and the Royal Electrical and Mechanical Engineers teams – not normal to Army practice.

Captain Western, who now had at his disposal the facilities of HMS *Messina*, naturally devoted most of his attention to the naval activities which were very considerable and needed a lot of organisation in the Port Headquarters on shore. This would, of course, increase when the operational ships of the Grapple Squadron arrived a few months later. It is the custom of the Royal Navy to name every shore establishment as a ship; so he applied through Commodore Gretton to the Admiralty, requesting that the Christmas Island port establishment be christened 'HMS *Resolution*', after the ship in which Captain Cook had discovered the island on Christmas Day 1777. This was approved and Commander John Holt, a very lively and extrovert officer, was appointed to command HMS *Resolution*.

On September 25th, the Task Force Commander with his aide arrived by the weekly Hastings shuttle from Hickam, partly to see for himself how things were going on the ground and partly to watch the drop of Operation Buffalo at Maralinga. So leaving Commodore Gretton to look after the shop in Whitehall, they had left the UK on September 16th to pay a round of high level visits en route. First to Montreal by BOAC, where they were picked up by a Royal Canadian Air Force aircraft and taken on to Ottawa. There the TFC's oldest and closest friend was, for the moment, the rather reluctant Deputy Minister of Defence, which made it very easy to call on the Chief of the Air Staff and other dignitaries to give thanks for the help being given to Task Force Grapple and to ensure that any further requests would be considered sympathetically. This was also a very pleasant break for the TFC who had a great affection for Ottawa and his Canadian friends.

Next on to Washington where, to his surprise and pleasure, they were met at the National Airport by the friendly and helpful Allen Crocker who over-rode all protestations and took them off to his home in Bethesda to dinner and to meet some of his colleagues in the US atomic tests programme. It was good to see that Britain was welcomed to the atomic club so warmly.

After calling on the ambassador and the Head of the British Defence Mission to discuss the progress of the Grapple programme, the TFC, and Squadron Leader Helfer were invited to visit the Washington headquarters of the US Joint Task Force 7, the organisation responsible for American atomic tests, in their offices in the old wooden First World War Navy Building on Constitution Avenue. There they were greeted most cordially by Rear Admiral 'Bull' Hanlon USN, the Commander of JTF 7 and by his second-in-command, Brigadier General Perry Griffith, USAF. This meeting rapidly developed into a very friendly relationship and two days later the visitors were flown by General Griffith in his 'private' Martin 504 aircraft to the JTF headquarters in Albuquerque, New Mexico. There they received a full briefing on American experiences in atomic tests. It was very comforting to find that the plans for Grapple seemed to be on the right lines. The hospitality was equally warm and next day the TFC wondered whether perhaps there had been another atomic test overnight!

Next, on to Travis Air Force Base of the US Air Force, just outside Sacramento and not far from San Francisco. This was to be a key staging post for all Grapple aircraft going or returning by the west-about route and the take-off point for the 2,000 mile leg to Honolulu. Here the visitors were very warmly welcomed by the Commanding General, the legendary General 'Kal' Kalberer, an outstanding pioneer aviator who had amassed the incredible total of 25,000 hours as a pilot. 'Kal' was a splendid character, rugged, decisive, very kind hearted, very much an admirer of the RAF, who he reckoned had saved his life by giving him sound advice and operational briefing when he was part of the first US Army Air Corps attack on the Ploesti oilfields in World War 2. He and the TFC became life-long friends. Things did not always work out smoothly for the RAF

176

staging post team at Travis, because the modes of operation were so different; but the American hearts were in the right place and RAF aircraft and crews in transit could always be sure of help when needed.

Honolulu next stop, after an eleven-hour flight in the Qantas Constellation. General Sory Smith was at the Terminal Building to greet the visitors and insisted on taking the TFC over to his residence on the Hickam AFB side to accommodate him there for the two day stay. Margaret Smith was a most charming English woman, who had met her husband when he was serving in Egypt during the war, and no doubt this had something to do with the sincere welcome extended to all British, and particularly the RAF at Hickam.

With a staff car and driver kindly put at his disposal by General Smith, the TFC and his aide made their round of courtesy calls. On leaving the office of CINCPAC at Pearl Harbour, the TFC was cheerily accosted by a distinguished looking Vice Admiral who boomed a welcome at him by name and went on to ask: 'and how's your young son? – the one who was born the morning after I dined with you and your charming wife in your quarters at the Joint Antisubmarine School at Londonderry ten years ago.'

Small world! And what a memory! And how like a US naval officer to remember and recall such a trifling act of hospitality!

'Have you got time to do a tour round Pearl and visit the Arizona memorial*? I'd be glad to send my aide with you.'

Of course he had time – or would just make it. This was an opportunity not to be missed and what a moving experience it was! Not only moving; for as the TFC and Helfer were chatting with their amiable guide after the tour, a guard of honour arrived escorting the Japanese Minister of Marine, who had come to lay a wreath and pay his respects to the Arizona memorial – the first time such a visit had been made. The

---

* The sunken battleship USS Arizona now fixed up as a memorial to those who lost their lives in the attack on Pearl Harbour.

177

rapprochement between the USA and Japan was still in its infancy, at least as far as the troops were concerned; and the TFC watched with sympathy and admiration the impassive stony faces of the US Marine guard of honour and USN escorts as they meticulously performed their duties. Something to remember.

Having had a long discussion with Squadron Leader Claridge and his 160 Wing staging post personnel the previous evening the two visitors were joined by Douglas Lovelock, who had just arrived in the early hours, and all three departed on September 25th for the eight hour Hastings flight to Christmas. The thought occurred that it was a hell of a long way to go for an extra pint of milk or anything else needed in a real hurry. Maybe they should have available a faster courier service for emergencies? Like a Canberra, perhaps?

Apart from a rough half hour going through the inter-tropical front, the zone of conflict between the air masses of the southern and northern hemispheres near the equator, it was a smooth and unexciting journey and on arrival at the old Christmas Island coral airstrip there was no interruption of work for any kind of formality; but Bower, Western, Stone and Woollett with beaming smiles were all there to greet the visitors. They were quickly transported to the main camp about two miles away and taken to the tents which would be home for much of the following year. The TFC looked round his tent and noted with approval its adequate simplicity. An army type iron bedstead with, in his case, a couple of inch-thick foot-wide planks under the standard mattress, a small chest of drawers, a wooden hanging cupboard, a writing table and two Windsor chairs. On the table, a telephone already. Well done, the Signals!

A steady breeze was blowing through the eaves of the tent, mitigating the heat and humidity and from the entrance there was a travel-brochure view of the shore line and the green, turquoise and white waves breaking over the reef with monotonous regularity. All very pleasant, compared with some places.

Off to the left was a shower house – a simple wood joist and corrugated iron structure with about a dozen shower stalls and a plain cement floor with slatted duck-boards to stand on, to serve this end of the line of tents. There was a similar structure beyond for the Elsan toilets. Some forty yards nearer the beach and off to the left was the small marquee of the Task Force Commander's staff 'A' mess, and beyond that the very large marquee of the main officers 'B' mess. All very practical. The sappers had done a fine job in a very short time.

There was daylight left for a visit to the port and port camp, a hive of activity, and to pay a call on the excellent Percy Roberts, the Colonial Service Administrator, who was being immensely helpful.

Douglas Lovelock was intrigued by the one man Civil Service set-up and at a later date went to have a chat with Percy Roberts, to find out how it all worked. Roberts, for fun, asked if he would like to have a Christmas Island passport, which Douglas accepted with great pleasure and amusement. Then Percy asked:

'Would you like a Christmas Island driving licence too?'

As Douglas hadn't even got a UK driving licence, not yet having taken the UK driving test, he thought this would be a great leg-pull and accepted laughingly. On his later return to London, he found that his Christmas Island licence was perfectly valid in Britain and so he used it for the next year. By that time he was such a proficient driver that he had no difficulty in passing the test.

By keeping the Hastings aircraft at Christmas for an extra day, the following morning the TFC with Western and Stone made a reconnaissance of Malden Island, where the first landing was to be made a few days later, and then a look-see circuit of Christmas itself, which extended some thirty miles well to the south-east of all the construction activity presently in progress.

Then came high speed tours round all the key work centres, talking for a few moments with as many of the men as possible, including for instance, the bakery housed in a tent where the temperature was well over 100 degrees. In spite of this the army cooks were clean, tidy, hygienic in their white overalls and working like beavers. Not much glamour for them, but no construction work without them. In fact, there was not one man on the island who was not himself essential to the Grapple programme.

Two days later, the TFC and Helfer continued on their way to Australia. Now HMS *Messina* was reloaded with the construction plant, equipment stores and living facilities required for the initial work on Malden, most urgently the airstrip. *Messina* sailed from Christmas on October 1st with Captain Western, Colonel Stone and Colonel Woollett on board as well as the sapper contingent under the command of Captain P S Wadsworth RE and she arrived off the north side of Malden on October 3rd.

The Naval Task Group Commander had ruled that if the cargo and troops could be put ashore by the LCMs and DUKWs, *Messina* herself should not be risked in a beaching. Accordingly, on arrival Commander De Vere attempted to anchor off the gap in the reef. This, however, was none too easy and did not at first succeed; for Malden is the pimple on top of a very steep submarine mountain and the anchor simply rolled down the underwater hill instead of holding. Then it had to be laboriously hoisted up again for another attempt. Eventually, about four o'clock in the afternoon, the anchor held firmly; but clearly this could not be the standard drill and the deep mooring to be laid by *Salvictor* was going to be essential.

Meanwhile, the two LCMs had been hoisted out from their athwartships stowage on *Messina*'s deck and lowered into the water by the ship's winches, while the two DUKWs had been driven out from the tank deck through the open bow doors. The LCMs, one at a time, had driven into the bow opening and lowered their ramps to rest on the ship's ramp. Vehicles were then able to drive under their own power into the LCM for transport ashore. Likewise the DUKWs could drive into the hold, load up and drive ashore.

There was a moderate sea running but the tidal set between the reef and the shore was not very strong; so the craft were able to negotiate the 80 yard gap in the reef, to beach – or to run up on to the beach – and start unloading. The first LCM ashore landed a large caterpillar tractor with a heavy-duty winch attached and a towing cable. This machine was driven up the steep little escarpment behind the narrow sandy beach and was dug into a firm position. As successive vehicles discharged from the LCM ramp on to the beach, the towing cable was hooked on and they were quickly winched up the steep sandy slope and were then well away. Similarly, the fully loaded DUKWs, initially carrying tents and domestic gear and everything necessary to set up the camp, were hauled up by the winch and could then drive easily to the unloading point.

Everyone pitched in on this operation. Senior officers rolled up their sleeves and worked equally alongside the sappers and seamen to get the job done as quickly as possible. There was something of a Boy Scout atmosphere about the operation and by the early afternoon of October 4th, the unloading was completed, plant vehicles and stores neatly parked. Finally, a beach roadway was prepared ready for the arrival of the construction force.

By that time the sea had abated to a near calm and there was vitually no tidal stream across the gap in the reef. It was too good an opportunity to miss; so Commander De Vere with the approval of Captain Western decided to try an approach to beaching the LST. As a 'prudent and seamanlike precaution' he stationed an LCM with a bow line on each bow of the *Messina* to check any tendency for the ship's head to drift off the centre-line and then gingerly steered for the gap. Just short of the beach, he lowered the ship's ramp to touch bottom in about one foot of water, so gently! They'd done it – to great satisfaction all round and without contravening orders. There followed an equally careful withdrawal and return to Christmas.

181

24

Maralinga – the first air drop

On leaving Christmas Island after his brief tour of inspection, the TFC and his aide flew on to Fiji, where at Suva they transferred to the superb New Zealand TEAL airline, which operated a 'Sandringham' flying boat service to Auckland. For interest, comfort on an imperial scale and a well managed operation, it was the epitome of all the best in air travel as well as being delightfully nostalgic for old flying boat enthusiasts.

From Auckland on to Wellington by internal air line to call on the Prime Minister and the Chiefs of Staff to give thanks for the splendid help which they were rendering to Operation Grapple by the support of the two RNZN ships *Pukaki* and *Rotoiti* and No 5 (Sunderland) flying boat squadron. They were informed of the progress made so far and were given an outline of the operational plan.

There was great interest in the British tests heightened by the news of the first ground burst at Maralinga on September 27th and they voiced the concern of the Government and people of New Zealand with the safety aspects of the tests and the possibility of radiation hazards, which were not well understood.

To help in allaying these anxieties, the senior RAF officer in the UK Services Defence Liaison Staff, Group Captain Hutchinson, gave a reception in his home to enable the visitors to meet a wide cross-section of senior New Zealand personalities and to explain the extensive and comprehensive precautions which were to be taken. One distinguished and elderly New Zealand scientist cornered the TFC not only to chat about the tests but also to reminisce about his early days working at RAE Farnborough. He went on to ask: 'There used to be a young fellow called Penney who was always making loud bangs when I was at RAE. Have you heard of him lately? I wonder if he is still making his bangs?'

The TFC assured him that Doctor Penney was in good health and was still making bangs - very loud bangs!

'Oh, that's good. I do hope he'll find some use for them.'

One thing about this pleasant and cheerful occasion intrigued the visitors, the local social custom whereby all the ladies congregated at one end of the room and all the men at the other. They thought this a shocking waste of the local talent and went over to talk to the many charming ladies present; but not for long. They were soon hauled back to their duties in the male enclave. Too bad!

On a more serious note, many officials and private citizens expressed their worries about the safety aspects of atomic tests and this was a good opportunity to give a detailed explanation of the comprehensive measures to be taken to ensure that, even in the extremely unlikely event of an accident, there could be no ill effect on the civil population anywhere.

These explanations did not, unhappily, satisfy everyone in New Zealand and at the airport on leaving Wellington, the TFC was paged to take a telephone call, which turned out to be from a very vehement and irate lady who abused him in a long tirade for his wickedness in carrying out these tests and so imperilling her and her family. He was not able to reassure her and felt badly to leave New Zealand on such a sour note.

It is quite a long way from New Zealand to Australia - over twelve hundred miles across the far from peaceful Tasman Sea. From the relative comfort of the Constellation aeroplane, the TFC mused on the heroic achievement of his friend Francis Chichester, who had flown his tiny De Havilland Gypsy Moth floatplane solo across that wild stretch of ocean, utterly dependent on finding the very small Lord Howe Island – roughly half way – to refuel. To find the island without radio aids, he had used a sextant and some cleverly pre-calculated astronomical data to get a position line by the sun. This was a most remarkable feat of navigation in the cramped open cockpit of the Moth, which could not be flown 'hands-off' for more than a few seconds and so having to hold the joystick between his knees while he took the astro shots. Fantastic!

Sydney was glamorous and exciting and there were old drinking friends in the Royal Australian Air Force training centre at Point Cook. But there was little time to spare for frivolity and so early next morning off to Canberra for a day – a raw building-site sort of Canberra, to which the Australian Premier, Mr Menzies, had only recently insisted that the key Government departments should move forthwith. The vast ornamental Lake Burley Griffin was then only a wide expanse of sun-baked brown earth and sad marshy rushes, with a handsome long white bridge running across the middle of it, apparently without reason.

The first priority was to call on the UK High Commissioner, the very youthful but extremely competent Lord Peter Carrington. He was no technocrat, maybe, but with his lively intelligence he took a genuine interest in the atomic tests, both from the point of view of the Australian public reaction to Monte Bello and Maralinga and of the world balance of power consequences of the Christmas Island series. The High Commission staff had been extremely helpful over both series of tests. The Defence Liaison Staff were, of course, deeply involved in Grapple and it was useful to discuss the operation with them and with the very co-operative Australian services and to render sincere thanks accordingly.

Back to Sydney and early next morning, October 4th, the TFC and Helfer were packed like sardines alongside the pilot and navigator into the constricted cockpit of a Canberra aircraft of 76 Squadron, RAF, part of the Operation Buffalo Task Force, and taken twelve hundred miles west to Maralinga, the 'aluminium village' in the South Australian desert. They arrived just before lunch to be greeted by Air Commodore Weir, the Task Force Commander for this operation, and were immediately hustled off to the spectator stand to watch the second ground burst of Buffalo.

From the point of view of a casual visitor, this was no great drama. A couple of dozen people were gathered in a very utilitarian wooden shelter, with the front open to the test range out in the desert some miles away. Over the Tannoy public address system came a calm voice, counting off the minutes, while the spectators – mainly scientists and engineers with a sprinkling of service officers, both Australian and British – chatted in a desultory manner. At minus five minutes came the order to turn backs to the range site. At minus one minute, shut eyes and hands over eyes.

'Thirty seconds. Ten seconds. Five-four-three-two-one-'

A great flash of light, shining even through hands and eyelids.

'Plus ten seconds,' said the voice. 'You may turn round now and look.'

There was a great cloud, brilliant white edged with brown and dark blue, ascending rapidly. Some moments later the shock wave arrived and the ground trembled. Everyone looked pleased – another successful shot.

Under the direction of the Air Task Group Commander, Group Captain Menaul, several 76 Squadron Canberras – followed by their contrails – converged on the cloud now reaching up to over thirty thousand feet, there to collect samples of particles for analysis. The spectators made their way back to the mess for a cup of tea.

That's all there was to it – on the surface. But like the analogy of the dignified swan paddling like mad below the placid surface of the lake, there was much more. Into this test had gone many years of planning and technical experimentation. This had been followed by hectic months of hard detailed work at Maralinga, out in the inhospitable desert forty miles from the nearest rail head and three hundred miles from any support.

185

All the accommodation and technical facilities had to be constructed, a complex communications system set up, the range comprehensively instrumented and the atomic devices transported safely and assembled. Not least of the tasks was the careful and painstaking negotiation with the Australian Government Atomic Weapons Tests Safety Committee to agree on safety procedures and standards and to ensure that they would be followed rigorously. Now, after the explosion, the atomic cloud would be tracked continuously by the specially equipped RAF Varsity aircraft until the residual radio-activity had dropped to an insignificant level.

In the mess that evening, the Grapple TFC renewed his acquaintance with Bill Penney, the Scientific Director of this series, listened to the anecdotes of Ginger Weir and Paddy Menaul recounting the amusing and the not-so-amusing episodes of the last six months and refreshed contacts with AWRE staff involved in both Buffalo and Grapple. There were introductions and discussions with senior Australian scientists, given to various and vigorous opinions. In offering congratulations on the day's success to Sir William Penney, the latter smiled over the rim of his glass of Foster's and remarked in his genial manner:

'Well, that was certainly a lot of bang from just a little plut.' Then the smile faded and he went on gravely – 'What a frightening thought that it was enough to destroy a city and what a terrible way to have to defend ourselves. There ought to be some better way of running the world.'

For a few moments this put a damper on the conversation and so this seemed a suitable moment to tell him of the comment of Doctor Morton in Wellington, thereby causing roars of laughter all round.

Amongst the many useful encounters that evening was the first meeting with Air Commodore Denis Wilson, a senior RAF medical officer who had made a speciality of radiation monitoring, the effect of radiation on the human body and the establishment of safe limits to the amount of radiation which a person might absorb. He had flown as a passenger in the Canberra aircraft sampling the atomic clouds at Monte Bello and Maralinga and he was to play a very important role in the forthcoming operation at Christmas Island. A modest man of great personal charm and technical competence, he became a highly regarded member of the Grapple team.

Another very interesting personality was Colonel Durrance, the Australian army officer who had been in charge of the construction of the Maralinga base and was now the resident Range Commandant. He had had a tough time and was well entitled to feel satisfaction for a job well done.

The original programme for Operation Buffalo had called for a third ground burst test before the air drop; but in view of the three weeks delay already due to bad weather in September, Bill Penney decided to bring forward the air drop as soon as possible and delay the third ground test. The two 49 Squadron Valiant crews – Squadron Leader Flavell and Flight Lieutenant Bates – had completed their training at Edinburgh Field, near Adelaide, and at Maralinga itself and were ready to go. The weapon was ready for final assembly. But for the next several days, medium level cloud made visual bombing impossible. Penney, Weir, and the Grapple TFC discussed this ad nauseam and even considered a blind drop using the aircraft's radar. Penney asked what accuracy could be assured and the two airmen felt confident about an error of no more than 400 yards. On that, Penney was prepared to go for a radar drop if necessary.

However, the forecast for October 11th was much better and it looked as if there would be a good chance of visual bombing from 30,000 feet in the afternoon with the upper winds in the right direction for safety of any fall-out. On the afternoon of October 10th, the assembly of the weapon was completed and it was loaded into the bomb bay of Valiant WZ366, Flavell's aeroplane.

At midday on the 11th it looked as though the operation might have to be postponed yet again because of a change in the upper winds; but by bringing forward the time of drop by one hour, this was avoided. At 1400 the crew were ready in their aircraft and were given take-off clearance. Without any fuss or ceremony, the Valiant taxied out, lined up on the runway, rolled and was airborne. Flavell did a check run over the dropping zone to allow his bomb-aimer, Flight Lieutenant Stacey, to line up his bombsight and to allow the scientists to make any last minute adjustments to their monitoring equipment. Then the final run along the dropping zone, commencing at 13.05, a calm 'Bomb gone' from Stacey in the nose of the Valiant and then the sharp turn away to take the aircraft clear of the effects of the detonation.

In the spectator stand: the same mixed group of people as the week before, the same drill, the same flash at the end of the count-down, the same drill for sampling the cloud and monitoring it until innocuous. Britain had successfully demonstrated her capability to launch an atomic weapon, albeit designedly of low yield and intended only as part of the technical build-up to a thermo-nuclear test.

Operation Buffalo was completed as far as the RAF Valiants were concerned and the Grapple TFC lost no time in returning that evening to Richmond, near Melbourne. Once again he and his aide were packed tight into a 76 Squadron Canberra, piloted this time by Squadron Leader Boyd, the Commanding Officer. Most of the 76 personnel, having moved their aircraft and equipment to Edinburgh Field, would return to the UK for leave and most of them had volunteered to come back later in the year to re-form and move to Christmas Island. Flight Lieutenant Lindsey Cumming, for his own good reasons, had volunteered to stay behind to look after the small care and maintenance party.

In Melbourne there was celebration of the successful conclusion of the Mosaic and Buffalo series. The Head of the UK Ministry of Supply Mission, Bill Wheeler, who doubled as Scientific Adviser to the High Commissioner, and his very charming wife Mary, threw a memorable party for the senior RAF visitors at their home in the Hawthorne suburb and this

The first Royal Air Force Valiant to pass through the US Travis Air Force Base, California. Wing Commander Hubbard and the crew of XD818 and Brigadier General A F Kalberer USAF (centre). (Photo: K G Hubbard)

A view of Malden Island, with HMS *Messina* in the foreground unloading. *(Photo: AWRE)*

The approaches to Malden Island – the beach and the airstrip. *(Photo: AWRE)*

A rare touch of Service protocol – a parade for the arrival of the Task Force Commander on Christmas Island. Left to right: Percy Roberts, Air Commodore C T Weir RAF, Commodore R Hicks RN, Wing Commander Helfer RAF, Colonel J C Woollett RE. The Task Force Commander takes the salute. *(Photo: AWRE)*

A Guard of Honour of Gilbertese Police. *(Photo: AWRE)*

(Above): The Task Force Commander greeting Mr M H Freeman, the Senior Meteorologist, and other members of the 'Grapple' HQ staff. (Photo: AWRE)

(Left): A handshake for Wing Commander R Boardman, the Chief Technical Officer of 160 Wing. (Photo: AWRE)

moved on exuberantly to the Chevron Club. The following evening Rear Admiral Welby, the Head of the British Defence Liaison Staff, gave a boisterous dinner party at his home, finishing with host, hostess and guests playing a rowdy game of drawing room rugby, using a lighted candle as the ball! Life in Australia seemed to be much more dangerous than atomic tests and the TFC thought he'd better 'get the hell out of it' and return to London, before worse befell! So he did.

They made one stop on the way back, to pay a courtesy call on Bill Marchant, the British Consul-General in San Francisco. This gentleman virtually ranked as an ambassador to the twelfth richest country in the world – California; and in view of the large number of British personnel passing through San Francisco in the next few months, it seemed sensible to make contact with him and put him in the picture.

The visit had its moments. On arrival at San Francisco International airport by an overnight flight from Honolulu, the first thing was to change from plain clothes into uniform. So down to the men's lavatories below the main airport concourse and the TFC and Squadron Leader took adjacent 'loo' cubicles. Five minutes later, as they were about to emerge as spruced up credits to the RAF, there was a loud wail from Helfer.

'I've dropped my cap in the bloody loo!' Consternation!

He emerged, the very spit and polish image of the perfect ADC, his uniform immaculate, his golden aiguillettes on his shoulder gleaming in the fluorescent lighting; and in his hand, this sorry thing, the blue, peaked uniform cap a sodden dripping mess.

'What on earth can I do now, sir?'

'Just give it a jolly good shake and hold it out of the cab window as we drive into town. It shouldn't drip much more after that.'

When they arrived at the Consul-General's impressive office on Pacific Avenue and introduced themselves to that genial and impressive man, Bill Marchant, the TFC was about to relate the incident as a funny story, but was one-upped by his host, bubbling with amusement over another episode. With apologies, Bill Marchant interrupted and said:

'I really must tell you this – it's hysterical.'

Apparently that very morning a young Californian had gone to a car showroom to collect a new Volkswagen 'Beetle' – they were all the rage among the young Californian jeunesse dorée at that time. Never having driven a European car before, or even one with a manual gear-shift, and being somewhat apprehensive, he had taken a friend with him and they had stopped at a local hostelry and taken a glass of beer, to calm the nerves.

With great care, he had driven towards home and had pulled up for a red traffic light on the highway behind the 'Cow Palace', as the San Franciscans call their main exhibition centre. Unhappily, ahead of him in his lane, waiting patiently for the lights, was a large elephant, properly qualified mahout on top. The new 'Beetle' owner slowed down but not quite soon enough and his front fender just touched the back of the elephant's knees. Whereupon the elephant sat down – on the Volkswagen! Flattened – completely! The mahout got down, exchanged insurance cards, expressed sincere regrets and explained that his elephant was trained to sit down on a touch behind the knees. Very sorry!

By this time the lights had changed to green again and the elephant moved on. Next event, predictably, was the arrival of a police car, and a burly, well-weaponed character got out, sauntered over to the wreck and demanded to know what all this was about. The distraught young man told him the simple truth.

'An elephant sat on it.'

The officer, though well aware that he was not intellectually highly qualified, nevertheless felt fairly confident that he was as good as the next man when it came to spotting an unlikely story. He grabbed the young man by the arms, pulled him close, smelt his breath.

'You're drunk. I'm taking you in.'

'And now' chortled the Consul General, 'the boy's lawyer is chasing all over the city looking for the elephant!'

It was hard to get back to a serious discussion about Operation Grapple, but they managed it eventually. An hour later the two visitors left and got a cab to take them out to Travis Air Force Base to reinforce the friendly relationship with General Kalberer and to check on the operation of the RAF staging post. All was well; and so speedily back to London.

25

Suez brings new problems

During the absence of the Task Force Commander at Christmas Island and in Australia, Peter Gretton had kept the programme bowling along at a spanking pace. HMS *Narvik*, the LST which had been Commodore Martell's command and control ship at Monte Bello, had returned to Chatham dockyard and was urgently being refitted and having installed the greatly increased technical facilities necessary for Operation Grapple. The work on the aircraft carrier *Warrior* at Devonport was coming along and a succession of freight and store ships was sailing on schedule to keep the build-up on Christmas Island adequately supplied.

The technical modifications to Valiant, Canberra and Shackleton aircraft were proceeding apace and the Dakota flight, No 1325 Flight, had formed at RAF Station Dishforth under command of an old Dakota 'hand', one Squadron Leader 'Joe' Hurst. The crews were commencing training and should be ready to leave for Christmas Island early in January. They would have to go by the eastabout route, not having the range for the 2000 mile leg from California to Honolulu.

The extensive network of stations for reporting weather, checking fall-out, pollution and measuring seismic shock had been agreed at a day long meeting of Grapple HQ staff, Mr Freeman the Senior Meteorologist and AWRE experts on September 24th. These reporting centres would be established at Penrhyn, Aitutaki, Suva in Fiji, Faleolo in Samoa and Fanning Island north of Christmas.

192

No 5 (flying boat) Squadron of the Royal New Zealand Air Force would be based at Lauthala Bay in Fiji. Their Sunderland aircraft would begin on November 1st to collect fortnightly samples of seawater, vegetation and fish from the Marquesas, Noumea, New Caledonia, Funafuti in the Ellice Islands and Papeete in the Society Islands. These would then be compared with similar samples taken after the nuclear tests to prove that there had been no appreciable pollution.

In his weekly signal on the progress of the construction programme, Colonel Woollett had reported that the two notorious Barber-Greene machines had started to lay the one and a half inch macadam topping on the runway and were working well at a rate of 300 tons a day. With luck and no break-downs they would just make the target date. Other work at the airfield was late, but they expected to catch up later on; and the DDT spraying Auster was keeping the fly menace at Christmas down to a bearable level.

For the moment, things seemed to be going fairly well. Western and Stone were back in the office and Ginger Weir turned up a few days later to take over 160 Wing problems from the overworked Grapple air staff. This seemed a chance for the TFC to take a week-end off and to pay a little attention to his forbearing and much neglected wife. So home to pack a tooth brush and a quick dash down to Sandbanks, a nice room in the pleasant little Harbour Heights Hotel overlooking Poole harbour and three nights of peace and quiet. Ha!

Sunday morning, sitting down to the breakfast table, there was the newspaper with the big black banner headline:

BRITISH AND FRENCH FORCES ATTACK SUEZ.

He had not been keeping up with the political situation vis-a-vis Egypt and had an uneasy feeling that this might not have been the best way to deal with it; but a moment later the real shock set in. The Dakotas could not go to Christmas Island eastabout! If there was a continuing war zone they wouldn't get through. If there wasn't, they would most certainly be commandeered. Dakotas would be more precious than the Crown jewels. What the hell to do now?

Then he remembered that ten years previously he had flown a Dakota non-stop to Cairo – of all places! – about the same distance as San Francisco to Honolulu, with a large internal fuel tank holding about 800 gallons. Now somewhere there must be lying around in some Maintenance Unit overload tanks which would do the job; but could it possibly be done in time?

Back to the office at opening time next morning, and Freddie Milligan and Doug Longley got to work on all their contacts. At the end of the day they had located some internal tanks designed for the Lockheed Neptune when one did a record breaking flight from Perth, Australia to Cape Cod, Massachusetts, over ten thousand miles. The RAF had bought several sets of these tanks when the Neptunes were bought for Coastal Command. So now could they be fitted and who could do the job in time? Scottish Aviation at Prestwick, a small but highly motivated company, undertook the task and to their great credit, by working right through the Christmas holiday, they completed it in time.

Another thing finished just in time was the runway at Christmas. The first civil charter aircraft bringing in the main body of the Air Task Group ground staff was due to arrive during the afternoon of November 4th. On the 3rd, Wing Commander Bower anxiously surveyed the scene as the last two hundred yards of runway were being laid with the macadam and hot rolled to produce the necessary fine finish.

'Can you do it?' he asked Colonel Woollett.

'Yes. Bring them in.'

November 4th, as the first aircraft made its approach, the last roller cleared off the end of the runway. Well done, those sappers! To celebrate the achievement Colonel Woollett as Garrison Commander decreed the next day, November 5th, as a holiday and a complete stand-down from all work. A very appropriate day for a place being set up to test some really large fireworks!

The glad word was signalled to London, to satisfaction all round. So what goes wrong now?

Willie Wright from the Foreign Office. The Quai d'Orsay was in an uproar over the threat which the British tests would pose to their sovereign territory of Tahiti. Apparently the French Governor there had been curious about the visit and activities of the RNZAF flying boats, which had been cleared at a low level. On being informed, he had discussed the sampling activity with a scientist friend, who had declared the British measures quite inadequate and demanded that he take charge of the whole affair.

'No way,' responded the New Zealander captain and the matter was referred to Paris and London, with the soothing assistance of the British Consul. Now Lovelock for Grapple HQ, Wright for the Foreign Office, Allen and Hall for the Colonial Office and experts from AWRE went into a long huddle to try to pacify and calm the French without upsetting the plans for the operation. In the end, the scientist flounced off, his dignity offended and life in Tahiti reverted to its normal peaceful and agreeable torpor. And the sampling operations went on as planned.

Nevertheless, as a result of this review, Bill Cook the Scientific Director concluded that the arrangements for sampling fish in the Christmas Island area were not adequate. It had been supposed that the Gilbertese natives could be persuaded to catch a sufficiency of fish for testing purposes, but this they would not do. Being sensible people, they could see the point of catching fish to eat; but to labour at catching fish to be cut up and thrown away was clearly nonsense and not for them. A plan to get the troops to catch fish as a pastime was equally inadequate. So Captain Western arranged for a ninety ton Motorised Fishing Vessel (MFV) to be taken out on one of the heavy lift ships, with a professional crew, and this in due course ensured a steady supply of the necessary several varieties of fish.

26

The construction force moves into Malden

During November 1956 another major piece of the planning jig-saw began to fall into place. In anticipation of completion of the technical and operational facilities necessary for the Air Task Group, the main body of RAF personnel began to move to Christmas Island, mostly by chartered civil aircraft. The Technical Wing, commanded by Wing Commander 'Ron' Boardman, co-operated closely and harmoniously with the Army engineers to achieve the best lay-out of the base maintenance area and the commissioning of the complex of specialist sections necessary for the first-line servicing of seven different types of aircraft. Second-line servicing was planned to be effected either in UK or at Edinburgh field in Australia.

The large wind deflector to permit changing aircraft control surfaces in the open was in course of erection and in due course worked well. Extensive power supplies of various ratings, air conditioning and clean air where essential and a good telephone network had been provided by REME and the Royal Corps of Signals. The wing had received and sorted out into discrete specialist units and locations over eighteen thousand separate containers of equipment, spare parts and consumable stores. In view of the speed at which these had been procured and shipped, inevitably there were shortages, misfits and breakages. Improvisation, self-help and local manufacture were brought to the rescue and the army technical units gave wonderful support to the RAF. There was a fair amount of traffic in the opposite direction too.

The air traffic control service of the airfield was now capable of handling any aircraft at a low rate and in any weather likely to occur. The Task Force Commander had been very concerned about this in view of there being no diversion airfield; but with a good M/F radio beacon useful out to 250 miles, a Eureka beacon good out to 110 miles, a manual VHF/DF homer with a range of 110 miles and a Plessey ACR 7(D) mobile 'talk-down' radar good down to 150 feet and ½ mile, there was now little anxiety. However, it is interesting to note that the 'talk-down' radar turned out to be a life saver on more than one occasion. Before the operational phase aircraft arrived, the manual VHF homer would be replaced by CR/DF* equipment and a more powerful M/F beacon with a range of 600 miles would be in operation. Likewise the current temporary flare-path for any unplanned night flying would be replaced in December by proper Class I runway lighting.

Not everything went smoothly, of course, and there were some mighty snags. For instance, the air cooling sets supplied for a variety of uses were quite inadequate. In the local atmospheric conditions they produced a great deal of water but no 'coolth'. This was reported to London, raised at the quickie morning meeting and the job went to Squadron Leader Duck. The latter reported, five days later, that much better coolers had been air-freighted to Christmas. The TFC, impressed, asked how he had achieved this. No problem, apparently. With the help of a senior supply officer friend, Duck had tracked down a West German firm who made good and suitable coolers, ordered them by telephone, had them trucked to RAF Northolt by Friday evening, persuaded a packing firm to work through the night crating them up, chartered an aircraft with Longley's help and the consignment had left on Sunday morning.

'Well done, Roly. Nice work! But how did you pay for all this?'

---

* Cathode Ray Direction Finding equipment, in which the direction of an aircraft transmitting on radio is indicated by a bright line on a circular picture of the neighbourhood.

'Oh, I just signed bits of paper and told them Mr Lovelock here would pay – I hope!'

No slouch, Roly Duck!

Meanwhile, progress was being made on the home front and Vickers, too, were no slouches. Mid-November the first Grapple – standard Valiant XD818, resplendent in its gleaming white external finish, was delivered to RAF Station Wittering and was taken over by the CO of 49 Squadron, Wing Commander Ken Hubbard, as his personal aircraft for the nuclear tests. XD818 was quickly followed by four others, each one being allocated to specific air and ground crews who would care for them like a hen with one chick. Thanks to the very helpful and co-operative Brian Trubshaw, later famous for his pioneer flying on Concorde, the final three Grapple Valiants were delivered in January.

The vast majority of the long list of special modifications had been incorporated, but more were still to come, including the vital Decca navigation equipment. The time taken in fitting these later modifications conflicted seriously with the intense squadron training programme, which was already in trouble because of the rarity of occasions when visual bombing training from 45,000 feet could be carried out.

49 Squadron was not the only unit approaching the starting line. On November 15th the TFC flew up to RAF Dishforth to visit the newly formed 1325 Flight and its reconstituted Dakotas. Four complete crews were in intensive training on their three aircraft, which would soon have to go, one at a time, to Scottish Aviation for the fitting of the internal fuel tanks and all the allied 'plumbing'. Squadron Leader Hurst seemed an excellent choice for this job and the TFC was very impressed by his thoroughness in the training for the long distance navigation, the North American radio procedures and operating into and out of improvised airstrips. The crews were all as keen as mustard and seemed to be very competent for their important task.

At Ballykelly, too, the two Shackleton squadrons were being

hard-pushed to recover from their trooping operations during the Suez crisis and to fit, and train the crews on, the special cameras, radio fit and other electronic equipment required for their role in Grapple.

While all this air side activity was being closely monitored in the Grapple HQ, it was agreed that Commodore Gretton should make another visit to Christmas Island to oversee the planned beaching of HMS *Messina* at Malden Island on December 7th, to land the main construction force. He was to go eastabout, taking in Singapore and New Zealand en route to make or confirm necessary naval arrangements and was due to leave London on the afternoon of November 28th. In the forenoon, before departure, he went to do a little last minute shopping near his home in Wimbledon. Because of the post-Suez threat of petrol rationing he rode to the shops on his bicycle and was knocked down by a lorry coming round the corner on the wrong side of the road. It shook him up and grazed a knee severely; worse still, although this was not immediately apparent, his spine was damaged. Being Peter Gretton, he left Heathrow on schedule but then, on arrival at Singapore, fell victim to a bad attack of the local 'tummy-bug'. Even so, he called as planned on Admiral Scott-Moncrieff, the Commander-in-Chief Far East and obtained the use of HMS *Alert*, the C-in-C's Despatch Vessel as a spectator ship for the second round at Christmas Island. Then on to Wellington, where he made friends and arranged facilities for *Messina* and *Salvictor* to refit there and to give the crews some rest and recreation. Feeling a little better, he readily agreed to play golf with his hosts and most unhappily this seriously aggravated his back trouble. On arrival at Honolulu in very great pain, he was put straight into the military Tripler Hospital, where he had to stay for three weeks, incandescent with frustration.

On December 7th, 1956, the LST HMS *Messina* – unhappily without Peter Gretton – arrived at Malden Island on schedule to deliver the Army construction force, forty sappers and an RAF signals section all under the command of Captain P S

Wadsworth RE together with the remainder of their plant, stores and materiel. On this occasion Commander De Vere decided to beach the ship without the benefit of restraining bow lines from two LCMs. Unfortunately, the current inside the reef was much stronger than it had been in September, the ship drifted a little to one side of the narrow gap and the bottom of the hull banged against a coral head, started a few plates and caused a leakage of sea-water into the fuel tanks. This would necessitate repairs when *Messina* later went to New Zealand for a short refit. Even so, she was able to put down her ramp and discharge much of her load directly on to the beach, but then had to withdraw and complete unloading by her LCMs and DUKWs.

The previously prepared beach road had been destroyed by the surf and it was necessary to use the winches of bulldozers already ashore to haul the stores and equipment out of the LCMs as they came in to the beach. The DUKWs managed much better than the LCMs and for a time they drove ashore without too much trouble; but then one broached in the surf and was lost. From then on the drill was established to snap a hook on the end of a winch line on to the D-ring on the bow of each DUKW as it touched the beach and so haul it up rapidly out of the surf.

Conditions worsened, but the Royal Marine and RASC crews pressed on gallantly and everything was landed safely. Work began immediately on setting up the temporary camp and then to the priority job of preparing the airstrip. Until that was ready, the Malden force would be isolated, except for one or two visits by *Salvictor* with food supplies.

However, to minimise the isolation it was arranged that the weekly Hastings aircraft shuttle from Hickam should stay for an extra day at Christmas and make a weekly run to Malden to air-drop mail and any urgently needed items which could be suitably packaged. The sappers had been briefed to mark out an air-drop zone with white strips and they would be in daily wireless touch with Christmas to list their requirements. This system worked very well for the six weeks until the airstrip was ready and the regular arrival of mail from home was always a great boost to morale and efficiency.

Woollett, Bower and Paton flew up to Hickam in the Hastings shuttle and had a whole day session briefing the Commodore on the Malden landing and on satisfactory progress in all areas – apart from the slight damage to *Messina*. Thereafter Gretton, with his characteristic resolution and determination and despite the vigorous protests of the doctors that he was not fit to travel, made his way home just in time for Christmas Day. Immediately after the break, he resumed his energetic activities in the Grapple HQ on a diet of pain-killing pills, to the great concern of his friend the TFC; but he was a sick man and inevitably the responsibility for the Naval Task Group fell increasingly on Captain Western.

However, there was no hitch in the naval programme and on December 27th the ammunition ship RFA *Fort Rosalie* sailed from the UK carrying the high explosive bombs necessary for the final stages of aircrew training and instrumentation calibration at Christmas and Malden Islands, as well as the basic Blue Danube bomb cases for the nuclear devices to be tested in the 'live' drops.

After discharging at Malden, *Messina* had returned to Christmas without difficulty, but clearly she could not continue with her planned programme in that damaged condition. She was therefore sent to New Zealand, a mere 4,000 miles away, for repair and refit in the dockyard. In the end this turned out well in that it gave the crew a break ashore for the Christmas holiday season before returning to the hectic operational phase of Grapple.

At one of the morning meetings early in December, Guy Western had commented on the steady flow of personnel to Christmas Island and that there would soon be nearly four thousand men there; and although each one of them knew his own job, practically none of them had any idea what the whole operation was about or even what was the role his own service was to play. Wouldn't it be a good idea to produce a small booklet to give to each man, saying in simple straight-forward language what the Task Force was required to do and why, how was it doing it and what the Royal and Merchant Navies, the Army and the Royal Air Force were each contributing to the total effort?

This suggestion was agreed with some enthusiasm and there were some wry remarks that this might be one way to learn what was going on in the Grapple HQ itself! So, sections of the proposed booklet were farmed out to individuals to do a first draft and AWRE undertook to provide a fifteen year old schoolboy's chapter on the physics of the devices to be tested.

The intention was to see that every man going to the Grapple area should have a copy as soon as possible, but certainly before the first live test; so it had to be a non-classified unofficial publication. In the event many problems arose and there were strongly held opposing views on content and presentation. These were eventually solved by un-democratic methods; but there were delays in printing at the price required and it was not until April 1957, and that only after some pretty fierce pressure by the TFC, that 4,000 copies were flown out to Christmas Island and sold to all interested personnel at the modest price of one shilling and sixpence.

Another consideration affecting morale was the fact that over two thousand men of the Task Force would be separated from their families at Christmastide, and this in time of peace. A splendid and warm hearted proposal was put forward, that each man out at Christmas Island should send a small Christmas present to some child sick in hospital in Britain. The idea was taken up with enthusiasm. A small fixed amount of money was collected from each man, together with a tie-on label giving the address of the donor. Captain Western did a deal with a neighbour who was a toy manufacturer to produce two thousand-odd gifts at a discount price. Volunteers packed up the gifts and tied on labels. Distribution was arranged to a number of hospitals and nearly every man out at Christmas

Island or Malden received, with his Christmas mail, a thank you note from some happier child.

27

Operational ships and aircraft

Early in January 1957 the Christmas Island base domestic, technical and operational facilities were almost complete and were rapidly being brought into full use ready for the arrival of the scientists and the RAF squadrons. The RAF Signals section had moved from the airfield to the new joint Navy/Army/Air Force communications centre alongside the almost completed Joint Operations Centre – the JOC as it was now referred to – leaving only 'approach' and 'local' control in the Air Traffic Control tower at the airfield. Wireless telegraphy and radio-teleprinter contact with the UK, with staging posts and with the network of meteorological and other reporting points involved in Operation Grapple as well as with aircraft in flight or ships at sea in the area would now be handled at this joint centre. For communications within the island, the army No 2 Special Air Formation Signals troop had laid and would now maintain 360 miles of telephone cable, including 95 miles of high quality circuits, a teleprinter link between airfield and JOC and four telephone exchanges. They had also, in conjunction with Royal Navy signals, laid submarine telephone cables to the deep moorings put down by HMS *Salvictor* for the use of ships lying off the port.

On Janury 7th, HMS *Narvik* sailed from Portsmouth under the command of Commander Tony Casswell. After the Monte Bello operation she had been refitted at Chatham dockyard and provided with a helicopter platform, a DUKW and a complex of instrumentation and communication equipment to enable her to fulfil her role of Command Post and Scientific Control for the Task Force Commander and the Scientific Director during the live drops at Malden Island. The ship was also carrying a great deal of the recording equipment to be positioned on the target island in the protective bunkers close to the burst point of the nuclear devices.

Two days later, the Dakota aircraft of No 1325 Flight, which were to provide the daily communication between Christmas Island and Malden during the installation of all those recording equipments, departed from Dishforth westward via Keflavik, Goose Bay, Namao, Comox (Vancouver Island) Travis AFB and Hickam, supported by a Hastings of 24 Squadron carrying the ground crews. Two of them arrived at Christmas on January 17th. The third had been held up by technical trouble at Namao, but almost caught up by taking advantage of a less unfavourable head wind to fly direct from Vancouver to Honolulu – a very long haul indeed – so arriving at Christmas only one day late. This route would, of course, have been impossible without the long range internal fuel tanks and the efforts of Scottish Aviation to get them installed just in time.

Meanwhile the Dakotas had been 'pipped' by a rather dashing Hastings captain. During the weekly mail and supply drop run to Malden on January 16th, he reckoned there was enough runway finished – about 900 yards – to put his aircraft down and he did so, to the delight of the isolated sapper work force, who were thus able to send home a lot of accumulated mail. Four days later, January 20th, the thousand-yard strip was finished, the internal tanks removed from the Dakotas and 1325 Flight began the daily service to Malden which was to continue without fail throughout Operation Grapple, plus many other routine runs as and when necessary. They soon acquired the title 'Christmas Airways' and painted it, airline fashion, on the side of their aircraft.

During this time *Narvik* was running into trouble. Half way across a turbulent Atlantic, Commander Casswell reported that he had a crack in the deck plating of *Narvik*, running from the corner of the main hatch and growing longer. Uneasy about this, Guy Western consulted the Director of Naval Construction who immediately sounded alarm bells. Because of the mode of construction of the LSTs, if that crack in *Narvik's* deck continued much further, the ship could disintegrate. Casswell was instructed to reduce speed and make for Kingston, Jamaica, while Western and a Naval Constructor hurriedly packed their bags and flew to Kingston on January 17th, there to search for suitable repair facilities. But despite having enlisted the aid of the very genial but unhelpful Governor and having fruitlessly combed the remnants of the Jamaican ship repair organisation, they still had not found the necessary repair facility when *Narvik* arrived safely a few days later. Meanwhile, of course, the TFC had been anxiously watching the daily report on the lengthening crack, concerned not only for the safety of the crew but also uncomfortably aware that in the event of disaster the mass of telemetry and other special equipment in *Narvik* could not possibly be replaced in time for the tests. What relief when the ship reported arrival at Kingston!

Eventually Guy Western found an industrial sheet-metal worker and welder who quite nonchalantly brought his equipment along and welded up *Narvik's* deck as good as new, even if not quite so pretty. No problem! Whereupon *Narvik* continued her voyage only a few days late, the Naval Constructor returned to London and Western went up to New York and joined the stream of bodies westward bound for Christmas Island.

On January 19th, the first five Shackleton aircraft of 206 Squadron, under the command of Wing Commander Preston, left Ballykelly for Christmas. Not being winterised to cope with Canadian winter weather, they flew by the southern route via the Azores, Bermuda, Charleston (South Carolina), El Paso (Texas) to Travis AFB (California) and so on to Honolulu to arrive at Christmas on January 28th.

Air Commodore Weir, the key members of his staff and the

first seventy of the RAF 160 Wing technical supply and administrative personnel arrived on February 1st in a chartered Qantas 'Constellation' and moved into their bare wooden hut HQ offices and the tented engineering and stores accommodation alongside the airfield. The RAF Station, Christmas Island, took on the standard format of organisation into three wings – Flying Wing, Administrative Wing and Technical Wing. Unusually, command of the Flying Wing, normally a post for a Wing Commander, was taken by Group Captain L E Giles, a very experienced and competent Bomber Command aviator. Again unusually he had a deputy, Wing Commander Johnny Ayshford, who had been the Grapple Liaison Officer at Bomber Command Headquarters and who had now carefully surveyed the westabout reinforcement route by flying out as extra crew member in one of the Dakotas of 1325 flight. Dougie Bower, who had initially opened the air base and brought it up to readiness, now became Wing Commander Admin, and Wing Commander Ron Boardman, who had already done a superb job in planning the aircraft maintenance facilities, became Chief Technical Officer in command of the Technical Wing. They made a first-class team and soon welded the steady stream of reinforcements into an efficient organisation.

No time was wasted and the very next day, February 2nd, the 206 Squadron Shackletons began their daily meteorological flights, initially at the easy pace of one per day. They used a route of about 1600 miles – twelve hours flying – chosen by the Met office staff to give the most important information for that day. All the aircraft had special instrumentation to collect the required data and each one carried a Meteorological Observer in addition to the normal crew.

Mr Freeman and his team of forecasters were already installed in the Meteorological section of the Joint Operations Centre and now began their first task of building up a picture of the weather pattern in the Grapple operational area, using every available input. In addition to data from aircraft, the newly installed Christmas Island Met station had begun regular observations and was already experimenting with the new radio-sonde equipment for high altitude wind finding. Standard weather reports were received from existing Government stations in Australia, New Zealand, Fiji and Hawaii and a direct link with the comprehensive American weather centre at Wheeler Field in Hawaii for much more detailed information would be set up later in the month. Other Grapple reporting stations – most importantly the major installation on Penrhyn Island – would come into use as their equipment and personnel were delivered during February and March.

While the Dakotas, Shackletons, Hastings and 160 Wing personnel were flowing westward from the UK to Christmas Island, the air and ground crews of No 76 Canberra B6 Squadron were returning from their rest period at home by civil airline or chartered passenger aircraft to Adelaide, where the squadron reformed at Edinburgh Field on February 1st under its new CO, Squadron Leader George Bates. After cloud sampling and tracking at Maralinga, the aircraft had been left at Edinburgh Field and were still usable for Grapple, although several had some degree of radio-active contamination and special precautions were required in servicing these. Also, strict and formal procedures would have to be observed when lightly contaminated aircraft transitted through international airports.

The reformed squadron included six new crews and an intense training programme, with emphasis on long range over-sea navigation, was necessary to bring all crews up to the requisite operational standard before the move to Christmas Island. Under the vigorous leadership of George Bates and thanks to the dedication and enthusiasm of air and ground crews, all volunteers for the job, this target was achieved.

The Naval Task Group was equally busy. *Messina* and *Salvictor* had now returned from their mini-refits in New Zealand and were engaged in delivering weather reporting stations, microbarograph recording equipment and Decca Navigator ground stations to designated islands. Some of this delivery task was done by Shackletons and Dakotas and the Air

Task Group and the whole programme was carried out in a splendid spirit of friendly inter-service co-operation.

During this time HMS *Narvik* had arrived at Christmas Island and, after a few days rest, went to take up her station on the deep mooring, off the north beach at Malden, where she would spend much of the next four months.

Meanwhile in a very different climate and in January, the aircraft-carrier *Warrior* had completed her refit and modification at Devonport, had commissioned under the command of Captain Roger Hicks and had moved to Portland for sea trials and practice in co-operation with a Valiant of 49 Squadron, to test and exercise the ship's radar control of the aircraft before leaving for Christmas Island. At the same time, opportunity was taken to give experience of landing on the carrier to the helicopter crews of 22 Squadron, RAF, who were to provide the Air Sea Rescue cover at Christmas Island.

The Task Force Commander took advantage of this exercise to pay a formal visit to the ship which was so vital to the overall operational plan. Arriving in one of the RAF helicopters he, together with principal members of the Grapple HQ staff, was very cordially received by Captain Hicks and his officers. There was a fine spirit of co-operation and camaraderie and of being all of one team. It all augured well.

Having embarked her aircraft, three naval Avengers and four naval Whirlwind helicopters, followed on January 30th by the two RAF Air/Sea Rescue helicopters and Squadron Leader Duck, *Warrior* sailed from Portsmouth on February 2nd. During her trans-atlantic passage she ran into extremely bad weather, which caused extensive damage. Accordingly, on February 15th she put into Kingston, Jamaica, for forty-eight hours to effect repairs sufficient to continue, and to the great satisfaction of the crew. On February 19th she passed through the Panama Canal – probably the largest vessel ever to do so – and Commander Robin Begg's careful calculations were vindicated. She had just a few inches clearance on each side as she passed through the narrowest part of the locks. After that, all was plane sailing. Avengers and helicopters were exercised en route and the ship arrived at the Christmas Island anchorage area on March 4th, picked up one of the deep moorings and was in telephone contact with the JOC.

There had been one light-hearted moment in the final part of the voyage when she was still 500 miles away. Tony Jillings, one of the inveterate humorists of the RAF Flying Wing staff, had filled a cannister with a vast number of land crabs and a bawdy message of welcome for his friend Roly Duck. A Shackleton, sent out as a navigation exercise to intercept and greet *Warrior*, dropped the cannister alongside the ship. Unfortunately it burst and sank. A suspicious but slightly anxious Robin Begg made a signal to Christmas reporting the loss and querying the contents of the cannister; to which he got only the laconic reply – 'Crustacea for Duck'!

On *Warrior's* arrival off the port area, the RAF helicopters had disembarked and flown to the airfield to join the Flying Wing and to take up their Air/Sea Rescue stand-by duties. This was quite a change of life style, from the relative comfort of cabin and ward-room to a tent and very basic meals in an improvised aircrew mess-tent alongside the parking apron. However, the beach was only a few hundred yards away and there were succulent ulua fish to be caught and grilled over a picnic fire when there was no air activity; so there were compensations.

Thenceforward, whenever flying was in progress, one of the rescue helicopters was on stand-by; but increasingly the second aircraft would be used for time-saving intra-island transport and the flight became one of the busiest units in the Task Force. They soon adopted the pseudonym 'The Yellow Cab Service' – a punning reference to the colour of their aircraft and their maid-of-all-work daily tasks.

28

Contaminated fuel!

Penrhyn Island, also known as Tongareva, more than six hundred miles south of Christmas, was to be the most important of the island out-stations and was planned to operate a principal weather station – the only one, other than Christmas itself, with a radio-sonde facility, a Decca slave station, micro-baragraph and radiation fall-out monitoring equipment and accommodation for a USAF special weapons monitoring team.

On February 14th that old Pacific hand Squadron Leader Church took a Shackleton, Air Commodore Weir and a mixed team of naval, army and air force specialist staff to reconnoitre the place. There was an old wartime airstrip there, long enough, but now surrounded by very tall palm trees. With the prevailing wind at 70 degrees to the runway, this produced a strong wind shear at 100 feet coming in to land. Very tricky! However, all was well. But Captain Gates, USAF, who was one of the party, was very concerned about this and opined that the C124 aircraft planned to deliver and supply the American unit could not use the strip unless the clear flight path was widened to 400 feet and the tallest palms lopped. Eventually a compromise was reached on this point.

Penrhyn was a lovely story-book tropical island – or rather a ring of small islands. It had everything that the troops had hoped for but had not found at Christmas – lush and beautiful vegetation, picturesque trading schooners and a pearl fishing fleet, a friendly and attractive native population and a small colony of warm-hearted and hospitable New Zealanders, headed by Mr D A Read, the New Zealand Liaison Officer positioned there for the duration of the tests. The recce showed that everything needed could be fitted in and the team returned to Christmas that evening well satisfied. Four days later HMS *Salvictor* landed the masts for the Decca slave station, and a small team to erect them.

Jarvis and Fanning islands were quite different – bleak and even less attractive than Christmas, although at Fanning there was at least cheerful company in the staff of the civil cable company. But beaching an LST was not possible at either of them and *Messina* put all the gear for the Decca master station ashore on Jarvis by LCM and similarly for the weather station on Fanning. These two places then had a weekly air drop of mail and other supplies and any necessary movement of personnel was effected by *Messina* or *Salvictor*. One of the mail drops for Jarvis hung up as it left the aircraft, fell into the sea and was not recovered. Very red and apologetic faces! But apart from that accident, the system worked well.

The demands for air movement of both freight and personnel began to increase rapidly. On February 2nd, a weekly Hastings service to Edinburgh Field in Australia was initiated. This enabled the Canberra squadrons, and to some extent eventually also the Valiants, to draw on supplies and engineering facilities there. The strength of aircraft in the Hastings flight was increased to four, rotating of course as they went back for major servicing, and this permitted an increase in the Honolulu shuttles to three a week. Squadron Leader John Claridge in command of the RAF Staging Post at Hickam AFB found himself a very busy man but it was all working well.

As usual in Grapple, the moment one problem was solved another took its place. Sunday morning – again! – the TFC's home telephone rang and a troubled Group Captain Milligan announced the day's catastrophe – all the fuel in the newly filled tank farm in the port area, over a million gallons of it, was contaminated. What to do now?

What to do, indeed, with a million gallons of hydro-carbon fuels! How do you get rid of it? And what hope of getting it replaced in time?

'Freddie, who supplied the fuel?'

'Shell, sir.'

'Get on to the Managing Director of Shell (UK) wherever he may be this morning, explain the situation and see if he can suggest anything.'

Later in the day, Milligan came back with word that Shell had an expert with experience of this kind of problem and who might be able to suggest a solution. Unfortunately he was away in Malaya doing his annual RAF Volunteer Reserve service. Milligan had asked HQ Far East for help and they had replied that the Shell expert was out on a jungle survival exercise and could not be contacted for the next week.

'Freddie, take down this signal and get the Resident Clerk in the Air Ministry to send it "Most Immediate" to SASO Far East. "Personal for Adams from Oulton. Would be most grateful for your assistance in locating Flight Lieutenant X, RAFVR believed to be out on a survival exercise and getting him soonest to Hickham AFB Honolulu for onward transit to Christmas Island".'

Alex Adams responded with alacrity, found the Shell expert and produced also a small fuel inspection team of the Aeronautical Inspection Service in the Far East. Unfortunately he couldn't get them to Honolulu or Christmas for weeks; so one of the precious Hastings from Christmas had to go to Changi – more than six thousand miles! – to fetch them.

However, ten days later the good word came back to Whitehall to say that the problem was not so severe as had been supposed and had now been cured by suitable local treatment. The AIS in Melbourne confirmed that the fuel was now within specification limits, so far as Avgas for piston engines was concerned. Full clearance for Avtur for jet engines was received on March 11th.

There were many other logistic problems. Over and above the

original tasks for which they had planned, as the scientific problems changed from day to day with rapidly advancing technology, and as experience showed up new requirements in the airfield, such as an additional asphalted area for running up jet engines on test, so extra demands were placed on the army constructors. So some of their unskilled jobs had to be unloaded on to the RAF, which meant using skilled tradesmen for stevedore jobs. This was acceptable for a few days, but could not be sustained for long. Furthermore, the situation was aggravated by the fact that part of the Army Group, 55 Field Squadron and 64 Field Park Squadron, had long exceeded their non-accompanied time overseas and were due to sail for home in the Troop Transport *Captain Hobson* on March 2nd. A cry for help was therefore sent to the RAF detachment in Australia, asking for twenty volunteers to come to Christmas to work as labourers for two months. The list was filled in a matter of hours and the workers arrived on the next returning Hastings shuttle. This more or less solved the problem caused originally by the planners not allowing sufficient bodies to do the chores; and this was the fault of the Task Force Commander for his over insistence on keeping the team lean!

214

29

Scientific preparations

With the completion of the operational facilities for the air and naval task groups and the commencement of routine flying and ship movements, the main emphasis now shifted to the Scientific Task Group, whose requirements overall absorbed thirty per cent of the sapper constructional effort for the entire operation. These, of course, fell broadly into two parts – the creation of the instrumentation base on Malden Island and the completion of the complex of activities at Christmas by March 1st, 1957.

Under the Scientific Director, Bill Cook, and his deputy, Charles Adams, the Scientific Superintendent (Malden) – Ken Bomford – and the Scientific Superintendent (Christmas) – John Challens – would each operate in an almost autonomous manner. But, for his work force, each of them would have to draw on the resources of some twenty specialist activities which fell into three groups, namely: Services, Weapons and Measurements. Broadly, these three groupings of activities corresponded to Personnel and Administration (including health and safety), Weapon assembly and functioning, and measurement and analysis of the result; and although the whole set-up was of and for AWRE, it must be mentioned that there was an important element of the Royal Aircraft Establishment, Farnborough, within the Weapons group.

Cook, with other onerous responsibilities at Aldermaston, was not due to arrive at Christmas until the end of April, by which time Challens and Bomford were to have their respective empires ready for evaluation and an intense period of rehearsals.

With the arrival of *Narvik* at Malden and the regular daily air service from Christmas, the work of landing the mass of equipment from the ship and installing it in the manner and place required by the scientists began to go ahead at a great pace. By early March, some fifty scientists and fifty sappers were engaged in this task, plus the Royal Marines and RASC crews of the LCMs and *Narvik's* DUKW. The DUKWs did great work, driving out to the ship a quarter of a mile off-shore, straight into the tank deck, loading up, driving back to the beach and being hooked up by the winch as the wheels hit the sand. Sometimes this was exhilarating fun. Sometimes, with a heavy surf running, it was very dicey indeed and not at all funny; but the timetable was inexorable and the work had to go on regardless.

On one noteworthy occasion, with strong surf and tidal set, the DUKW broached and rolled right over, a few yards short of the beach. Lieutenant Evans, RASC, the beachmaster, was standing ankle deep in the water with the snap-hook of the winch-line in his hand, ready to hook on. As the DUKW began to turn over, Evans appreciated the situation in a flash and hurled himself forward into the surf, regardless of the local shark population. Reaching up with his hand, he managed to snap the hook on to the D-ring on the bow of the DUKW just before it submerged and to give a wave of his hand before he himself submerged. The quick witted winch operator, having watched all this, immediately put tension on the cable and hauled away carefully. The DUKW came bow-on to the beach and continued its roll until it was right way up again! This was claimed as the first time a DUKW had been slow-rolled! Fortunately there were no casualties. Well done, Evans!

All the recording and measuring equipment of so many different types had to be positioned to point directly to that place eight thousand feet south of the bombing marker and eight thousand feet high where the nuclear device would detonate; but all the processing circuitry had to be protected against

216

damage. So most of the equipment was buried deep in protective bunkers, leaving just the receiving head peeping over the top. In some cases the circuitry was of such a sensitive nature that it had to be enclosed in welded-up sheet metal cubes, buried below ground level.

Most of the equipment was to record at very high speed and so could only be switched on very briefly before the detonation. This then required telemetry receiving aerials and more equipment.

Living conditions for this Malden work force were even more spartan than those at Christmas. Absolutely everything except the actual recording equipment had to be dismantled and buried below ground before a live drop; and then it had to be exhumed and set up again quickly to prepare for the next test. So there was nothing superfluous in the way of comfort.

As well as providing domestic and technical support for the scientists, the army had one other job, to make a clearly visible bomb-aiming marker on the south-east corner of the island as an aiming point for the bomb-aimer in the Valiant. This was a fifty-yard sided triangle of ten foot wide concrete, coated with orange day-glow paint. This was a key element in the accurate delivery of the bomb.

While Bomford and his chosen team were fixing up Malden, Challens and his cohorts at Christmas were making their arrangements for the assembly and checking of the devices to be tested. Perhaps the most important building in their plan was the Assembly Building, a large aluminium structure as big as a small hotel, temperature controlled, air conditioned with clean air and fitted with mechanical, electrical and electronic facilities. It had its own aircraft parking apron, well away from the main apron, and its own taxi track to the main runway. The area where the Valiant would, in due course, be parked for the loading of the bomb was protected from the vulgar gaze by a large square of something like a fence of cricket screens. The 'need-to-know' principle was being rigorously applied and only those scientists and supporting RAF technical personnel actually involved in its preparation would get within sight of the 'Blue Danube' bomb-case, let alone its 'innards', until the moment when it would be loaded into the chosen aircraft.

Adjacent to the assembly building were several others, each dedicated to some specialist activity which had required esoteric techniques of installation by the army. There were also several telemetry vans of pantechnicon size which simulated the electronic environment in which the bomb would be aimed and released off Malden Island.

Working largely independently of either Bomford or Challens were the Theoretical Predictions, Decontamination and Photographic sections. The first of these, headed by the bright, cheerful and popular Mr Ernest Hicks, was located next to the Meteorological Office in the JOC. Their job was to calculate the pattern – or 'foot-print' – of radio active fall-out from the bomb both in the case that all went well and also if it didn't. This they did daily on the basis of the Met Office forecasts, until they arrived at a very slick standard of drill, on which would depend the Task Force Commander's decision to go ahead with a drop – or not.

The Decontamination Centre, manned jointly by RAF Medical and AWRE Health Physics experts, was at a site off the airfield taxi track and well away from places where other personnel worked. Here air and ground crew could be monitored for any radio-contamination, could change out of contaminated clothing, shower and put on fresh clothes. The effluent water would be safely disposed of. This also applied to a small aircraft apron where aircraft could be hosed down to remove most of the contamination from cloud sampling, and where the samples could be removed from the B6 Canberras and packed into the 'Forth Bridge' in the PR7 which was to take them to England. Personnel working in this section would be continuously and rigorously monitored to ensure that they did not receive more than the agreed absolutely safe amount of radiation.

The Photographic section was to have a busy life, dealing with a wide variety of cameras in differing installations. There were cameras in the tail cones, underwing and side-windows of every type of aircraft and others on *Narvic* and *Warrior*.

All these facilities had to be brought into being and then exercised until they were free of 'bugs' and could be relied upon to work perfectly on the day.

30

Commissioning the base

The final phase of the movement of Task Force Grapple to Christmas Island was planned to begin March 1st, in order to allow sufficient time for working-up exercises and rehearsals together of all elements taking part in the first 'live' test in May. On February 26th, No 240 Squadron Shackletons under the command of Wing Commander C R Alexander left Ballykelly by the southern route, arriving at Christmas on March 12th to augment the 206 Squadron aircraft already there. Alexander took over command of the total Shackleton force from Preston on March 16th.

The team who were to staff the Joint Operations Centre and the Task Force Headquarters, together with most of the AWRE scientists left London on March 1st by Pan Am, BOAC and Quantas to Honolulu and then by the Hastings shuttles to arrive on March 3rd or 7th. The JOC was manned and began to control all operations in the Grapple Area on March 7th. At the same time Ken Bomford and John Challens and their assistants began to install and commission their special equipments at Malden and Christmas.

HMS *Warrior* arrived on March 4th, becoming flag ship of the Naval 'Grapple Squadron', including *Narvik*, *Messina*, *Salvictor*, *Fort Beauharnois* and such other RFAs and merchant ships as might be in the anchorage from time to time. On the arrival of Commodore Peter Gretton, she would wear his broad Pennant as Commodore Grapple Squadron.

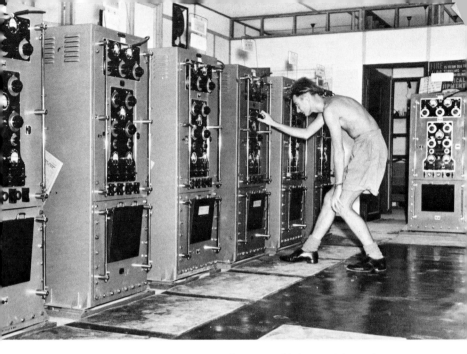

Part of the Joint Communications Centre on Christmas Island. *(Photo: AWRE)*

he Joint Operations Centre on Christmas Island. *(Photo: R Townsend)*

The Aircraft Carrier HMS *Warrior* off Malden Island during inert drop rehearsals. *(Photo: AWRE)*

Shackleton (foreground) and Canberra aircraft preparing for Meteorological flights. *(Photo: AWRE)*

e new Royal Air Force
ristmas Island airfield,
Shackleton, Canberra
Valiant aircraft. On the
right a Dakota and a
tings. Lower right, the
oon assembly and the
screened-off weapon
loading area. *(Photo: AWRE)*

(Right): Some of the
,000 packing cases of
res and equipment for
Air Task Group being
loaded at the airfield.
(Photo: AWRE)

J G T Western RN and
oup Captain L E Giles,
e Officer Commanding
Flying Wing, on the air-
ld. *(Photo: K Bomford)*

The Main Camp on Christmas Island, with all essential living facilities for three thousand men, but no luxuries. *(Photo: AWRE)*

Main Camp mess tents and cookhouse. *(Photo: R Townsend)*

Next day, March 5th, Squadron Leader Bates arrived in a Canberra of 76 Squadron. His purpose was to survey the route from Edinburgh Field via Amberley (Brisbane), Nandi (Fiji), Canton Island to Christmas which had not previously been flown by a jet aircraft. His squadron was busy completing the advanced training of new crews and would not be required for rehearsals at Christmas until the end of the month. It was arranged, however, that two of his aircraft should come earlier on March 15th to provide a fast courier service between Christmas and Hickam AFB. Cases were arising when it was inconvenient for personnel or urgently needed stores to wait for the next Hastings shuttle or even for a two-day round trip by a Shackleton. The Canberra could carry two passengers in considerable discomfort and quite a fair load in the bomb-bay pannier and it was less than a three hour trip.

It was not only the aircraft which ran shuttle services to Honolulu. Early in March, at one of the frequent impromptu meetings in the Task Force HQ to discuss and deal promptly with new problems as they arose, John Woollett raised with Western and Milligan the point that many of his army personnel had been working for nearly a year without a break. Would there be any way of giving them a change of scene? The occasional trips given in aircraft or ships had been much appreciated, but this could only affect small numbers and it wasn't practicable to take some hundreds of them by air to Honolulu or Tahiti.

Guy Western came up with the idea that it would be useful to the Naval Task Group to send *Warrior* to Pearl Harbour for forty-eight hours and she could probably take all the longest-time-on-the-island men. This suggestion was immediately agreed since, in addition to meeting Woollett's point, it would also serve to put would-be protesters-against-the-tests off the scent of any imminent trial.

So Western and Woollett flew to Hickam in the next Hastings to make the necessary arrangements. No trouble at all in arranging for *Warrior* to have a minor repair done in Pearl Harbour and Woollett received a warm welcome and much help from the US Army, who generously offered the use of the facilities of Fort de Russy, an old army post mid-way between Pearl Harbour and Waikiki. The question of shore patrols for the maintenance of good order was discussed with the US Military Police and it was agreed that mixed US/UK shore patrols should operate with a reasonable degree of latitude to curb any excessive high spirits during the forty-eight hour visit. Woollett's slight anxiety was allayed by the US Provost Marshal declaring: 'I can assure you, Colonel, that there will be no *brutality*.'

So all was amicably arranged and this fitted in well with a plan to cope with the very considerable out-cry against the forthcoming 'H-bomb' tests, both from the Labour Opposition in British Parliamentary circles and from an apparently serious Japanese threat to halt the tests by sailing a thousand small ships into the danger area. Chapman Pincher of the *Daily Express* helped by putting out, on April 29th, a story that Sir William Penney was going to Australia in June (true) and presumably on to Christmas Island to supervise the 'H-bomb' test (quite untrue). This, it was hoped, would delay the sailing of any protest fleet until after the tests had been completed. *Warrior*'s visit to Honolulu fitted in well with this story.

March 1st was also the target date for the 'Prime Ballerine' of Task Force Grapple, the first four beautiful gleaming-white special Grapple-standard Valiant bomber aircraft of No 49 Squadron, to commence moving, one at a time, to Christmas Island. Their dedicated ground crews had already gone ahead by civil charter aircraft, to be settled into their new environment and ready to receive their charges on arrival. By dint of enthusiastic efforts by the air and ground crews, the squadron had reached the necessary high standard of operational efficiency, but had been unable to complete the prescribed programme of high level visual bombing practice. Also some few of the aircraft modifications – notably the Decca Navigator installation – were not yet completed. These deficiencies would have to be rectified at Christmas Island.

Wing Commander Hubbard had selected the four crews who were to go forward to carry out the tests, leaving the other four crews and aircraft behind at Wittering to act as couriers carrying the special components of the bombs at the latest practicable date before the test. Initially these were Hubbard himself and Squadron Leaders Roberts, Steele and Millett.

The Valiants had not yet been fitted with under-wing long range tanks and were limited in the headwind component they could accept on the long legs of the journey. This caused a short delay and it was March 3rd before the first Aircraft, XD818, with Hubbard driving, could leave for Aldergrove in Northern Ireland. There again, there were three days' delay waiting for weather at Goose Bay. At last, on March 7th, they were on their way via snow-bound Goose Bay and Namao, grey rainy Travis to the pleasant sub-tropical sunshine of Honolulu and then to the humid heat of Christmas Island. The white Valiant created great interest and admiration at each stage, and nowhere more so than at the two USAF bases.

On arriving at Christmas in the early afternoon on March 12th, the aircraft made a tour of the ships in the anchorage, a low level high speed run across the main camp and the airfield to impress the 'locals', and then a more dignified approach and landing on the excellent runway. Under instruction from the tower, it back-tracked to the turn-off and taxied to that part of the parking apron which was to be the 49 Squadron dispersal. Hubbard was astounded and somewhat taken aback to see not a soul in sight, save a solitary airman marshalling him in. In some dudgeon at this cool reception, the crew shut down engines and disembarked, staggering a little under the first impact of the heat and humidity, wondering what the hell was wrong. Then a whistle blew and the enthusiastic ground crews suddenly rushed out of hiding to welcome them. A bomb-trolley, towed by a Land Rover and luxuriantly 'dressed over all' with palm leaves and manned apparently by a native Gilbertese crew, rolled forward alongside the aircraft and the 'natives' gestured to XD818's crew to get in and sit on the row of chairs awaiting them. Half-coconut shells of some suitable beverage were proffered and then the whole scene collapsed into laughter as it was realised that the 'Gilbertese' were none other than XD818's own ground crew. Ginger Weir's sense of humour had been at it again! The trolley drove them over to the tent which was now to be their squadron office. Quite a change from Wittering!

The second, third and fourth Valiants arrived in the course of the next few days and the squadron quickly slotted into the operational and technical organisation of 160 Wing. On March 15th a programme of high level visual bombing began to complete the training schedule, using a target marker on the south east corner of Christmas Island similar to that at Malden, in roughly the same topographical configuration and using the same overshoot bombing technique as would be used in the actual live test. In this drill, the navigator set the pilot on the right line of approach to the target and gave the bomb-aimer the wind speed and direction, which was set into the bombsight. The bomb-aimer conned the pilot with minute alterations of course to bring the target marker under the cross-wires of the sight graticule and pressed the release button as it did so. The pilot then flew steadily on for ten or eleven seconds while the bombing computer ticked off the exact time necessary to give the right overshoot distance to deliver the bomb to the required point in space and then activated the switch to release the bomb from its rack. The moment the bomb was gone, the pilot made his hard turn to the left in the so-called 'escape manoeuvre'. About a minute later the bomb splashed into the sea and its position was observed and plotted by two range markers who were then able to calculate the bombing error.

This programme to complete the visual bombing training was pressed forward at maximum speed but was frequently frustrated by the amount of cloud cover over Christmas and this delay was unacceptable. Two weeks later, Air Commodore Weir made the decision to switch the bombing practices to Malden, setting up the necessary range observation posts there. This worked well and that particular programme was completed on April 5th.

With ships and aircraft moving into position and taking up their operational roles, it was time for the Task Force Commander to go and take control of this massive organisation. Leaving Colonel Jack Stone and a small team behind in Whitehall to act as 'Rear Link' looking after the UK end of affairs, he departed westward on March 12th, to touch base with helpful friends in Canada and USA and to check that all was going smoothly. In Ottawa he stayed as usual with his old and dear friends, the Deputy Minister of Defence and his wife in their very pleasant house overlooking Echo Drive and the Rideau Canal. Forty-eight hours of relaxation, apart from some courtesy calls in the Department of Defence and Government.

Early in the morning of the second day – that telephone!

'Someone calling you from London, Wilf – from the Admiralty.'

'Hello?'

'Clifford here,' said a deep voice.

Why on earth would the Deputy Chief of Naval Staff be calling him now? Disaster?

'I'm very sorry to tell you that we have to withdraw Gretton. He is ill and won't be fit for duty for some time. What would you like us to do about it? Do you want a replacement?'

Hell's Bells! Very sorry about Peter Gretton, who must be desperately disappointed; but what a blow! – to lose his Deputy TFC and Naval Task Group Commander at this stage of the game and the only one, apart from himself, with such close contact with Bill Cook and the AWRE boys. Think! After a few moments of reflection –

'I'm extremely sorry to hear that, Admiral. What rotten bad luck for Gretton; and it's very good of you to call me personally. Thank you. I don't think it will help to have a new boy in such a closely integrated team at this stage. I have the greatest confidence in Western and I believe he can run the Naval Task Group. If you could up-rate Hicks to be Commodore Grapple

Squadron for disciplinary purposes, we can manage.'

'Very well. We'll do that. Let me know if you change your mind. Good luck!'

'Thank you, sir. Goodbye.'

That was very sad – particularly after Peter Gretton had made such a great contribution to getting the Christmas Island base established, and thank goodness for that! But Guy Western had proved himself to be absolutely first class and had in fact been doing most of the naval job before going out to Christmas. As for a Deputy TFC, that would have to be Ginger Weir. He would cope very well, should it become necessary. So, a telephone call to Jack Stone to instruct him to send word to Weir.

From Ottawa on to Washington, Travis and Hickam, where the Sory Smiths again insisted on putting him up overnight. Before leaving the next morning, a little housekeeping business in the RAF Staging Post. Newly-promoted Wing Commander Helfer was instructed to go to the PX – the American equivalent of the NAAFI, to get a large supply of instant coffee, and coffee-mate and a couple of dozen sturdy mugs. Coffee at all hours of the day or night was essential for the running of any operations room and it didn't necessarily come in the RASC scale of rations. And so on to Christmas Island by the faithful Hastings shuttle, with time to ruminate about the task ahead.

During the flight a radio message of typically warm welcome from Air Commodore Weir, who was there, immaculate in his well-cut number one tropical uniform, to meet his boss on arrival; and there were senior staff to be greeted, a small parade and a smart guard of honour to be inspected – a mixed platoon of Army, Navy, RAF and Gilbertese Police and a nice bit of protocol; but he privately wished they had not diverted troops from their heavy work schedule for any ceremonial.

Corporal Beall, in tropical rig and a wide grin of welcome, was waiting with the white-painted twin of the Humber Super-Snipe staff car left behind in London, pennant fluttering in the strong breeze and starplates shining to bolster the image of the Compleat Task Force Commander.

226

Then to the 'A' Mess and the smiling faces of Freddie Milligan, Guy Western, John Woollett and others. It was a very simple little mess - just a single-room wooden hut with some easy chairs and a small help-yourself bar in one corner. The back end of the room opened into a small marquee with a long dining table and chairs to seat about twenty. But simple as it was, the warm welcome and a glass of cold beer made it seem positively luxurious.

Then across to his tent, only some twenty yards behind the 'A' mess, and just as he had left it five months previously, except that there was now a dead-beat old cabin trunk in the corner, courtesy of a Valiant bomb-bay pannier a few days previously. Off to the left in front of the line of some six or seven tents allocated to senior officers and Bill Cook, was a simple structure of shower stalls - wooden uprights with a corrugated iron roof and half side panels, cement floor with wooden slats to stand on. Each cubicle had a shower rose overhead, fed by a pipeline which ran right round Main Camp supplying a number of similar structures. The water came from a hole in the ground a little distance away in which it collected and was then pumped up to a tower tank with sufficient 'head' to give quite a decent pressure even at the end of a long pipe. The water was slightly saline, but one could get a lather with it with lots of soap. It served well enough for washing both body and drip-dry clothing, saving the limited supply of fresh water from the distillation plant for cooking and drinking and the main camp laundry.

So after a quick shower and change into the evening rig of a white shirt, with tie, and light-weight slacks, both the TFC and his ADC made their way back to the mess for a meal and to get down to business.

Ginger Weir was in his usual good form, light hearted and amusing, but effectively covering the salient points about which the newly arrived TFC was anxious to hear. He was also unobtrusively waiting for some particular comment and at last the penny dropped - there was a night flying programme in

227

progress and the sound of taking off and approaching to land on the runway some three miles up-wind made a steady background to the conversation. This was re-assuring, for there had been some anxiety about night operations in the un-supported vastness of the central Pacific ocean and he had hoped to avoid it. This had proved to be quite impracticable, as the programme developed to require intense and continuous flying operations throughout the forty-eight hours prior to a 'live drop'. Weir had chosen a neat way to make the point – 'no problem'.

It was now time to review the entire Grapple set-up and to see how all the many bits of the jig-saw puzzle were fitting together.

Next morning at ten minutes to eight local time (Greenwich Mean Time minus nine hours) Corporal Beall and Helfer were waiting with the white staff car under its sun-shelter of plaited pandanus leaves behind the double row of tents. The TFC joined them and they drove off along the line of tents at a modest speed, partly to avoid raising dust from the loose coral surface and also to have a good look at the camp site as they went by.

Opposite the main officers 'B' mess they turned left into the approach road and so up to the main airfield-to-port-area road where it ran along the edge of the inland lagoon. Ten minutes later they pulled up outside the cluster of large wooden huts which constituted the JOC, as the Joint Operations Centre was now always referred to in Grapple jargon.

The spacious operations room itself was the heart of things. This was simply a large wooden Thorns type hut, making a room about fifty feet long and thirty wide, sufficient to seat about a hundred aircrew and others for briefing sessions. On the walls, large boards displaying ship and aircraft locations and movements, tasks programmed for the next twenty-four hours, maps and charts of the Grapple area and routes from UK and Australia, weather, communication instructions and advices and so on. About the room, all the impedimenta involved in running operations.

Across one end of the ops room was an enclosed gallery, raised some two feet above the general floor level to give anyone there an overall view. Above desk level this long cubicle had sliding glass screens, normally moved to one side but which could be slid across to shut out all the hubbub and give quiet working conditions for the two controllers on watch, one Air Force – one Navy, when they needed to use telephones or radio-microphones to talk with aircraft or ships.

Wing Commander 'Butch' Surtees had now taken on the very important role of RAF controller and his opposite number, Commander Felix Neville Towle, performed the same task for the Navy. Each had two watch-keeping deputies and between them they directed and monitored the movement and activity of aircraft, ships and – in the event of an evacuation for safety reasons – all ground personnel within the Grapple area, ensuring that the Task Force Commander's orders were being properly implemented. In the event of any deviation or difficulty, they reported upwards to Group Captain Milligan or Captain Western for revised instructions. They in turn would refer to the Task Force Commander if necessary. The latter, now glancing round this scene familiar from days and nights spent in other operations rooms during the war and afterwards, noticed the current activity chalked up on the ops boards – two Canberras and two Shackletons on the daily weather flights, a Shackleton en route to Aitutaki with a micro-barograph station, a Valiant on a bombing practice detail over the Christmas range and another doing a fly-over trial at Malden, a Dakota on the daily run to Malden and another on a supply-drop to Fanning Island, a Hastings en route returning to Hickam, the Auster fly-sprayer airborne locally, one Whirlwind and one Shackleton on Air/Sea Rescue stand-by. Another board showing aircraft serviceable and available, including 76 Squadron at Edinburgh. Then ships: *Narvik* at Malden, *Messina* en route to Penrhyn, *Salvictor* en route to Jarvis Island, *Warrior*, *Fort Beauharnois* and the tanker *Wave Prince* in the anchorage. Fuel state at the tank farm – over one million gallons – OK. In the background, Towle talking to *Warrior* and on the loudspeaker, volume turned down, a running commentary from a Valiant captain as he ground through his bombing practice runs and escape manoeuvres. All busy routine stuff, as it should be.

Adjacent to the controllers' gallery was the Joint Communications Centre, manned by a mixed team of Navy, Army and Air Force signals personnel. It contained the main telephone exchange and the operating positions of all the wireless telegraphy, voice radio and teleprinter facilities for communication with ships, aircraft, out-stations, staging posts, meteorological offices in Hawaii, Fiji, Australia, New Zealand, and the Grapple Rear Link in London. Voice radio could be switched through to the controllers' desk, so that Surtees and Towle could talk directly to the aircraft or ship concerned. Such conversations or running commentaries on an operation in progress could also be relayed through loud-speakers in the operations room and, for special occasions, by the Tannoy public address system throughout the port, main camp and airfield areas.

Also linked to the JOC was the meteorological office and it was one of the major concerns to see how effective the forecasting of weather and winds forty-eight hours ahead was going to be. Mr Freeman reported that he was now getting the necessary weather information from most of the planned reporting network. The data from high and low level Met aircraft, ships, island weather stations, Hawaii and New Zealand was coming in well and this would soon be completed with the inauguration of the full weather station on Penrhyn, with its radio-sonde, and the arrival of the two New Zealand frigates in the near future. The only serious technical deficiency at the moment was with the radio-sonde equipment. At the extremely low temperatures well above the tropopause, dry-cell batteries gave insufficient power to operate the transmitters. The stand-by solution, the fuel cell, was not working properly as yet. So he was lacking wind information above about 70,000 feet but hoped this would be solved in time.

The really big trouble was that the standard drill of plotting isobars, interpreting and forecasting was not working. He was finding cyclonic patterns of weather with no apparent variation of barometric pressure – the essential data on which forecasting was normally based. However, he had found that in areas where wind directions converged, there was cloud formation. Where wind directions diverged, either there was no cloud or it was dispersing. He was hopeful of developing a procedure for forecasting based on this convergency/divergency idea and might be able to extend it to get some guide to upper level winds. With a steady accumulation of statistics and a hoped-for improvement in the performance of the fuel cells for the radiosondes, he expected to be able to cope.

Closely allied with Freeman's Met section was the AWRE Theoretical Predictions group, run by Ernest Hicks. Co-operation was good and practice exercises were producing credible fall-out patterns, despite being currently handicapped by lack of actual and forecast high level winds. So far, so good.

Moving on to the next element of the JOC set-up, a door in the corner of the ops room led through a short corridor into another hut, sub-divided into a number of offices – the Headquarters office block. Task Force Commander in the middle. ADC and secretary, Deputy TFC, Naval Task Group Commander, Naval staff off to one side. To the other side Bill Cook the Scientific Director, Noah Pearce his Scientist Staff Officer and Charles Adams his deputy. In the next hut again, the offices of the AWRE supporting Services Group – all very compact. There was no distinction of Service here: they were all of one team and, apart from Service headgear, all wore the same uniform of open-necked khaki shirt, shorts, stockings and desert-type shoes. There was one exception, in Bill Cook when he eventually arrived, who favoured a dark green shirt instead of khaki, which gave him sartorial distinction to compensate for lack of a badge of rank. Not that he needed it!

So the HQ set-up was satisfactory. Now for a spot of protocol. Into Guy Western's office.

'Guy, do you think it would be convenient for us to go out to *Warrior* to call on Commodore Hicks – round about noon?'

'I'm sure it would be, sir – I'll just check.'

A few minutes to glance through the stack of signals and correspondence waiting on the plain table which was to serve as his desk, and Western came in with a welcome to the proposed visit.

'He'll send a chopper for us at 11.45, sir.'

'Right. That gives us half an hour to look round the port area. Let's go.'

31

The Naval Task Group

The TFC, Western and Helfer left the shade of the office block and went out into the blazing sunshine. An unusually fine clear day with not much cloud about – not much breeze, either, and the heat was oppressive. The leaves on the palm trees hung listlessly and the distant rumble of man-made noise only served to emphasise the somnolent silence of flora and fauna. The white staff car, irreverently dubbed 'Moby Dick' by some wag, was pretty hot to the touch after standing in the sun for an hour; but even so, it was a good ten degrees cooler than it would have been without the white paint. Wonderful stuff, this high technology!

Off they went down the dusty and wrinkled road, a ten minute drive round the north-west corner of the lagoon and southward for a mile along a very narrow neck of land, which then opened out into a peninsula about half a mile square, surrounded on three and a half sides by the waters of the ocean, the channel and the lagoon. Here, on the water's edge, free of the palms, there was more breeze and the air much fresher, which was accentuated by the gentle roar of the surf washing up on to the beach on the ocean side.

The first call was on the Commanding Officer of HMS *Resolution* in the tent which served as his office – Commander John Holt, an outrageously cheerful and irreverent character, much given to practical jokes and quite unlike his forbidding father, an admiral of the old school under whom the TFC had served many years before. But make no mistake – John Holt was doing a first class job. He introduced himself as 'the manager of London Airport', then laughed and took them to see the neatly laid-out helicopter pad with its well-kept 'H' ground sign.

Before embarking on a quick tour of inspection, they walked over to Percy Roberts' bungalow, to pay respects to that very friendly and helpful representative of the Colonial Office. He insisted on giving them all a cup of coffee, over which he mentioned that the Gilbertese natives were going to have a party the following week – a 'Maneaba' as they called it – and would be very pleased if the Task Force Commander and some of his staff would like to attend. How about it?

'Sure thing, Percy – I'd very much like to come. You too, Guy? and Terry? Perhaps one or two more, if that is in order. But could you please write for me a short friendly speech in phonetic language. I ought to make some right kind of noise.'

No problem, assured Roberts, who then joined them in a walk around.

The port area had been cleared up after the removal of the original army camp to the main camp. There were still a few tents about, for the personnel working the port, and several of the old semi-derelict US Army huts had been refurbished and brought into use as stores. The jetty had been repaired and extended and the channel had been dredged sufficiently to allow small tankers and fuel barges to come alongside to discharge directly into one of three pipelines – one for each class of fuel, Avtur, Avgas or diesel – which ran to the tank farm some six hundred yards away on the furthest point of the port area. The farm of ten bolted steel tanks, each holding 80,000 gallons, was laid out very tidily in textbook fashion and had been erected in only three weeks by a team of fifty sappers who had received only a modicum of special training at MEXE. After one early snag due to incorrectly tensioned torque spanners, resulting in the joints of one tank leaking and a hurry to get a fresh set of spanners flown out from England, the installation had passed a severe routine test and was now working very satisfactorily. The fuel was drawn off from these tanks into 5,000 gallon bowser vehicles and transferred to a similar but smaller farm of seven tanks at the airfield, from where it was drawn off as required for issue to vehicles, plant or aircraft. This was all now working quite smoothly. No more pollution.

From the tank farm they walked back along the shore line, observing the unloading going on at the jetty and the activity on the two NL pontoons moored end-on to the beach, each with two LCMs alongside discharging stores of all kinds. Apart from ready-use naval stores, there was now only a small dump in the port area, as all other stores and supplies were immediately loaded from the LCM or ship's boat into waiting trucks and driven directly to the main stores dump at the main camp. There they were checked in and catalogued and then distributed either locally or by Christmas Airways to Malden.

The naval Whirlwind helicopter clattered in and put down neatly on the H marker at the heliport, raising a great cloud of squawking sea birds – mainly white terns – from the nearby coconut-palm plantation. The three visitors climbed into the very utilitarian cabin and a few seconds later they were airborne, cruising at eighty knots ten feet above the light aquamarine sea, the pale green sandy bottom showing up clearly for the first few hundred yards and then turning to dark turquoise over the much deeper water as they approached *Warrior*, on her mooring a mile off shore.

As the pilot gently put the chopper down on the flight deck near the 'island', the TFC noted with some dismay that Commodore Hicks, Commander Begg and the Officer of the Day were awaiting their arrival, immaculately attired in tropical white uniform – crisp white open-necked short sleeved shirts with gold-striped epaulettes, well-ironed white shorts with fore-and-aft creases, white knee-length stockings and shiny shoes – the 'beau monde' of Christmas Island. What a rag-tag scruffy lot the TFC and his entourage were going to look in comparison! Couldn't be helped now.

As they jumped down from the cabin door of the chopper, the

bo'sun's pipe shrilled, salutes were exchanged, hand-shakes and how-nice-to-see-you-again and the party went below to the Commodore's day cabin.

'Just twelve o'clock, sir,' said Hicks with a twinkle in his eye. 'What will you take for your health's sake?'

'Thank you, Roger. A dry sherry would do nicely, please.'

A smart steward handed round drinks and the talk was about the voyage out, the damage still under repair, the completion of the Decca fit, the move to Malden in a few days time to fit in with the shift of 49 Squadron's visual bombing programme to the Malden target. The carrier's Aircraft Direction Room team would get much better and much needed practice there in communication with and tracking of the Valiant during its bombing runs. Commander Begg was also eager to try out the Avocado minespotting radar, now installed to one side of *Warrior*'s flight deck, in front of the 'island'. Of course, it might not work with the small 100 pound bombs which the Valiants were using for training at this stage, but the practice would be useful in getting the equipment accurately set up.

'Will you stay to lunch, sir? – the Wardroom would be very pleased if you could.'

'Thank you very much, Roger, but not today. I hope you will ask me again at a later date; but I would like to show myself in the Wardroom briefly and meet a few of the officers. I didn't see much of them on my last visit off Portland. Could you then kindly send us ashore by boat and arrange for us to make a quick call on Gausden in *Fort Beauharnois* on our way? If so, would you please warn him and make it clear that this is just a quick working visit – no formality.'

'Certainly, sir,' with a look and a nod at Robin Begg, who quietly went off to arrange matters.

The Commodore led the way along the corridor to the Wardroom, which for the benefit of those readers not familiar with arrangements in Her Majesty's Ships – was the social centre of life on board for all officers except the very junior and the captain of the ship himself. In a large ship such as an aircraft carrier there would be a fairly spacious lounge or ante-room, easy chairs arranged all round the walls, a long table with newspapers, magazines, journals, reference books. Across one corner a decorative mantlepiece with a large radiant electric 'fire'. In this case, above the mantlepiece was a large oil painting of an extremely attractive and luscious blonde who was evidently serving in the Women's Royal Air Force – at least one might assume so, since she was wearing a WRAF uniform cap, if nothing else. Very inter-service, this Operation Grapple!

Overhead, four large electric fans, their wide wooden paddles rotating slowly to give circulation of air and some easement of the rather oppressive humidity. Through the many open port-holes, glimpses of the sea and the contrasting white surf breaking over the reef a mile away.

There were a couple of dozen officers in the Wardroom as the visitors came in, some in the easy chairs reading, some chatting in little groups. Some were drinking coffee, having just had an early lunch in the dining room next door before going on duty. Others were having a drink before lunch – mainly long drinks, soft or beer, with a sprinkling of traditional pink-gin devotees; but in this climate, it was strongly advisable to stick to long drinks as a defence against stones in the kidney.

Here in the Wardroom Robin Begg was host. Standing at ease against the wall were two stewards – Royal Marines in white jackets above their khaki uniform trousers, hands loosely clasped behind their backs, waiting to be summoned to fetch drinks from the bar next door. With a gesture of his hand, Begg summoned one of them and asked his guests, including the Commodore, what they would take. Sherry with ice and soda, please – beer – lemon squash – pink gin. He then called up several officers in turn to meet the TFC, beginning with the ship's doctor, Surgeon Lieutenant Commander Pugh, wearing a thin red stripe between the gold two and a half stripes on his epaulettes. A hawk-faced intelligent and humorous looking young man, prematurely balding but compensating for this with a very rakish, very black beard. The doctor, in addition to his usual duties, was running the laboratory dissecting sample fish and analysing those organs which would concentrate any radio-active contamination picked up from the sea water. There would always be a certain level of this, but the object was to show up any difference before and after the forthcoming bomb tests. He talked with great interest about this work and the criticisms of the Japanese and French protesters.

Meanwhile, Commander (Flying) – Paul Whitfield – and Squadron Leader Roly Duck, the RAF liaison officer, came in and joined the group, with their comments and anecdotes of the voyage from UK and earnest invitations to take another drink. With long experience of such situations, the TFC could see that unless he was very firm right now, this would develop into one of those memorable sessions and he could not afford the time today. So with a promise to come and see the Aircraft Direction Room in action sometime in the near future, the visitors took their leave, were escorted to the starboard gangway, saluted the quarterdeck, were piped over the side and down the gangway to the waiting Commodore's barge – an immaculate motor launch all gleaming brasswork and white paint and scrubbed teak decking. In a smart and seamanlike manner the crew pushed off and the launch rapidly made its way towards *Fort Bo* on the next mooring. It was then that the TFC noticed that the boat was wearing an Air Vice Marshal's pennant. Where the hell had Robin Begg got that! A nice piece of one-up-manship. There would have to be a return match!

Handsomely alongside *Fort Bo* and up the gangway again. Very different here. *Fort Bo*, like all Royal Fleet Auxiliaries, had a civilian crew taken on for this job only. The Master, Captain Gausden, met the visitors as they reached the deck. A very pleasant, affable man, he had already demonstrated his professional competence early in the operation. After intro-ductions by Guy Western, they chatted for a few moments while watching the ship's derricks hoisting heavy nets full of cartons and cases up from the hold and lowering them over the side into the LCM waiting below. This could be a very tricky operation

with a sea running, but today there was only a gentle swell
heaving the LCM slowly up and down and the transfer
proceeded quickly and effectively.

'Are the frozen meat carcases handled the same way?' queried
the TFC.

'Yes. They come straight out of the freezer and go straight
into the net, just like those boxes.' replied Gausden.

'So by the time they get to the refrigerators ashore, they've
been exposed to these air temperatures and humidity for two
hours or more, I suppose?'

'Well yes, I suppose so.'

'Hm!'

They made a quick tour of the ship, the TFC stopping
occasionally to speak to one of the crew at work, asking what he
thought of the place and the job. None of them had any idea
what it was all about or what it was all for. Just a job.

Promising to return one day to have lunch on board, they said
their farewells to Captain Gausden and the outstandingly
competent Mr Geoffrey Clark, the civilian Victualling Supply
Officer and went down the gangway into the waiting launch.

A five minute exhilarating high speed run to the jetty, 'thank
you' to the efficient and courteous coxswain and into the waiting
staff car. Corporal Beall ran a very good intelligence service and
was always there when wanted. Twenty minutes drive back to
the main camp, a quick wash and brush up and into the shade
and relative cool of the mess for a cold orange juice and a light
lunch. Most of the others had already finished and were chatting
over their coffee before returning to work.

'Ginger, would it be convenient for you, and you Freddie and
Richard Brousson, to meet in my office at 2.30? Yes? Good!
And if you're free, Guy, when you've had lunch could you join
us too? Fine! Terry, I'm sorry to rush you, but we leave for the
JOC in half an hour. OK?'

32

Operational problems

On entering the HQ office block, they met the ebullient Lieutenant Tony Wallington-Smith, one of the original small Grapple team and secretary to the unlucky Peter Gretton.

'Hello, Tony, nice to see you here. I had thought we might have lost you. What are you doing now?'

'Hello, sir. I'm glad to say I've just been re-appointed Secretary to Commodore Grapple Squadron; but as there is already a ship's secretary in *Warrior*, I'll be working for Captain Western here ashore and dealing with the Naval Task Group paperwork and admin, with John Ducker as my assistant. I'm sure that will work out all right.'

'That's good, Tony. I'm glad you'll be staying with us, with all your background knowledge of the operation.'

In the TFC's office, the little meeting began without more ado.

'I'm sorry to have upset your plans for the afternoon, but it's much too long since we had a staff meeting and I want to be sure we have a firm grip on the situation. I just want to hear about any major problems and to bring up a couple of points myself. Firstly, is there any word on the Grapple booklets for issue to all the troops?'

'Not a cheep since I arrived here, sir,' replied Milligan.

'This won't do. The few men I've talked to so far have only the vaguest idea, or none at all, of why we are here and what we are trying to do. With the live tests only a few weeks away, it's very important that everyone, be he cook, coxswain or Canberra crew, should know that his individual job is vital to the whole enterprise and how it fits into the plan. I want a stiff signal sent to Jack Stone – something he can wave in the faces of the Ministry of Supply people – insisting that the first four thousand copies be air freighted to us by April 1st. Over to you, Freddie.

'Next, the leaflets for dropping on any ships straying into the danger area. We had the English language draft approved before we left London, but I expect some of the translations are delaying things. Ask Jack to ensure that they are printed off ready for air-freighting by April 15th.

'Notices to Mariners and Notices to Airmen, declaring the danger area and warning off all shipping and aircraft. I know it was said to be all lined up, but let's ask Admiralty and Ministry of Civil Aviation to confirm that the Notices will go out before the end of this month.

'Hello, Guy,' as Captain Western came in. 'Thank you for rushing your lunch and getting here so quickly. We've just made the point of reminding the Admiralty to send out the Notice to Mariners.

'Once those notices are out, we shall have to watch out for intruding protestors of one kind or another – particularly Japanese tuna-fishermen. Some measures have been taken to divert would-be protestors, but we can't rely on that working. Ginger, would you please check that we have adequate security at the airfield and would you, Guy, please confer with John Woollett and see if we need to do anything further about the port area.'

'On that point,' interjected Weir, 'last week a Shackleton reported seeing a periscope some miles off the north shore. On investigation nothing further could be seen; but it's not likely that a good Coastal Command crew would make a mistake over a thing like that and it is reasonable to suppose that the Russians would be interested in whatever is going on here.'

'That's very likely; but I don't see what we can do about it, except to take care not to let the world have any idea of when we plan to do the first test. What do you think, Guy?'

'I think all we can do is to warn all ships to report immediately any contact and we'll have to decide what's best in the light of the circumstances at the time,' replied Western.

'OK. What else, Ginger?'

'On the whole, things are going pretty well according to plan,' replied Weir. 'As you know, the bombing range here at Christmas has been a bit of a failure, because of the almost continuous five-eighths cloud cover the past two weeks. So we're shifting the bombing range to Malden, which is no bad thing except for the extra consumption of precious Valiant flying hours; but we should be OK there.

'Although we are managing well enough, I'm concerned that aircraft servicing is proving a much heavier load than we estimated. The plan to have only first line servicing here at the normal RAF level was far too simple. Boardman and his chaps are doing wonders, but his facilities are overstretched. Maintenance in this climate is much more of a load than we had supposed, with greatly increased arisings of unserviceabilities – mainly electrics and electronics – due to corrosion and humidity.'

'I'll support that,' came in Group Captain Brousson, the Chief Technical Staff Officer. 'Corrosion is very bad, not only on the aircraft, but on tools and test-gear as well. We have to put quite a lot of effort into repairing tools.'

'Even so,' continued Weir, 'we are keeping up the scheduled flying programme, thanks to some heroic work by the ground and maintenance crews late at night. Transport – I mean light transport of the Land Rover type – is another problem. We haven't nearly enough. We had to divert some of ours to help out the army and now we find already that the AWRE chaps are needing much more than they calculated. Obviously we have to help them too; so we are short. We've managed to cut out some of the constant running backwards and forwards at meal times between airfield and main camp by setting up a ground crew/aircrew canteen in the maintenance area and that is working very well, thanks to John Woollett's support; but we are still short and this is aggravated by corrosion, which means that many vehicles have to be started up by towing first thing in the morning. On the aircraft equipment side, we're having some trouble with Green Satin. Flying over a smooth sea, the doppler won't lock on, which sometimes means a serious gap in the wind reporting for the Met boys. We have a couple of Marconi chaps doing their best to improve the situation. If they don't succeed, when it comes to a live drop we may have to put on an extra PR7 to find the 45,000 foot wind over Malden and pass it to the Valiant.

'Decca, too, isn't fully operational yet, but Peter Harris – their senior rep here – reckons he'll fix it. The trouble stems from the long and narrow base line and the aircraft/master station/slave stations relationship in the vertical plane. Harvey Schwartz is confident it will come good in the end.

'My last problem is birds – with feathers. At this season there are thousands of many types of birds around – many of them white terns – and sometimes they rise in a cloud at the upwind end of the runway, just as an aircraft is taking off. I'm a bit worried about the effect of a bird-strike on the Valiant – or a Canberra, for that matter.'

This was another serious worry for the TFC. Maybe that one in a million figure he had suggested at Aldermaston was over-confident. He asked:

'If they take wing for a noise, like a take-off, why not make another noise first to get them out of the way? What about a maroon – or even a 100 pound bomb exploded off the upwind end of the runway just before take-off?'

'That's an idea. We'll try it and see,' replied Weir.

'Now your turn, Guy,' – turning to Captain Western. 'How about the naval side of things? Is the Naval Task Group/Commodore Grapple Squadron arrangement working all right?'

'Yes, sir. It was obviously an unhappy blow losing Peter Gretton, but with a very understanding attitude on the part of

Roger Hicks, it's all working pretty smoothly.'

'That's good; and *Narvik* at Malden, are the arrangements for Bomford and his scientists functioning smoothly?'

'Yes, sir. The only snag so far is the excessive time taken getting personnel to and from the shore by DUKW or LCM; but when *Warrior* goes to Malden next week, we can put a chopper full time on *Narvik*, which will solve that problem.'

'Thanks, Guy, and that brings me to a point in our D-day schedule. You will all remember that initially I proposed that Bill Cook and I, after the decision meeting here, would be flown to *Warrior* in a couple of naval Avengers, and then by chopper to *Narvik*. Much as I have complete confidence in Paul Whitfield and his boys, I now think on further consideration that this is not a 'prudent and seamanlike' arrangement – to borrow Guy's phrase. So we'll go by Dakota to Malden, the Dak to have sufficient fuel to take off and stooge around out of harm's way for two or three hours until re-entry to Malden is authorised by the AWRE Health Physics team. Then the Dak can land, pick us up and bring us back to Christmas. Naval chopper to lift us – and the Dakota ground crew – to *Narvik* before the shot and back afterwards. Will you please make that amendment in the plan, Freddie.

'That will do for this afternoon. Let's get on with our jobs. Thank you.'

The TFC mused on the transport problem, which was wasting the precious time of key personnel already struggling to keep up to schedule. He sat down at his desk and wrote by hand a note to General Sory Smith at Hickam Air Force Base, asking if it would be possible to borrow two or three jeeps for a few weeks, since it would be impossible to get them from UK or Australia in much less than a couple of months. Five days later he got back a semi-official letter in which General Smith expressed his appreciation for the facility which the RAF so kindly extended to the Globemaster aircraft of the Military Air Transport Service to refuel at Christmas Island. Not wishing to be a burden on the fully extended British organisation, would it be convenient for MATS to locate six jeeps at Christmas for the use of the Globemaster crews? Perhaps these could be accommodated in the RAF transportation section and used occasionally to guard against the severe corrosion. They could indeed! Two days later a Globemaster on a training flight refuelled at Christmas and left six jeeps behind.

33

Military life on a coral island

Working hours, except for those on duty or urgent maintenance, now ended at six o'clock in the evening. By local time on the equator, the sun always set at approximately six o'clock and there were only a few minutes of twilight. But Christmas Island operated on Daylight Saving Time, so there was an hour of sunshine to give everyone a chance to go for a swim – or at least a splash in the sea – or for sports of some kind after the day's work. As the army engineers had finished most of their priority jobs in February, they had been able to divert some effort to making football, hockey and cricket pitches with the lagoon mud which was excellent for that purpose. The Gilbertese were particularly good at cricket and gave the British teams some surprises, not to mention a trouncing from time to time.

One of the facilities which helped so much to maintain morale was an 'in house' newspaper – the *Mid-Pacific News* – produced as a hobby by a small inter-service group of enthusiastic amateur journalists. Some four or six sheets of mimeographed paper gave the key items of the BBC home news – by courtesy of the Joint Communications Centre – and, most importantly, all the UK sporting results, including of course the football and/or cricket matches played that very day. This provided the basis for many vigorously partisan arguments over a drink in the NAAFI in the evenings and helped the troops to feel in contact with home.

The sea wasn't very good for real swimming. The water inside the reef was only two to four feet deep, depending on the state of the tide, except where there were shallow depressions in the coral; and an incautious kick against the bottom would usually cause a nasty cut which took a long time to heal. So one had to proceed with considerable care and there wasn't much chance for a vigorous crawl or trudge to work off the frustrations of the day. But snorkelling was a different matter altogether. To drift slowly, face down, round the coral hills and dales of every conceivable shade of red, rose, pink, pale blue, the crystal clear water teeming with aquatic life, was a delight for the senses. Occasionally dense shoals of small fish would shove their way past the swimmer, for all the world like the contrary flood of commuters when one tries to make one's way against the rush hour crush at London's Oxford Circus tube station. It never failed to be an exhilarating experience. Fortunately it was easy to get an ample supply of inexpensive snorkels sent down from the PX at Hickam and this was the most popular after-work activity. It was, however, a firm rule that no one went out beyond the reef, where one man had been drowned already. Months later, one other poor young man thought he knew better – familiarity having bred too much contempt. Despite the most valiant and courageous efforts of the winchman of the beach patrol helicopter, he was lost. These were the only fatal casualties at Christmas Island during Operation Grapple.

A third incident had a happier ending. At last light one evening, one of a small group of soldiers had gone too far beyond the edge of the reef and had been carried out some three hundred yards by the strong off-shore current. Despite the onset of darkness, the strong surf and the sharks, Senior Aircraftsman C J B Matthews swam out to the soldier and brought him in safely. Matthews was later awarded the George Medal for the brave action.

So another day was gone and the next was to be devoted to inspecting the splendid achievements of the Army Task Group in creating so quickly an environment in which the other services could securely accomplish their difficult tasks. Colonel Woollett and the TFC, having agreed on a planned tour, set off early next morning to inspect all living facilities, beginning with the cook-houses and mess halls. Napoleon's dictum about the importance of stomachs was even more valid in this age of advanced technology and the over-stretching of human performance.

At the time of the initial landing at Christmas, the food had really been pretty bad, though not enough to upset the seasoned campaigners of 28 Field Regiment. Other and tenderer stomachs had been less happy but resigned. During the interval from the issue of meat and vegetables from the *Fort Bo* to their arrival at the mess tents where food was prepared and cooked, meat could go 'off' very quickly and vegetables – particularly potatoes – deteriorated. But now the main camp was fully established, well organised and working smoothly, food was transported ship to shore much more quickly and mostly went straight into the six big ten-ton deep-freezes, from where it was issued as required to the fairly spacious and well-equipped hutted kitchens. Even so, no bricks without straw, and the hard-working army cooks had trouble in making appetising meals out of the issued rations. Oddly enough, the average British trooper of whatever service was not greatly enamoured of the fresh salads obtained with so much trouble from Hawaii. He wanted meat and two vegetables for his main meal, including specifically European type potatoes – not the American sweet potatoes. Such potatoes were very difficult to procure and more difficult to keep in fair condition in that climate; and according as they were available in the mess tents, or not, so morale and working efficiency of the Task Force went up or down.

The reader might well ask what has all this to do with nuclear tests and the answer is – a very great deal. Heroic efforts by well-motivated individuals are often made in spite of poor living conditions and are all very well for a relatively short time; but for a long sustained effort requiring a high level of efficiency by highly technical and skilled operational personnel, if the food isn't reasonably satisfactory, neither is the overall perform-ance.

So things were better now, although not perfect by a long way. The conditions were difficult and one had to admire the army cooks for sticking at their jobs and doing as well as they did. In the bakery, producing about six thousand loaves a day, the ambient temperature was about 110° F and the humidity very high. In the main kitchens it wasn't much less. Despite this, the cooks did the best possible with the materials and facilities available.

Living quarters in the main camp were reasonably good for campaign conditions. Most of the personnel tents were of the EPIP (European Private Indian Pattern) design, furnished from Malaya and now arranged in neat rows over three large levelled areas some two hundred yards from the beach. They were well designed and fairly spacious, a little snug for six men but fine for four or less. The sides could easily be rolled up to allow the breeze to blow through and each man by his bed had a locker for the stowage of personal possessions, although this was no great problem since wardrobes were scanty. The only trouble with these EPIP tents was that the fabric deteriorated in the strong sunshine and eventually rotted.

The camp was well equipped with shower structures, fed with an ample supply of very slightly saline fresh water, obtained from a number of small underground water holes and one large excavated water hole some four miles away. The really fresh water produced by the antique and unreliable distillation plant on the beach was sufficient only for the cook-houses and the laundry, and even the laundry fresh water had to be cleaned and recirculated. The laundry could only cope with bedsheets and uniform clothing. Everyone did his own personal 'smalls', off-duty shirts and sports gear, in one of a number of large wooden troughs, amply supplied with the brackish underground water, which worked well enough. Sunday mornings at the troughs were social events, brightened by the rainbow arrays of exotic underpants and aloha shirts, which later lent the camp a holiday

249

air as they dried off on the improvised clothes lines, strung from tent to tent.

For relaxation after dark there was a good NAAFI recreation room and bar, set up in a very large Romney type hut, part of which was partitioned off to make the WVS club, run so very successfully by the two WVS ladies. Adjacent to the tented area was the open-air cinema, which ran quite up-to-date film programmes two or three times a week. So with mail arriving from home regularly once a week, taking only about five days, the personal side of life was reasonably well looked after.

Then to the airfield, to be joined by Wing Commander Bower and – with clearance from Control Tower – to inspect the runway. This was very good and a great credit to the sappers. It had a good asphalt surface, accurately levelled and cambered, quickly shedding all surface water except in the heaviest rain and was never out of action for more than thirty minutes during the following months.

'The one snag,' said Bower, 'is that it collects coral chips, which cut the aircraft tyres and at first we were using up tyres at too great a rate. But now the runway is swept every day to remove the chips and we have no more trouble.'

The Control Tower was now working well and, with the recent bringing into use of the Cathode Ray Direction Finder in place of the original manual homer, was well equipped to handle a volume of traffic larger than any which would occur during Operation Grapple and was presently operating eighteen hours a day. This would soon increase to twenty-four hours a day.

The airfield tank farm was working smoothly and trouble-free; so all was well for the moment with the infrastructure and 160 Wing could be left to another day.

A little east of the airfield and well off the runway approach line was the novel army repair workshop area, manned by a mixture of Royal Engineers, Royal Electrical and Mechanical Engineers and Royal Army Ordnance Corps personnel.

This team of sepcialists had done a fantastic job in continuously repairing broken-down plant and equipments of

250

all kinds and restoring them rapidly to useful service. Mangled construction machines, victims of the climate, harsh terrain and maximum output usage, were restored to a functioning state nearly as good as new, even if not quite so pretty. The young officer in charge of his activity, Major Keith Bean, was of necessity a most capable engineer and also a very cheery character to boot, with a great sense of humour. He shared a living tent with Tony Jillings, the RAF Navigation Leader, also a humorist and there were high jinks when these two were around together on a Saturday night.

Further east again, on the north-east corner of the island and some three miles from the airfield, was the coral rock excavation and crushing plant, which earlier had been producing seven hundred tons a day of crushed and graded coral aggregate for runway, hard standings and road construction. Now it was working at an easy pace, producing only sufficient for repairing and extending the forty-five miles of new and reconditioned roads and for patching up the hard standings as required.

Finally, back to have an initial quick look at the AWRE site – John Challens's parish – comprising the weapon assembly building and its associated laboratories in their remote and screened-off area to the south-west of the airfield. The Weapons groups were still busy settling into their working environment, but were already analysing and assessing the results of the 'fly-over' trials which had begun at Malden Island on March 16th. The scientific staff were very pleased with their working facilities and fairly happy about their living accommodation; but there was more than one grumble about the food.

To sum it all up, in eight short months the Navy, with a little help from the RAF, had transported and delivered to a site nine thousand miles away everything necessary to build a first class operational base for the Air Force and the scientists. The Army had built it all, with a little help from the Gilbertese and Percy Roberts, completing in the process all the essential infra-structure of a small town, a V-bomber base and a high-class scientific establishment.

Now for the target island. At eight o'clock the following morning, March 23rd, the TFC, his ADC and Colonel Woollett caught the Christmas Airways commuter to Malden – a noisy two-hour forty five minute flight conducted impeccably by the conscientious and earnest No 1325 Flight Commander, Joe Hurst himself. VIP service today, of course, that is to say a folded blanket to sit on instead of the bare metal of the jump seat and lots of hot coffee served in large earthenware mugs. Very much appreciated, too. There were, of course, some other passengers, some mail and a load of assorted freight. A very busy airline, this, and on arrival no time was wasted in the turn-around. Half an hour later the Dakota was already on its way back to Christmas.

They were to have a full twenty four hours in the forward area, returning on the next day's commuter, which barely gave time for the full programme of inspection. Captain Wadsworth, the sapper officer in charge of the construction work at Malden and Ken Bomford, the scientist responsible for the forward area were there to meet them and to show them round. First of all, the air side. The airstrip was well made and more than adequate for Dakotas. One RAF Air Traffic Controller, with a mobile VHF set and a W/T link to Christmas JOC handled the air traffic. Two 1325 Flight ground crew doubled in turning round aircraft and manning an improvised fire tender – a Land Rover equipped with heavy fire extinguishers. For air navigation aids there was an M/F radio beacon with a range of about eighty miles and a Eureka beacon good out to about fifty five miles. This was all quite adequate for the job and the service was evidently working well.

Bumping round the four mile by three mile island on a rough track, one was struck by the lack of scenic charm – a dull greeny-grey-brown sort of perimeter with a dried-up lagoon in the middle, all rather evocative of Kipling's 'great grey-green greasy Limpopo river', except that there was no water and not even fever-trees. But the bird life was spectacular in that the booby birds made great splashes of colour – red, blue, black and

252

The WVS ladies – the Misses Billie and Mary Burgess. *(Photo: AWRE)*

Sunday morning Do-It-Yourself 'dhobi'. *(Photo: AWRE)*

John Challens (left), the Scientific Superintendent Christmas Island.
(Photo: AWRE)

The Weapon Assembly shed. *(Photo: AWRE)*

The AWRE testing and weapon loading area with its security screens – no peeking! *(Photo: AWRE)*

One of the AWRE laboratories. *(Photo: AWRE)*

High technology in high temperatures! *(Photo: AWRE)*

Some of the AWRE weapons team. Note the over-dressed Service members. *(Photo: R Townsend)*

white – where they clustered together on occasional half-hearted shrubbery or in the shade of some out-crop of coral rock. But on closer inspection, even the booby birds weren't particularly attractive – just rather lumbering, clumsy and dim-witted goose-like creatures. Even so, it was very sad to think that some of them were going to be hurt or even killed by the tests; but nuclear deterrence was a grim business and this was no time for sentiment.

At the southeast corner of the island was the large triangular bomb-aiming marker, very clearly defined; and a mile to each side of it sappers were setting up range observation posts, ready for the armament staff to mark the fall of the 100 pound practice bombs which would be used to complete the training of the Valiant crews. Then running up the east side of the island was the heart of the matter – the whole instrumentation base. Rows of excavated bunkers, many with corrugated iron roofs to shelter their precious tenants from the worst of the fierce sun, their recording heads or lenses all focused on that point one and a half miles south of the marker and eight thousand feet high. These instruments, peeping over the edge of their protection, would measure the heat, light, blast and radiation of every kind produced by the explosion and ultra-high speed cameras would photograph some one hundred thousand times a second the development of the fireball. Such equipment could only run for a few seconds and had to be switched on by telemetry from HMS *Narvik*, which on the day would be some twenty miles to the north. So there was great activity in fixing up and testing the communication links with their aerial systems and power supplies.

Accommodation for the hundred sappers and scientists preparing this base was a very small and spartan tented camp, so organised that it could rapidly be dismantled and buried in bunkers for each test and then just as quickly be re-activated for the preparation of the next round. So life here was pretty primitive and basic; but oddly enough, the hundred or so inhabitants seemed to find this boy-scout existence more fun than Christmas Island.

253

Having covered Malden itself fairly thoroughly, out by DUKW through the gap in the reef to *Narvik* at her mooring, a quarter of a mile off-shore, there to be greeted by the courteous Commander Tony Casswell. Here the centre of interest was the operations room, originally installed for Operation Mosaic at Monte Bello and now, extended and re-equipped, to serve as the command post for the Task Force Commander and the Scientific Director for the thermo-nuclear tests. Bomford's deputy, Wally Long, a young sandy-haired scientist, was in charge here and showed the visitors round the installed equipment.

There was a great deal of communications equipment, every vital channel being duplicated, and across one corner was a simplified version of an aircraft carrier's Air Direction Room air plot to display for the benefit of the Task Force Commander the position and movement of all aircraft and ships in the area. The most important item, however, was the oscilloscope-like display unit of the telemetry receiver tuned to transmissions from the Valiant on its bombing run and from the bomb itself. As each event in the prescribed sequence took place, the trace on the scope would form a series of 'steps' to indicate the switching-on of the telemetry sender in the aircraft, the opening of the bomb doors, the switching on of the bomb's own sender and so on. On the day, the control-room team would check against the detailed check-list that each necessary action had been taken correctly and could immediately abort the operation – up to the point of bomb release – if any one was missing or inadequate.

Adjacent to the control room were scientific facilities and a photographic dark room, rather cramped but adequate for the purpose. After thorough inspection of all these and a tour round the ship, noting particularly the helicopter platform and its approaches, the visitors accepted a welcome drink in the small and overcrowded ward room and went ashore. Although warmly pressed to stay aboard for the night, it would have been a problem for the hospitable Commander Casswell to accommodate them in his overloaded ark. So the evening was spent very informally with the Malden pioneers and after some useful time devoted to going over their problems again next morning, the visitors commuted back to Christmas and the accumulated office work.

34

Penrhyn Island

On March 20th, HMS *Messina* embarked a small team of
RAF, sappers, meteorologists and Decca technicians – 32 men
with 18 assorted vehicles and 100 tons of stores and equipment –
to take them to that delightful island of Penrhyn, 600 miles
south of Christmas. Commander Harry De Vere, Captain of
Messina, was to be in command until the detachment was put
ashore, when Flight Lieutenant G A Morgan-Smith would
become CO RAF Penrhyn. The operation had been carefully
planned and, following on the earlier visits by HMS *Salvictor* to
deliver the Decca masts and their erection team and Ginger
Weir's later reconnaissance in force, Morgan-Smith had made
two other short visits to ensure that all would go well on the day.

Partly because Penrhyn was about the only bit of glamour in
Operation Grapple and partly because the establishing of a
supporting base there, although much bigger than the rest, was
fairly typical of the business of planting weather stations, Decca
stations, micro-barograph recording and fall-out monitoring on
a number of similar small islands, the reader may be interested
in Morgan-Smith's initial report, written a week after the
landing. The narrative, part of a full report to Air Commodore
Weir, is therefore reproduced in full as follows.

The detachment arrived at Penrhyn early on Sunday, March
24th. HMS *Messina* beached without difficulty and a small
recce party got ashore at 11.00 hours. Final sites were chosen for

both Met signals and stores areas. *Messina* commenced off-loading at noon and first stores off were Avgas, Hydrogen, Compo (rations), these being deck loaded and covering hatches. Working parties were arranged both for ship and shore duties. Much movement of tank deck cargo (vehicles) was required in order to enable the off-loading of fork lifts, dumpers and Land Rovers. However, it was well planned and the vehicles did get ashore Monday. The fork lifts and dumpers have been invaluable throughout the operation (heavy trucks would have been useless.) The Matador winch was u/s but we managed most jobs by direct towing. Old vehicles with flat batteries, etc, were winched ashore by use of the bulldozer. Those vehicles which were off-loaded with small troubles were quickly serviced and moved to site or to work.

The 25th, 26th and 27th saw all equipment landed and 110 cases etc accounted for. Various sorted dumps had been organised and this made the job fairly easy. A twelve hour day was worked. Lunch came from *Messina* daily until she sailed on Thursday, 28th March.

Tuesday afternoon our tentage and accommodation stores were landed. By Wednesday 27th a good camp was installed. A temporary field kitchen produced a good meal at 6 pm. Temporary electric lighting was in all tents. Staff Sergeant Ridden really did a fine job.

Mr L McKay's Met vehicles and equipment received priority and his installation was complete by Thursday 28th, except for the balloon shed which again caused difficulty. The tubular construction went up slowly but the roof had to be modified, certain parts being missing. When Staff Sergeant Ridden has completed the kitchen, he is going to try to get the balloon shed completed correctly. This may not be possible however. The kitchen has not gone together easily. Parts were missing, door and window frames, self-tapping screws, and small snags which are being put right. The kitchen should be completed by Monday, 8th April. Meanwhile we enjoy good food which is being prepared and cooked out of doors. Two Soya stoves borrowed from *Messina* and a fire pit with grill cover seem to be working out very well.

Each day a gang of local labour reports to Headquarters and we allocate jobs. They work well and display plenty of intelligence. Typical jobs are handling fuel drums, assisting in construction of showers and kitchen, assisting in the distribution of stores, rubbish clearance, topping off tree tops and attaching VHF and other radio aerials. About twenty four men turn up each day. By April 8th only a few men will be employed.

The organising of the camp routines has been planned to get the best results from our small party. In this respect Flight Sergeant Seabrook has been of great assistance, for apart from his technical job he has spent hours with me working on all kinds of little snags which inevitably crop up. The attached list of orders was produced by him and they will, I think, show up our transport problems.

Air field installations have gone on well. Met, W/T, VHF, MF and Eureka were positioned on the last two aprons at the south end of the runway on the west side. The balloon shed is set in amongst the trees opposite the Met site.

The heavy rain has penetrated the VHF and MF cases and at this date they are unserviceable. Every precaution has been taken but the rain has been really severe at times. We hope to be fully operational within this week. All installations on the airfield are behind or in line with the tree line. These sites were the only possible ones to take our equipment. From the early reports it seems that the Met and radio aids will function well from these positions.

The Canteen is a great success. I managed to open it on Thursday 28th. To date the sales are over £50! The lock-up shed supplied by Mr D Reid is just the right thing. It was the local jail! Corporals Barnes and Derby jointly run the canteen and I think all will run smoothly from now on.

It was a blow to lose SAC Firkins, especially as he had the Swing Fog. The weather was really bad, of course, and he was just stranded on *Messina*. Flies and mosquitoes are very bad here. Several men are covered in bites – mostly got whilst working on the airfield.

Liaison with Mr Reid is most gratifying. He has helped us in many ways. Our men are popular among the natives and everyone gets along well together. Courtesy prevails on both sides.

Of all our stores, all that was lost was 8 plastic wardrobes. Everything else is 100%. Some items of accommodation stores were broken in transit and I am writing to GHQ giving exact details. Colonel Woollett assured me that such items would be replaced.

Morale is high. General health is good. The men have worked very hard, very long. The climate is severe. One feels pretty tired after a full day's work. We work Penrhyn time now and work ceases at 1600 for day workers. Swimming is good, extremely popular and safe.

Food is good and plentiful. We can keep fresh meat six days. The cooks are keen and competent. Messes are well equipped and I have no complaints at all. If only we can beat the flies and mosquitoes, life will be pleasant on Penrhyn.

We look forward to your first visit to our camp.

> GA Morgan-Smith,
> OC 160 Wing Detachment,
> Penrhyn.

So there was one very happy detachment – and with a weekly supply and mail service into the bargain. There were some other very pleasant small detachments of two or three men, such as Apia in Samoa or Aitutaki; but the only two other sizeable detachments on Jarvis and Fanning Islands were in an environment bleaker and even less attractive than Christmas – although at Fanning there was at least cheerful company in the staff of the civil cable station. Beaching an LST was impracticable at both these places and neither had an airstrip. So the Decca Master station had to be put ashore by LCM at Jarvis and the Met station likewise at Fanning. Both had a

259

weekly air drop of mail and supplies and any necessary movement of personnel was affected by occasional visits by *Messina* or *Salvictor*.

35

Saturday night relaxation

It would have been inefficient and ineffective to work the Task Force personnel more than six days a week – with occasional unavoidable exceptions – and everyone looked forward to Saturday evenings as the beginning of twenty four hours relaxation and letting off steam, in the NAAFI or the Sergeants Mess or the Officers 'B' mess. Informality of dress and behaviour was the keynote, and most people would don a brightly coloured and wildly patterned aloha shirt with plain civvy slacks, to make fairly merry over a glass or two with colleagues they hadn't had time or opportunity to talk with during the week.

The top brass in 'A' mess were no exception and they were always invited over to 'B' mess next door, to mingle with the real workers on a free and easy basis. The large marquee serving as an ante-room wore a holiday air and buzzed – or rather uproared – with the conversation of innumerable groups discussing their own recent experience and exchanging news, views, and many a ribald anecdote evidenced by occasional roars of laughter.

After chatting for some time with the younger members of all four services, the TFC noticed that nothing was being done about the piano on which he had insisted and which stood lonely and neglected in the corner. He got hold of Wing Commander Alexander, that robust and piratical Welshman who so ably commanded the Shackleton squadrons and who had served with him in 1939 at the outbreak of the war.

'Alex! Come on – let's have a sing song.'

Immediately some of the Shackleton boys were rounded up to start the ball rolling and the TFC sat down to play a sequence of the old service songs, beginning with the Air Force version of Waltzing Matilda, which soon brought in a further fifty lusty voices. Then on through 'Shaibah Blues', 'Shire, Shire, Somersetshire', 'The Dying Airman' and anon to that old Mesopotamian lament which begins:-

> In the year Anno Domini one nine two four
> In the Kingdom of Baok there started a war;
> HQ got excited and sent for old Bert
> To pull Operations Room out of the dirt,
> Singing...

and goes on, in the rollicking chorus, to indicate the unhappy fate of those who allowed themselves to run out of petrol!

This greatly amused and intrigued those of different cloth and so the switch was made to 'What shall we do with a drunken sailor', 'I Don't Want to Join the Army' and then on to more ecumenical themes ranging from 'Clementine' and 'Green Grow the Rushes Oh' to a complaint about shortages in Mobile.

It was all good thirsty-making fun and did a lot to ease the loneliness of those missing their families and homes and to divert the anxieties of those thoughtful ones concerned about what might happen to them in a few weeks' time.

It wasn't all just fun. Beneath the light hearted veneer and in this relaxed atmosphere, junior officers could voice frustrations and worries and senior officers could often pick up early warning of emerging problems and so deal with them before they became serious.

Sunday mornings were evidently a time for thoughtful reflection and after the colourful 'dhobi' session, the DIY laundry activity, quite a lot of people went to Morning Service at one or other of the 'churches'. These had begun as plain wooden huts but sincere and enthusiastic parishioners had transformed them into very attractive and restful places of worship. The Task Force was very fortunate in having two very good padres to officiate there. Most of the Navy, of course, attended Sunday 'Divisions' on one of the ships; even so, the shore services usually ended with the very moving hymn – 'Those in peril on the sea'.

As would be expected, there was occasionally a light hearted touch even about church. When 55 Field Squadron had dismantled their camp in Korea, one very large packing case was marked 'Fragile' – 'Ecclesiastical Embellishments'. Unhappily, when it came to setting up the first church, no trace could be found of this case and it was only later that someone remembered that, during the initial weeks, the only place to get a glass of whisky was in the 55 Squadron mess tent!

This, then, was for most people the pattern of the week-end. But Monday, precious Monday, was Mail Day – Calloo, Callay! Oh frabjous day! By the beginning of April, the Hastings shuttle service to Hickam had increased to three times weekly and the mail service was correspondingly better. In order to check that the Post Office in England was playing its part in the game, test letters were sent with each outward mail from Christmas and the date and time of arrival were signalled back from London. The service proved to be consistently excellent, so much so that, taken in conjunction with the reporting same day of UK sporting results in the Task Force *Mid Pacific News*, the troops were able to play the pools. This was another great help to morale.

And so the weeks rolled on.

36

The Maneaba

It was the evening of the Maneaba – the Gilbertese party to
which the TFC had promised to go with Percy Roberts, the civil
administrator of Christmas Island. What on earth did one wear
to play the pompous role of Big White Chief? Not much choice,
so he settled for Number One khaki drill uniform and gold
peaked cap – if it hadn't rotted away already! – and told his ADC
to do the same plus aiguillettes. Ginger Weir and Guy Western
said they would come too, in full rig. That ought to make some
kind of impression. He also asked Doctor Bradley, the head of
the RAF hospital, to join the party, as Jack had had quite a lot to
do with medical care of the Gilbertese families and had even
delivered three babies – so far.

So after sunset down to the port area to join up with Roberts
and then on to the Gilbertese long house in the little village, set
in a grove of coconut palms at the back of the port area
peninsula. The hut itself was about a hundred feet long and
about forty wide, consisting of a long palm trunk acting as a
ridge-pole, supported at intervals by pairs of inward sloping
palm trunks, making a long V-shaped roof. The whole was well
thatched with palm leaves, with other clusters of leaves making
wind-breaks at the otherwise open ends. At the entrance end of
the hut was a low dais, about a foot high and running the whole
width of the hut, and on this was arranged a row of plain wooden
windsor chairs, almost certainly borrowed from the main camp,
with one extra chair out a little in front.

The party was met and greeted by a dignified elderly Gilbertese, obviously the head man, who shook hands European fashion with each visitor and led them all up on the dais. The others to take seats, the TFC – clutching his prompt card in the palm of one hand – to stand at the front of the dais. The floor was packed solid with rows of seated Gilbertese, mainly men in wrap-around cloth skirts or kilts, some wearing a singlet, some topless. There was a fair proportion of women, some with small children. All wide-eyed absolutely silent and quite still – even the tots.

In front of the dais and a little to one side was something like a large, flat, wooden packing case – it might at one time have contained aircraft ailerons or other control surfaces – about fifteen feet square and eighteen inches high. Sitting on the ground along each side of the box, like the crews of four rowing eights going round the box in a square, left arms resting outstretched on top of the box, were some thirty young men. Waiting.

After a few seconds of mutual inspection, the TFC thought he had better begin and opened – as per Roberts' briefing – with a loud clear:

'KO NA MAURI!'

Immediately, in a roar that fairly rattled the palm leaf thatch, some three hundred lusty and mainly deep bass voices came back with a mighty shout of:

'KO NA MAURI!'

Delighted smiling faces and more silence. Then, with many a surreptitious peep at his 'crib', the short address of greeting and thanks, which was apparently recognisable. Then to take his seat on the egregious chair.

As if on that signal, the packing-case team began to beat in unison on the top of the box, making it resonate like a drum; and according to the distance from the edge at which their hands smacked the top surface, the pitch of the note varied. It was soon apparent that the box was playing bass-fiddle-like counterpoint to a tune which the team were humming, pianissimo at first and

265

gradually increasing in volume – and very pleasant music it was.

Then the principal guest's eye was caught by a movement at the far end of the hut. From behind a palm leaf screen emerged unwillingly and apprehensively a small girl of about six or seven years of age, dressed in a classic pale straw-coloured grass skirt and a T-shirt top of some gold-coloured material. Round her curly dark hair a chaplet of bright yellow blossoms and in her hands, held out at rigid arms length ahead, was a garland of the same golden blossoms. Poor child! She was terrified and wide-eyed, but walked slowly and steadily and with dignity the length of the hut, as one who knows that some awful doom awaits her but is determined to go to it bravely.

As she neared the dais, the 'music' got louder and this apparently gave her more confidence. The TFC could hear the suppressed merriment of those unsympathetic characters behind him, but was more concerned for the child. At last she stepped quite smartly up onto the dais, he lowered his head and she gracefully draped the garland round his neck. He took her hands in his, thanked her gently in English – nothing in the phonetic brief to cover this – and she backed off the dais with aplomb. Then dignity forgotten, she scampered off to sanctuary at the far end of the hut, to a roar of approval from the audience.

Then were the tables turned. The 'music' diminuendoed to begin a repeat performance and now at the far end appeared four even younger little girls, too young even to feel nervous and giggling joyously, each with a similar garland clutched in one chubby hand. They swayed their way forward in a hilarious attempt at the hula movements of their elders, made a final rush at the dais and without much ceremony plonked the garlands more or less round the necks of the other visitors. The TFC said nothing, but felt much better.

There followed some community singing by the entire audience with its music box accompaniment, some of it very beautiful and somewhat reminiscent of American negro hymn singing – but no syncopation. Then Percy Roberts wound up the proceedings with some evidently well chosen words and the guests moved off the dais and met several of the Gilbertese men who had a few words of English. One of them greeted Doctor Bradley warmly and was then brought to be introduced as Doctor Simione Peni. Speaking in pretty fair English, he explained that he had been born and grown up in the Gilbert and Ellice Islands, but as a young man had studied medicine in Fiji. He had been unable to take the Pathology part of the course and so was not properly qualified, but was nevertheless a very useful medical practitioner, particularly as a diagnostician, asserted Bradley. This place was full of surprises and the Maneaba evening had been something to remember.

Duty done, the team made their way back to the 'A' mess and some suitable refreshment. Over the rim of his glass, Guy Western looked sombrely at the TFC and said:-

'I'm sorry to tell you this, sir, but we have to have a funeral.'

Immediate consternation! What had happened and to whom?

'Well, I don't know how it happened, but somebody pinned on me the job of being bar-officer, which in turn involved me in a tragedy. Five thousand cans of Watney's Pale Ale have gone "off" and have been condemned as unfit for Task Force consumption. Terrible! Watney's have immediately undertaken to replace them, but only on condition that the faulty lot are certified as destroyed. So we're having a burial party tomorrow. John Woollett is providing a bulldozer to excavate a suitable tomb near the beach and the corpses will be 'dozed over. Corrosion will look after them in a very short time. Sad, isn't it?'

'Then we'd better have one more now, in case this lot goes off too!'

37

Live drop procedure at Malden

By the end of March, all training and other preparatory work should have been completed in time for the operational phase to begin on April 1st. The visual bombing training for the Valiant crews was still in progress and the Decca equipment was still not functioning correctly, but on the whole things were going pretty well to programme. Someone, however, evidently thought the Task Force was becoming over-confident and on March 28th the Inter Tropical-Front moved south and dumped six inches of rain on Christmas Island in a few hours. The average reader must find it difficult to visualise what it means to be rained on at that rate; it was like standing under a bath-tub full of water and having the bottom suddenly disappear. Aircraft having to return to base in such conditions would experience the most violent turbulence, often with very heavy hail which could in a few minutes strip all the paint off the forward fuselage of a Valiant and come close to shattering the windscreen; and it would take the combined efforts of the pilot and co-pilot to handle the controls in such circumstances. Most fortunately the ACR 7 (D) talk-down radar continued to function well and all aircraft caught out in these conditions were safely recovered. There was nowhere else to go.

All praise to the sappers, who had made a fine job of grading and cambering the runway, so that the water normally drained off pretty well as fast as it fell; but the whole of the Air Task Group maintenance area and the aircraft hard-standings were knee-deep in water. Alexander, he of the Shackleton force, made fun of the whole thing by sitting in an inflated rubber dinghy moored in his office tent to do his admin work – to the general amusement; but it was not so funny for all the technical maintenance and equipment-supply personnel of 160 Wing, who worked long and hard to ensure that serviceable aircraft were available as required by the programme. Great credit, not for the first or last time, to the Technical Wing.

The main and camp roads were under about a foot of water and those which had been surfaced with lagoon mud were washed away in places. Luckily the far-sighted sappers had constructed a relief road from port to camp to airfield, following a rocky coral outcrop. It was a slow and bumpy route, but it kept communications open until the standard roads could be restored.

Next day was fine again and there was little outward sign of all this watery trouble. Equipment and clothing were drying out and the belated visual bombing training programme began at highest intensity at Malden. During the following three days, about a hundred bombing runs were made to complete that programme and most of these were used to exercise the co-operation between the Valiants and HMS *Warrior*, on station to the north of the target island.

The opportunity was then taken for *Warrior* to return briefly to Christmas and en route she did a good samaritan job by calling at Jarvis Island, where the Decca technicians were working hard in miserable conditions to get their system working properly. One of *Warrior's* helicopters flew ashore, picked up the Decca team, brought them on board, for hot baths and a good meal and then returned them to their 'salt mine', feeling much better.

On April 3rd the operational phase began in real earnest, with just six weeks to go to the first live test, and from now on all flying effort would be restricted to and devoted to supporting the scientific programme. Charles Adams, who was to be deputy to Bill Cook, the Scientific Director, arrived on this day and with his help the Task Force Commander began daily to practise like everyone else the role which he would have to play on D-day. At eight o'clock each morning, six days a week, there would be a full briefing session covering all current aspects of the operation, particularly the meterological situation and the predicted 'fall-out' pattern. At the conclusion of the briefing, the TFC and the Scientific Director (or Adams for the time being) would give a decision on whether or not they would give the order to start the sequence of events leading to a live drop forty eight hours hence; and similarly they would confirm or not the decision made twenty four hours earlier. Then during this practice period leading up to D-day, they would analyse with hindsight whether the previous decision had been valid; or – if not – then where had they gone wrong, and so adjust their parameters of judgement.

Also on April 3rd, the 49 Squadron Valiants began the programme of 'Inert Drops' at Malden Island, under the control of the Operations Room in HMS *Narvik* and monitored by the air-guard radar and the Avocado plotting radar in HMS *Warrior*, just as would be the case during the live drop on D-day. The purpose of these 'inert drops' was to test – and if necessary correct – the communication and telemetry links between the aircraft, the weapon and the control room in *Narvik*. To this end the Valiant carried a replica of the real bomb, a 'Blue Danube' ten-thousand pound bomb-case filled with concrete in place of the nuclear device but having all the electronics and telemetry as per the real weapon.

The procedure is described in great detail in K G Hubbard's excellent book,* 'Operation Grapple'; but, in brief, the Valiant was to rendezvous with the ships at a point some 75 miles north of Malden Island at the bombing altitude of 45,000 feet. It would then fly on a southbound track which would take it along the eastern side of the island and directly over the bomb-aiming marker. At what would be the release point of the bomb, the

---

* Ian Allan, 1985.

aircraft would make a rate 1 turn to port on to a reciprocal track some five miles to the east, continuing northward for some forty miles and then another turn to port to bring it back on to the original southbound track. This made a flight pattern resembling the normal horse-racing track and in Grapple jargon was always referred to as 'the race-track', and on it were five check points at which the aircraft would report its position.

If all went well, in making any kind of a drop – be it inert, high explosive or nuclear – the Valiant would make the southbound run three times. The first was the 'Navigation Run' to enable the navigator to assess the wind speed and direction and to enable the bomb-aimer to line-up his bomb-sight. The second, called the 'Initial Run', was to enable the aircrew and the scientists in *Narvik* to check that all the electronics in both ship and aircraft were switched on and were functioning correctly. If everything was in order, at Point Charlie, half-way up the northbound leg of the 'race-track', the controller in *Narvik* would give clearance to drop on the next southbound run.

Having completed the race-track pattern, on the third southbound run, the aircraft would be lined up accurately on the bombing line, all windows except the bomb-aimer's viewing panel already blocked off with anti-flash screens. *Warrior's* Air Direction Room and Avocado radar would monitor the track of the aircraft and would intervene if there were any error. As the aircrew went through the extensive drill of opening the bomb doors, arming the weapon and setting up everything ready for release, the controller in *Narvik* would check that he was receiving the correct telemetry indications and would cancel the drop if this were not so. As the target on the south east corner of Malden came under the centre point of the bomb-aimer's sighting graticule, he would press the bomb-release. The pilot would hold his course, flying straight and level for about eleven seconds, while the computer calculated the exact time and then activated the bomb release to deliver the weapon to the required point in space. As soon as the bomb had left the aircraft, the pilot would commence the 'Escape Manoeuvre', rolling into a 60 degrees bank and a steep turn to port and holding 1.7g on the super-sensitive g-meter until the aircraft had turned through 135 degrees and was thus tail-on to the point of explosion. During this turn, the bomb aimer would have placed the screen over his window, so that the crew were now in a completely light-proof environment. The turn would have taken forty seconds; after a further twelve seconds the bomb – in the case of a high-explosive or nuclear drop – would explode and the aircraft would be far enough away to be beyond risk of serious damage. If the calculations were correct.

This drill would be practised over and over again until each Valiant crew had demonstrated that they could do it consistently well and deliver the bomb within the required accuracy.

On this first 'inert drop' on April 3rd the weapon was not actually released, all effort being concentrated on ensuring that everything worked smoothly. This was just as well, as there were still some problems. Three days later, on April 6th, Wing Commander Hubbard carried out the first actual inert drop, achieving an accuracy of 245 yards, which was well within the required limits.

While 49 Squadron was starting on these 'inert drops', and later on a series of 'high explosive drops', the weather flights by the Shackletons and Canberra PR7s were stepped up and now began at the earlier time of 04.00 hrs daily. This was necessary to provide the information for Freeman's Met assessments and forecasts in time for Hicks' Theoretical Predictions group to make the 'fall-out' pattern prediction in time for the Task Force Commander's decision-making practice at 08.00 hrs.

As this process of exercising and tuning up the entire Grapple machine proceeded, snags were bound to occur – and did! After the first inert drop in April, Freddie Milligan came in to tell the TFC that the Valiant pilot's running commentary during the bombing run and in the escape manoeuvre was almost unintelligible, both in *Warrior* and in the JOC. The signals people had tracked down the trouble to having both the VHF and the H/F transmitters wired to the pilot's microphone, causing mutual interference and it wouldn't work. So what to do?

'I still want the broadcast on both frequencies, Freddie. Let's see now. I don't know if they still do it, but Naval Aviation used to use throat microphones instead of face mikes. See if *Warrior* has got and could let 49 have half a dozen throat mikes and get Hubbard to try putting the H/F on to that.'

They did and they did and it worked well.

Guy Western came in a few days later with a different sort of problem. The crew of the RFA *Fort Constantine*, a supply ship temporarily replacing the *Fort Beauharnois* which had gone to replenish, had downed tools and refused to work. It appeared that the ship had a Pakistani Moslem crew who now complained that the MK (i.e. Mohammedan Killed) mutton which comprised the main part of their diet was phony – not genuinely slaughtered in accordance with Koranic regulations – and they wouldn't eat it; and without eating they certainly weren't going to work! No more work until they could be satisfied that they were being fed genuine MK mutton.

Shades of the Indian Mutiny!

'What the hell do we do now, Guy? I suppose the nearest pukka Imam or whatever would be in Jakarta, but the nearest supply of sheep plus a freezer plant would be Australia? Could we get the Aussie navy to locate a Moslem priest in Brisbane or Cairns and get him to do the proper ceremonial slaughter on some fresh sheep, freeze it and fly it up here plus the priest and a Certificate of Authenticity? There is a Hastings coming up from Edinburgh very soon and maybe that could pick up a ton or so to keep us going until the Director of RFAs can sort it out.' A week later *Fort Constantine* was back at work, but this wasn't the end of food troubles.

While the safe and adequate nourishment of the Task Force was one constant pre-occupation, that of the rest of the world was another and equally important. Eventually it would be politically essential to demonstrate that the nuclear tests had not

273

caused any harm to civil populations or any significant pollution in the environment – particularly in edible fish or vegetation. To this end, on April 10th the first Sunderland flying boat aircraft of number 5 Squadron, Royal New Zealand Air Force, came into Christmas Island to inaugurate a programme of fortnightly visits. They would bring samples of fish and vegetation from Tahiti and other island groups in the Grapple area.

The Sunderland draws much more water than some flying boats and so Commander Paton, the naval surveyor, had made a survey of St Stanilaus Bay, the south-west area of the main lagoon, which appeared to be the most suitable alighting area and had indeed been planned for use by the temporarily suspended South Pacific Air Lines. He found, however, that there were quite a number of coral heads and these mushroom-shaped colonies of coral, growing up from the bed of the lagoon to about two feet below the surface, could be a great hazard. So Gilbertese pearl divers were employed to move them, by rocking the columns until they broke off at the base, and then carrying them underwater to shore, clear of the alighting area. Eventually the necessary area was cleared and checked by a hawser being dragged across the length of the alighting run.

The Task Force now had operating outstations dotted about over an area as big as the whole of Europe and the Mediterranean, from the North Cape down to the Sahara and from Dublin to Moscow; and where there were people, there had to be regular supplies of food, mail, technical spares and medical attention when necessary. The intention was to have a weekly supply of some kind to each of these outposts and this task was now beyond the capability of the very hard-working 1325 Dakota flight, loaded as it was with many more runs to Malden Island than had been envisaged in the planning stages. So the Shackletons were brought in to assist in the weekly runs to Penrhyn, Raratonga, Aitutaki, Jarvis, Fanning and all the rest. They even substituted on occasions for the Hastings shuttle to Honolulu when the Hastings went unserviceable.

Wing Commander Alexander was very enthusiastic about this, particularly that earthly paradise Aitutaki where Mr Gladney and the resident New Zealand families were so very hospitable. The Dakota boys complained that the Shackletons pinched all the nicest runs and Alexander soon earned the soubriquet 'Alexander of the Islands'. But the insidious result was that the available Shackleton flying hours and spares were being used up much more quickly than had been planned. This was a great anxiety and one not easily remedied.

There were occasional light hearted moments to relieve the anxieties. There was increasing concern about rumours that a Japanese protest fleet of fishing boats would enter the area to prevent the tests taking place and this gave Commander John Holt of HMS *Resolution* opportunity to pull one of his practical jokes. After the completion of the Valiant visual bombing training and the first set of inert drops at Malden Island, HMS *Warrior* was to return to Christmas for a short break, arriving at dawn. Guy Western was awakened by his telephone and JOC relaying a signal from *Warrior* reporting that she had been hailed by a boat, apparently manned by a Japanese crew and displaying a very large banner saying: '*Warrior* go home'. Request instructions. Western, on a hunch, replied 'Don't go home' and went back to sleep. Meanwhile the 'Japanese' boat came alongside *Warrior* and the heavily disguised John Holt called out to the anxious Robin Begg, leaning over the rail:

'Good morning, Robin! Welcome home!' Roars of laughter.

Not much laughter, however, when Charles Adams came in to see the TFC to report that there was great complaint amongst the AWRE staff, principally amongst the technician grades, about the quality of the food and that this was now affecting their work and their morale. Would he agree to see a representative group of them, hear their complaints and try to do something about it? Of course – that very afternoon at 17.30. He appreciated that when the messing was pretty poor even for service personnel more or less inured to such conditions, it must be very miserable indeed for civilians who might never have been away from home before.

Assembled that afternoon in a conference room in the AWRE office hut adjoining the JOC was a group of about twenty, representing the various sections of the AWRE contingent. The TFC came straight to the point.

'I know the food is not very good and the airmen are grumbling as well, particularly at this moment because of some trouble in one of the supply ships. I'm sorry and I sympathise, but if you'll give me your specific complaints, I'll do my best to improve matters.'

At that moment a truculent and angry man pushed his way forward aggressively and thrust a dinner plate at the TFC.

'That's my dinner. Would *you* like to eat that muck?'

The TFC glanced at the grey, unappetising serving of some kind of meat stew.

'No, I wouldn't. It looks bloody awful and I'm sorry you've been faced with that. Meat is a great difficulty at the moment and it is always not very good. How do you get on with the fish and how do you find the vegetables?'

The general opinion was more moderate and it was agreed that the vegetables weren't too bad. Meat was the chief trouble and some people didn't care much for fish – at least in the way it was served up by the army cooks. With sympathy and understanding, the situation was eventually defused; but something had to be done, despite the Whitehall negative.

After some brain-storming in the headquarters, a fish and chip fryer was purchased in England and was flown out in a hurry. With good fried fish and chips available in the NAAFI at minimal prices, morale shot up. At the same time, a clandestine purchase of canned turkey in Honolulu made it possible to introduce a little more variety into the diet and the grumbling and complaints were kept down to a tolerable level.

38

The 160 Wing squadrons

With so many other and varied problems to deal with, the TFC had not so far devoted much time to the RAF 160 Wing, knowing that their affairs were in the extremely capable hands of Air Commodore Weir. But with the arrival of the first 100 Squadron Canberra PR7 on April 1st, with others following in quick succession, and eight Canberra B6s of 76 Squadron on April 18th – two had been left behind at Adelaide as reserves and possible couriers – it was time to make a more obvious show of interest in all aspects of the work of the Air Task Group. In company with Ginger Weir, the first thing was to meet the 76 Squadron crews – some of whom he remembered from Maralinga – and their new CO, Squadron Leader George Bates. A tall athletic and extrovert character, Bates had a keen brain and an attractively informal and animated manner, but without any trace of brashness or discourtesy. He was a highly professional aviator and had just spent two years as personal pilot to the Commander-in-Chief of Bomber Command.

76 was well organised, well trained, with high morale and ready for their cloud-sampling task, which they had already performed with such distinction at Monte Bello and Maralinga. They had been advised of impending essential improvements to the oxygen system and the cloud sampling equipment, but as yet there was no sign of the modification kits and they were getting anxious about the time factor. Then they were running into another problem which had not so far seriously affected the

PR7s of 100 Squadron, namely the intolerable temperatures in the perspex-canopied cockpits of the B6s when the fierce sun had been roasting them for hours before flying mid-morning. The PR7 flights were all in the early morning or late afternoon, when the air-coolers had some effect; but late morning the coolers didn't cope.

'Ginger,' said the TFC, 'get some of those big beach umbrellas from Waikiki beach and stick them up on stands to shade the cockpits. That'll help.'

'Of course. Why didn't I think of that myself. We'll do it.'

The squadron aircraft were drawn up in a neat line on their allotted part of the extensive concrete hard-standing. Just behind this were the office tents, one for the CO, one for the adjutant and the engineer officer and one for the aircraft handling party. The squadron maintenance personnel were absorbed into the specialist sections of the Technical Wing, responding to the demands of the squadron engineer officer, but all economically under the overall co-ordination and direction of the CTO.

Squadron Leader 'Duggie' Hammatt, CO of the Canberra PR7 Squadron, was a different sort of character, tall but slightly built, quiet and introspective, but had proved himself to be an excellent squadron commander. 100 Squadron had an enviable reputation for its long-range world-wide photographic recon- naissance activities and was now efficiently and without any fuss carrying out its allotted task of medium and high level wind finding, out to a thousand miles from Christmas Island. It was not a glamorous job, but to fly out to the prudent limit of endurance of the aircraft day after day and to return maybe to fine weather, maybe to three hundred feet, half a mile and no possible diversion required a high standard of airmanship, high morale and good leadership.

Unglamorous it may have been, but there was excitement and hazard enough in the high level Met recce flights. The movement of the Inter Tropical Front north and south of the island meant occasional flooded runways on early morning take-off and it was often necessary to send a Land Rover down the runway to check the water level before releasing the aircraft. Strong turbulence and icing were often found in climb and descent; on one occasion the ice crystals were large enough to damage the engine impellor blades, necessitating a double engine change.

High level turbulence, both in cloud and in clear air, caused problems. Climbing above it often meant temperatures of –70°C or lower, the cold causing engine surge and a possible 'flame out'. A small but abrupt change in aircraft attitude in the rarifield cold air had the same effect. Climbing above the turbulence sometimes meant running at right angles to the required track.

There were radio problems too. On one occasion, because of a slip-up in ground organisation, one of the PR7s was almost lost and was only saved by quick thinking and a splendid effort on the part of Group Captain Giles, the CO of the station Flying Wing. The PR7, WJ822 piloted by Squadron Leader Hammatt himself, returning from a long Met sortie, was unable to make radio contact with Approach Control and had apparently over-shot the island. Giles was just taxiing out in another Canberra B6 to do some local flying, heard the PR7 failing to make contact and appreciated the situation in a flash – there is a radio blind spot below and behind the Canberra, in which sector reception is poor and the PR7 was apparently not hearing the tower. He immediately took off and chased after the receding PR7, eventually contacted him, instructed him to turn 180 degrees and maintain height to conserve fuel and then acted as relay between the tower and the PR7 to carry out a successful homing and the safe return of the wanderer. Giles, angry at this near miss, investigated and found that the normal high-powered VHF transmitter had been taken out of service for maintenance some time before the ETA of the PR7 and had been replaced temporarily by a low power stand-by transmitter adequate only for local flying. This was the result of the earnest efforts of overworked technical personnel trying to keep up with their task and to cope with problems caused by the exceptionally heavy rain. It should never have happened with an aircraft out on a long distance sortie. Of course, had the Decca chain been in operation, the aircraft would not have overshot the island and shortly thereafter this situation was rectified.

This brief summary does not do justice to the epic nature of Squadron Leader Hammatt's sortie and it is perhaps worth telling in the pilot's own words.

'With myself at the controls and Flt Lt Dave Andrews (navigator), the Canberra was airborne at 05.15 hrs for a Met survey of weather conditions between Christmas Island the Carolines. The track was almost due South, a distance of approx 1000 nautical miles. The take-off was normal, except for some drag from the partially flooded runway – a not uncommon occurrence, following a night visit from the Inter Tropical Front. As we gained height to 43,000 ft in order to commence our cruise climb, we could see, in the dawning light, continuous cloud ahead extending above this altitude. We entered the cloud almost immediately, trusting, as we did so that we would avoid the very large Cu-Nimbus with its massive anvil top. Surprisingly, we met very little turbulence, and by the time we had reached 47,000 ft an hour or so later it was possible to break the tops here and there, and thus avoid the more ominous looking cloud still extending above the aircraft.

'Navigation was by "Green Satin", which operated perfectly except for the odd period of "unlocking" of the Doppler system in conditions of low wind speed at sea level.

'Since we were still in cloud, or just above it, our arrival at the Carolines had to be on calculated ETA. At the estimated position we commenced our descent on instruments to the scheduled levels to record temps and pressures, experiencing as we did so, some medium turbulence and a little icing. The task complete, we commenced climbing on a reciprocal heading to Christmas Island. The return journey was again an eighty percent instrument flight and it was always a welcome relief to break the surface of the cloud and bask in the heat of the sun.

'At an estimated 500 n.mls. from base we switched on the Radio Compass. Signals were received from the beacon, but to our horror, the Compass sensing unit failed to respond. The indicator needles continued to revolve, without pause, like "whirling Dervishes". (This discovery provoked some bad languages from the crew. The equipment had been working perfectly when tested at the beginning of the sortie).

'Note: (The R/C equipment on this aircraft had given this type of trouble before. Despite exhaustive ground checks and subsequent air tests, no faults could be traced. It was only after this sortie, when I had ordered a complete replacement of all units in the system, that workshop investigation revealed a "Dry joint" in the sensing unit. The technical explanation for the failure appeared to be the intense cold, which only after several hours of flight caused a circuit disconnection in that unit).

'We had now estimated that we were in easy range of Christmas Island and completing our final weather report to H/F control, we informed them that we were changing frequency to VHF approach control. Contact was not obtained on VHF. A check on Rebecca also came up zero. ETA arrived without radio contact. We decided to carry on for another 10 minutes, but again without success. At this point, since we were now above cloud, we turned on a reciprocal course roughly due South to take "Sun shots". Calculations confirmed that we were on track, but not whether we were North or South of base. It was then I heard an aircraft on the R/T. I made contact and ascertained that it was a Canberra from 76 Squadron. Explaining my predicament I requested his position – the pilot reported that he was over Christmas Island. I then said that I would give a series of transmissions in the hope that he would be able to report any change in my signal strength as I flew south. In conversation, the pilot reported that the Island had been subject to a heavy rain storm which had affected radio conditions. I decided at this point, to shut down one engine to conserve fuel.

'Very little loss of height occurred. The aircraft now being almost at its minimum weight. R/T checks were inconclusive, the signal strengths between our aircraft and the contact aircraft, remained 5 by 5.

'I don't know how my navigator was feeling at this moment. I know that I was beginning to perspire somewhat freely at the thought of making a bit of a splash somewhere.

'It was about this time, and on sudden inspiration, I asked for a cloud report for Christmas Island from the pilot of my contact aircraft. This was given as broken at 12,000 ft. On realisation that throughout our return flight we had not encountered anything but solid cloud this report suggested that we must be south of Christmas Island. Presumably, just out of range of ground R/T and the Rebecca beacon, i.e. some 200 n miles or more.

'It was with a dry mouth and crossed fingers I resumed our Northerly course, and remaining on my single engine. Fuel was now on the low side. Our good friend the contact aircraft remained in touch, and shortly afterwards the pilot informed us that Approach control was calling us. Contact was made, and a homing bearing confirmed that we were only a couple of degrees off course. The ground signal was weak, confirming, that we were indeed roughly 200 n miles distant. What a relief!

'Fuel was now heading towards the critical stage. I estimated that at our current weight and height of some 40,000 ft we could, if necessary, glide at least 350-400 miles. With engine throttled back we made a gradual descent, arriving over Christmas Island with a good 4000 ft to spare, and with just over 800 lbs of fuel remaining, completing some 6½ hours of flight.

'After landing, we checked the navigation plot, but failed to locate the "lost" 300 miles. I think that in flight we had met a southerly jet stream or very strong wind at a time during which the "Green Satin" had unlocked perhaps without showing the red indicator light warning the operator to switch to manual operation.' An interesting story.

Technically, the PR7s only had one real trouble and that was the occasional failure of the 'Green Satin' doppler radar to lock on to a smooth sea. However, excellent co-operation between the manufacturer's representatives and the Technical Wing eventually reduced the problem to acceptable levels.

The organisation of 100 Squadron on the airfield was similar to that of 76 and this boy-scout life seemed not to bother the crews – most of them very young – one bit; in fact they were thoroughly enjoying it.

The Shackleton air and ground crews of 206 and 240 Squadrons had taken Christmas Island and the whole Pacific Ocean in their stride without batting an eyelid. They were all veterans of many overseas detachments to Masirah, Muscat, Singapore, Cyprus, Malta and you-name-it: and two of the crews had carried out in 1955 the survey of the central Pacific islands which had led to the choice of Christmas Island for the tests. They were comfortably (by their standards) installed in their tented squadron headquarters, craftily sited on the seaward side of the vast aircraft parking area and so with quicker access to the beach and plug fishing during awaiting periods. For the time being, their Met flights and Air/Sea Rescue stand-by did not fully use all their resources and they were glad to help out the 1325 Dakota flight on the supply runs to the many islands with small recording detachments and on occasion replaced an un-serviceable Hastings on the run to Hickam. There were other odd jobs too and on one occasion a Shackleton crew had saved the life of a critically ill sailor by dropping a supply of vital drugs to a US Navy ship, the USS *Glacier*. On April 15th, Wing Commander Alexander took a 'knocked down' micro-baragraph hut and the equipment and the operating team to Faleolo, the airport of Apia in British Samoa. The aircrew had a very pleasant overnight stay in the famous 'Aggie West's Hotel' and before leaving next day, at the request of the British Resident, put on a flying display to impress the locals and 'show the flag'. Everyone was delighted – and impressed. These supply runs to the islands were always utilised to give trips to soldiers and sailors, both to give some of them a break and to foster the inter-service one-team spirit.

49 Squadron had a similar set-up – a tented squadron headquarters behind the Valiant parking area – but this was a much more formal organisation. Wing Commander Hubbard and his hand-picked and highly trained air and ground crews had a spirit of dedication to the awesome task in hand; and the delegation of responsibility to carefully selected leaders – training, navigation, electronics, bombing – produced a standard of squadron efficiency well above the norm. This showed in every aspect of their work, but they were not pompous about it and could relax with the best on Saturday nights. It was they who pioneered beach picnics at night, fishing for crayfish on the inner edge of the reef by the light of Tilley high-pressure kerosene lamps and then roasting them over a beach fire. Delicious!

1325 (Dakota) Flight ran like a small, highly intensive airline with a mixture of scheduled and non-scheduled services. Their adopted title 'Christmas Airways' was well chosen. Squadron Leader 'Joe' Hurst proudly showed off his task charts and the accomplishment of much more than the planned amount of flying and freight delivered. Of necessity they had developed a relaxed attitude to the constant flow of unexpected jobs thrust upon them, but they always performed very conscientiously and well. The TFC was one of their regular customers on his visits to Malden.

At the end of the line, the health-saving Auster fly-sprayer was all on his own – one pilot and two ground crew – and without him the rest might well not have been able to operate at all. He did a great job.

So the flying wing was in good shape and seemed to show that all the planning, procurement, preparation and training had produced the required result – the capability to meet AWRE's requirements for the tests.

But at the next level down, this impressive operational capability depended on the Technical Maintenance Wing, run

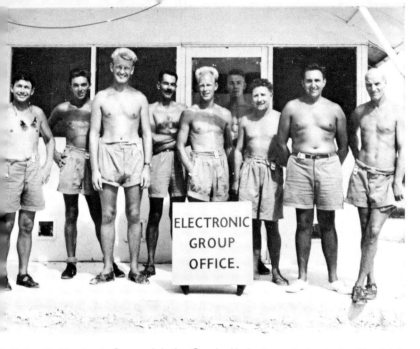

e Scientific Electronic Group. Join the 'Sunrise' industry and win a better life-style! *hoto: R Townsend)*

Dr Bean (with shirt!) and his Explosives Assembly team. *(Photo; AWRE)*

Some of the instrumentation on Malden Island in its protective shelter and aimed at the point of burst. *(Photo: AWRE)*

Ken Bomford – Scientific Superintendent, Malden Island. *(Photo: K Bomford)*

hip to shore transport by 'chopper' at Malden Island. *(Photo: AWRE)*

Penrhyn Island: ting up the camp for the teorological and scientific teams. *(Photo: Racal-Decca Co)*

Mail for British Forces Post Office 170. *(Photo: Ministry of Defence)*

Penrhyn Island: laying out the Decca slave station equipment.
(Photo: Racal-Decca Co)

by Wing Commander 'Ron' Boardman, an extremely competent organiser and practical engineer with his feet firmly on the ground. He showed the TFC round his empire with restraint, encouraging the NCOs in charge of the many specialist sections to speak for themselves and to explain their tasks and their difficulties in what was for them a hostile environment.

The technical stores held many thousands of different items of spares and of consumable stores, most of them held in banks of small weather-proof containers in rows of tents. The NCO in charge claimed proudly that he could locate and produce any required item in about five minutes.

Many of the technicians working in the specialist maintenance sections such as radio or hydraulics, seemed very young indeed and appeared to belong to that long-haired 'hippie' stratum of youth so much criticised by the stuffy and pompous middle-aged; but Boardman assured the TFC that they worked like heroes and there was no question of knocking off for the day before a job was finished.

It was not all sweetness and light. As Ginger Weir had already reported at a staff meeting, the arisings of unserviceabilities were much greater than had been planned for and there should have been a much greater second-line servicing capability. But that was a counsel of perfection. The logistics were already strained to the limit; and by the dedication and enthusiasm of the troops, the Tech Wing could just about cope for the next two months. That would do – but only just. It must be kept under review.

The difficulties were aggravated by the fact that nearly all work on the aircraft had to be done out in the open, where damp and dust inevitably got into whatever system was being opened up for inspection. It would have been quite out of the question to have considered hangarage sufficient to take aircraft inside; but the planners had helpfully provided one small Bessoneaux hangar – a canvas stretched over a wooden framework – into which the nose of one aircraft could be pushed to allow some work to be done under cover, and this was a great help. So also was the special wind deflector, which not only worked well for changing control surfaces and aerodynamic seals, but also provided a degree of shelter for other work.

It was quite late in the afternoon when this tour round the Air Task Group was completed and the TFC decided to walk back to the main camp, about three miles away. Having sent the staff car back, he set out along the taxi-track past the AWRE Assembly Building area and on across country, where he came upon one of the scientists, Dr. Bean – a gentle, kindly character – who had lengths of cable of some kind spread out all over the topography and connected to a test equipment. Bean explained that he had 'lost some micro-seconds' and was looking for them – all to do with exploding the weapon at the right moment – and he hadn't got it right yet.

In the course of the ensuing few minutes of amiable conversation, the TFC mentioned the trouble with starting cars and trucks first thing in the morning. 'Oh,' exclaimed Bean, 'I think I might be able to help with that,' and the next day he produced a silicone liquid to be sprayed on to the vehicle ignition systems. No more trouble after that and the stuff inevitably became known as 'Beano'.

'And that,' mused the TFC, 'is the most useful thing I've done today!'

39

Personnel safety measures

Japanese and other protestors were not the only shipping which might hold up a live weapon test. There could always be some ship whose master had either not seen or had ignored the Notice to Mariners declaring the Danger Area and prohibiting unauthorised shipping from entering it. Prior to a nuclear test, any such intruder would be located by the searching Shackleton aircraft, which would then drop a shower of leaflets on the ship, explaining the danger and advising it to steer at full speed away from the hazard. These leaflets, bearing the awful message in many languages, now arrived at last from London, as did also the first four thousand 'Grapple' booklets to tell the participating troops all about the complex operation in which they were involved. Late, but at least in time to be of some use in explaining to each man how important was his own role to the success of this vital operation. On the whole, people were pleased with the booklet, except that many could not cope with the alleged 'schoolboy' physics of the section on nuclear fission. The latter did at least, however, make it clear that radiation was something to be taken seriously.

It was then time to initiate the arrangements for safeguarding the Task Force personnel against possible radiation hazards, either foreseen or accidental. Short of an accident, no personnel other than the air and ground crews of the Canberra B6 sampling aircraft or, to a lesser degree the AWRE bomb assembly team, should ever be exposed to any radiation at all other than normal background which is always about us to a greater or lesser degree, depending on the local geology. The Canberra and AWRE crews were being carefully monitored and if any one of them were to receive in total anywhere near the permitted safe dose of radiation, he would immediately be transferred to other duties.

But it had to be considered that, however unlikely, there was a finite possibility of the Valiant carrying the bomb crashing on take-off, in which case there could be a nuclear explosion of unpredictable dimension. Planned measures were necessary to safeguard the great majority of the Task Force personnel against any consequent radiation effects. Therefore, at the time of take-off of a Valiant carrying a live weapon, all personnel on Christmas Island other than those actually required for the handling of aircraft at that time would be assembled and checked by roll call in the main camp or in the port area. Gilbertese families would be put on board one of the ships. In the event of such an accident, personnel would then be moved out of the path of the ensuing cloud.

Each man – and the two WVS ladies – was now issued with a personal dosimeter, which he wore constantly pinned to his shirt or shorts. This was a small plastic envelope, such as might contain a rail season-ticket or an identity-card, containing a small sheet of material sensitive to radiation. This dosimeter continually indicated the total amount of radiation received by that person and should it ever exceed the permitted safe level, remedial action would be taken.

But radiation was not the only hazard to which personnel were exposed. Other risks were more likely, as on another day when the friendly neighbourhood Inter Tropical Front was visiting, complete with heavy rain and low cloud. A Canberra returning from a Met flight was making an instrument approach and was being talked down by the duty Air Traffic Control officer using the ACR 7 D radar. At half a mile from the runway threshold and still in cloud at three hundred feet, the talk-down commentary suddenly ceased. The pilot (with no diversion and insufficient fuel to overshoot, climb and make a new instrument approach) decided to continue his descent and present heading in hope. A few seconds later he had the runway in sight and landed safely. It might not have been so and he complained vehemently to the tower, but go no response. The Air Traffic officer had collapsed with a serious case of food poisoning.

An irate Air Commodore Weir stormed into the Task Force Commander's office to demand some action – 'What if this had happened to the crew of a Valiant during a live drop?' Moments later the ear of the apologetic Captain Gausden of the *Fort Bo* was burning under the blistering comments coming down his ship-to-shore telephone. He promised a shake-up and no more such incidents and invited the TFC to that long delayed lunch on board, to discuss improved procedures. Meanwhile, Doctor Bradley and the RASC staff would certainly be tracking down the origin of the present trouble.

Troubles tracked back to the source could usually be dealt with and those which had bedevilled the Decca Navigator system were eventually sorted out before the end of April. This was a great relief, since it was the primary method of putting the Valiant on the correct bombing line if there was any appreciable amount of cloud and the only method of doing a 'blind' drop should this be necessary. The Decca Company team of experts had worked indefatigably to solve the problems caused by the very long base line and the unusual geometry of the requirement. There were anomalies in the propagation of the radio waves and a kink in the display pattern. With the help of new and improved Decca charts, these were largely overcome. At the same time, Wing Commander Boardman, the Chief Technical Officer, became exasperated with the frequent unserviceability of the equipment in the aircraft. So he had the 'black boxes' stripped down and thoroughly cleaned and dried. The sum of this joint effort was that the Decca system then worked well and during the 'inert drop' phase at Malden, was used to effect at least one blind drop from above cloud, well within the required accuracy.

289

40

The Dress Rehearsal

As the last days of April raced towards May and the target date for the first thermo-nuclear test, the final reinforcements began to arrive at Christmas Island. The Royal New Zealand Navy frigates *Pukaki* and *Rotoiti* had joined the Grapple Naval Task Group and almost immediately went on station as weather ships, to augment the daily flow of data arriving at Freeman's central meteorological office. This now included full reports and forecasts from the American principal met office at Wheeler Air Force Base on Oahu, not far from Hickam, where an RAF Signals section manned continuously a teleprinter and signals link with Christmas. The weather reporting network as planned was finally complete, better results were coming in from the radio-sonde units and the technique of forecasting based on converging/diverging wind velocities was proving to be very useful. So the daily 'go/no go' practice decisions were working out correctly in most cases.

At Aldermaston, too, they were racing to beat the clock. Group Captain McLachlan, the Senior Superintendent of Weapons Production, was responsible for the manufacture of the various elements of the weapons to be tested. The designs were constantly being changed as the technology developed and he was being very hard pushed to meet the required programme for shipment of the components of the first device to be tested. The first 'ball' of radio-active material, safely enclosed in a 700 pound lead container was transported to RAF Lyneham early on Friday, April 26th and left immediately in a special Hastings aircraft, escorted by Air Commodore Denis Wilson and Group Captain Paul Wood. No other passengers or freight. Only two days late on a programme drawn up six months previously. Nice work!

Even so, time was short, every effort was being made to accelerate the programme and therefore a reserve Hastings had been positioned at Namao, in case of any technical delay to the first.

The aircraft with the special load and escort duly left Lyneham, refuelled – both tanks and tummies – at Aldergrove and smartly left again for Goose Bay. An hour out over the Atlantic Ocean from Aldergrove, the captain came back into the cabin and enquired of Denis Wilson if there was anything in the special load which could affect the radio, as they had been unable to contact base or any other ground station. Wilson assured him there was nothing about the special load which could do that and nothing more was heard from the flight deck.

Some eight hours later they joined the circuit at Goose Bay, but went round and round and round, until eventually the control tower fired a green Very light and the aircraft landed. Only then did it transpire that there had been no contact with any ground station since leaving Aldergrove and a mighty panic had been set in motion, culminating in a special report arriving on the desk of the Chief of the Air Staff! The reserve Hastings had been despatched from Namao to Goose Bay and now took over the special load and its escorts. An enquiry into the radio malfunction was left to Transport Command to handle.

Two days later they arrived at Hickam AFB, Honolulu, where rumours of the panic and the nature of the special load had preceded them. The USAF was taking no chances and several fire-engines were lined up to each side of the runway as the Hastings came in to land. As it touched down, the fire engines raced alongside, bells clanging madly, and pursued it as it taxied to the ramp. The doors opened and Wilson and Wood emerged, to find themselves looking down the muzzles of the hoses of fire engines surrounding them on all sides – very sinister and un-nerving! However, everything calmed down in due course, they stayed overnight and next day continued to Christmas Island, to arrive on May 1st.

On April 28th, perhaps the most important final reinforcement in the shape of Bill Cook, the Scientific Director, at last set off from UK bound for Christmas Island. At the same time, the slip crews for the two courier Valiant aircraft, which would carry other vital components of the first nuclear device to be tested, were despatched to be in their take-over locations by May 2nd. Two complete crews from the B Flight rear echelon of 49 Squadron, under the command of Bailey and Bates, left Wittering for the RCAF Station, Goose Bay, Labrador. David Roberts, Millett and their crews left Christmas by Hastings to Hickam and thence by Qantas to San Francisco, to position at Travis AFB. A back-up Valiant left Wittering via Goose Bay, and Namao to position more or less mid-way at Travis, ready to replace either of the two scheduled couriers if necessary.

On May 5th, the two courier Valiant aircraft, XD825 and XD827, were loaded with the precious vital components of the first bomb to be tested. Flown by Flavell and O'Connor and their crews and still limited in range by lack of overload underwing fuel tanks, they departed from Wittering first of all for Aldergrove, where they refuelled quickly for the Atlantic crossing and continued without delay to Goose Bay. There the aircraft were again refuelled and taken over by the slip crews captained by Bailey and Bates, off the ground again in thirty five minutes. Five hours later they were on the ground at Namao, refuelled and were off again in thirty minutes.

At Travis Air Force Base, apprised of progress so far, Millett and Roberts were on their toes and determined to beat the clock and so to impress their friendly American hosts. Alas, it was not to be. They were indeed ready to go only twenty five minutes after Bailey and Bates had landed, but then the last minute Met report showed headwinds too strong for their range on the leg to

Honolulu. There was nothing for it but to wait until the headwind eased off.

After twenty-four hours of delay and no reported sign of improvement, anxiety in the AWRE staff at Christmas began to increase and Ginger Weir began to wonder if the American forecasters were playing it a little too safe. He sent a Canberra PR7 up to Hickam with orders to check the 40,000 foot wind every six hours. Three days later the headwind had reduced sufficiently, Roberts and Millett left for Honolulu where they refuelled quickly and pressed on to Christmas, arriving for a night landing at 06.00 hours on May 9th. As they shut down engines and opened bomb doors in the 49 Squadron dispersal the AWRE crew moved in to collect their precious burdens and hustled them off to the AWRE assembly building, carefully closing the security screens behind them.

Meanwhile, Bill Cook's progress had been a little more sedate. In order to support the deception plan, aimed at conveying to the world the impression that the tests would be delayed and so avoid the unwelcome intrusion of protesters, it was essential that his passage through Honolulu should not attract attention. He therefore flew from San Francisco by United Airlines instead of Qantas, arriving mid-afternoon on May 1st. John Claridge, CO of the RAF Staging Post, inconspicuous in the usual very informal beach attire affected by most people, met Cook at the airport arrival hall, took him and his baggage unobtrusively to an unremarkable rented car and drove him round to his own living quarters at Hickam Air Force Base. There the Scientific Director remained incarcerated overnight, shunning – at least for the moment – all Hawaiian blandishments, thankfully untroubled by any curiosity and able to work quietly on his papers. Early next morning he stepped straight into the waiting Hastings shuttle and was soon on his way south, accompanied by a vast assortment of freight and a miscellany of other passengers. Eight hours later there was the usual reception party waiting as the aircraft doors were opened in the Hastings dispersal at the Christmas Island airfield. Both the reception party and the steaming late afternoon atmosphere took him aback a little. However, the party ignored Bill – it was the mail and urgently awaited aircraft spares they were after. But there just beyond the crowd were the TFC, Ginger Weir, Charles Adams and John Challens to welcome him and to lead him to the waiting white staff car, while Corporal Beall collected his baggage.

'Hello, Wilf! Nice of you all to come to meet me. Phew! It's a bit hot, isn't it?'

'Welcome, Bill. You'll soon get used to the warm. Right now you need a cool shower, a couple of hours sleep and then a very large whisky and soda.'

'Or even two!' responded the weary traveller.

It was probably the first time – or at any rate the first time for many years – that Bill Cook had been shown into such austere living accommodation as he found in his tent, next door but one to the TFC's; but he took it with complete nonchalance as though he had lived that way all his life. Two hours later, refreshed and coolly dressed in white shirt and light slacks, with his pipe going well and his whisky and soda – and ice! – in one hand, he was completely on the ball as the TFC gave him a succinct run-down on events and achievements in the past two months. There was a very free and easy camaraderie amongst the dozen or so members of the little mess and the light-hearted badinage was even brisker than usual; but beneath all that was a sense of approaching the moment of truth as Cook's presence heralded the imminent first test.

The TFC explained to the Scientific Director the philosophy of the daily morning 'go/no go' meeting but suggested that he might wish to spend the first day or so being briefed by his own staff, beginning with Adams and Challens and then going to see Bomford and the Malden set-up. This was agreed. So while Bill Cook on his first morning began a detailed tour of all the AWRE and RAE sections at Christmas, the TFC took the opportunity to visit *Narvik* and Malden to see the last of the High Explosive drops. There would be no more until the dress rehearsal for the real thing.

As the aircraft carrier *Warrior* was then to return to Christmas for replenishment and a few days stand-down, he accepted Commodore Roger Hicks' invitation to go back by sea and to enjoy the luxury of the Admiral's cabin for the overnight voyage. This gave the pleasant opportunity to chat with a number of the ship's officers in the wardroom. In the course of conversation with the ship's doctor and Commander Begg, the TFC observed that bath water always goes out of the plughole anti-clockwise in the Northern hemisphere and clockwise in the Southern, thus giving rise to that 'shaggy dog' story about the goats on Tristan Da Cunha. Admittedly it sometimes starts the wrong way round, until it is sure of its latitude; but in such cases, just before the final gurgle, it will reverse and always finishing up emptying the last few drops in accordance with the Law devised by that eminent Norwegian scientist, Buys-Balot. The question arose, what happens exactly on the equator?

In the interests of scientific enquiry, the TFC agreed to take a bath in the Admiral's bathroom ten minutes before 'crossing the line'. Robin Begg would attend to the navigation and would telephone the count-down as the ship approached the line, the plug would be pulled and the observation made. With some hilarity this exercise was performed and the only conclusion which could be reached was that the water wouldn't run out exactly on top dead centre, but waited a moment to find out which way it was supposed to go! Or maybe peering 'through the bottom of a glass, darkly' had diminished the accuracy of visual observation!

At first this was thought to be the most likely explanation of an extraordinary sight the next morning, when he was being shown round the Air Direction Room and the bridge by Roger Hicks and Paul Whitfield, the Commander (Flying). To his shocked amazement, there was a Shackleton aircraft at about two hundred feet, wheels and flaps down, making an approach to the stern of the carrier as though in the process of 'landing-on'. It couldn't be true! – or possible, with the aircraft wing span greater than the width of the flight deck. Nevertheless, there was the batsman with his 'ping- pong bats' on his little platform at the port corner of the round-down, signalling corrections to keep the approaching aircraft level and on the right line of approach, all in accordance with standard naval aviation landing-on procedure. It took several seconds for the penny to drop, to notice the batsman's signals were a caricature of the normal and that the whole thing was a well organised joke. As the Shackleton neared the round-down, that is the rear edge of the flight deck, full power went on, wheels up, flaps up and the aircraft climbed and turned away to port, well clear of the 'island' and the ship's masts. Cameras had been clicking madly at this unusual sight and no doubt it was all good clean fun and in the interest of good inter-service co-operation and teamwork. But it was a bloody silly thing to do and contrary to his firm orders that there should be no high spirited larking about until the tests were over and no longer any need to eke out overstrained resources of all kinds. He would certainly tell Ginger Weir so on his return. Still it *was* an impressive sight and the sailors were all delighted.

A couple of days later Bill Cook came into the TFC's office.

'Wilf, I think the Army have done a wonderful job in setting up the facilities for us and I would like to put our appreciation and thanks on record. To whom should I send the message?'

'I agree with you, Bill. Woollett and his team have been first class in every way. Best to send the signal to the War Office for DCIGS.'

'How about this then?' – and Cook, having entered in the addressee, handed over the signal form. It read:

'Am very pleased with the arrangements made here by War Office units. AWRE Scientific Groups are well satisfied with accommodation, offices, laboratories. They did not expect conditions to be so good. This is having very marked effect not only on morale but on ease and efficiency of working. The help

received by AWRE Groups from Army is tremendous. Army co-operatioan extremely good and
difficult work goes on regardless of hours and
weather.'

'Very nicely put, Bill. A well earned tribute. If you wish,
Terry Helfer will get that sent off for you right away.'

Next morning, alas, Bill Cook wasn't feeling quite so
cheerful. After taking part in the morning briefing, he said he
wasn't feeling too well and would go back to his tent and rest a
while. Oh Lord! Not another case of food poisoning! Not that,
reported Doctor Bradley. Just too much sun too soon. Cook had
faithfully followed the advice always to wear his Panama straw
hat when going out into the sun and not to sunbathe until late
in the afternoon; but no-one had warned him that the dazzling
white crushed coral surface of roads and levelled areas reflected
the sun's rays upwards very strongly. His shorts were unusually
wide in cut in the leg and his thighs had been badly burnt. With
aspirin and staying quietly in his tent he would be fit again in 48
hours. Breeze in the shady tent and aspirin – OK. He had his
own ideas on the best medicine. But as for keeping him quiet –
not a chance! He worked by telephone.

As soon as Cook had recovered, the TFC suggested that they
went out to the *Fort Beauharnois* for a breath of sea air and a
leisurely and special lunch with the penitent Captain Gausden.
This was agreed with alacrity. It was a pleasant day, with little
cloud, lower humidity than usual, the sea sparkling and exotic
bird life performing aerobatics for their entertainment. A nicely
recuperative day and the fifteen minute trip in a launch out to
the *Fort Bo* was very agreeable. The captain met them most
hospitably and produced his special Glen Fiddich for the
delectation of the Scientific Director. After five minutes' stern
finger-wagging over the food poisoning incident, all was relaxed
and it was a very pleasant lunch party with a menu rather
different from the plain fare ashore.

As they returned ashore, the afternoon was wearing on and it

297

seemed late to go back to the office; so back to the tents to sleep it off before the evening swim. An hour or so later, however, the TFC was far from happy. He habitually ate very plainly and maybe smoked salmon and all that highlife had been unwise. Better just see that Bill was all right. Indeed he was not. William Cook was green in the face and in a very poor way. Fortunately he was able to get rid of the trouble and, after a night's rest, he was back on the job although still fragile. Meanwhile the TFC was about to have words with Captain Gausden, but was beaten to the draw by the telephone from Gausden himself in an exceedingly feeble voice.

'Are you all right, Air Marshal? I think that smoked salmon must have been off.'

'No, we're not!'

'Oh, dear! We appear to have done it again. I'm so sorry!'

There was no point in saying anything more, other than thanks for hospitality. All quite funny in retrospect, but not very funny against the operational background of the moment.

But all that was soon put aside and forgotten. In a quiet moment after the evening meal a few days later Bill Cook suggested a short stroll along the shore and when he and the TFC were out of earshot of the others, he said:

'The good news is that we have the first non-nuclear rehearsal round assembled and running tests. We'll be ready to go in forty-eight hours.'

'That's splendid, Bill. We'll go for the dress rehearsal right away and try to save a day on the programme.'

The whole Task Force was now working to a target date of May 16th, for the first thermo-nuclear weapon test and was aware that every effort would be made to improve on this. Accordingly Roger Hicks, Commodore Grapple Squadron, had sailed in the aircraft carrier HMS *Warrior* from Christmas Island on Tuesday morning, May 7th, arriving off Malden Island next day, ready for the final dress rehearsal and the live drop. *Warrior* rendezvoused with *Narvik*, the technical control ship, replenished *Narvik* with oil fuel and then lay off Malden awaiting the progress of events at Christmas Island. Most of the time she just drifted with the tidal set and periodically steamed to regain position. On one occasion, however, when wind and tide were right, she anchored for the day off the south-west point of Malden, with the bow over a shallow shelf and the stern a thousand feet away over unplumbable depths. Other ships of the Grapple Squadron – *Messina*, *Alert* and their passengers – arrived in due course and took station some twenty odd miles north east of the island. They were later joined by HMS *Cook*, carrying Task Force personnel from Christmas Island as spectators.

On May 9th the TFC opened the 8 am briefing meeting with the word that this was no longer a practice run. This was for real, for the full dress rehearsal in 48 hours time. Every aspect of the operation would be exercised exactly as it would be for a nuclear test, the only exceptions being that the bomb burst on which the instrumentation was focused would be chemical high-explosive, not nuclear, and the Canberra PR7 with the 'Forth Bridge' would not actually depart for Hickam and the UK. So on with the decision-making.

First, forecast weather and winds in the Malden area 48 hours ahead. Freeman explained lucidly his forecast for both the operation and the danger area. All his reporting stations, including the RNZN ships *Pukaki* and *Rotoiti* were functioning correctly and he was confident that conditions would be favourable.

Secondly, the fall-out patterns from the expected air-burst or an accidental surface explosion. Ernest Hicks produced his forecast charts based on Freeman's high level wind predictions. Satisfactory 'all clear' of any populated area.

Next, radiation safety. All personnel both at Christmas and on board ship were now wearing dosimeter badges. Roll calls were prepared and assembly areas designated for all personnel, other than those required for handling departing aircraft or for duty in the Joint Operations Centre. Sufficient motor transport was allocated to the assembly area to move the personnel if necessary.

299

The weapon. John Challens had the non-nuclear duplicate of the actual device ready for installation in the aircraft.

Warrior. Could she be on station at Malden 48 hours later, with aircraft (Avengers and helicopters) and radar serviceable for the D-day programme? 'Yes,' said Western.

'*Narvik, Messina, Salvictor, Alert, Fort Beauharnois* and one cargo ship all ready?' 'Yes.'

Valiants XD818 and 824? Serviceable. Aerodynamic seals to be changed to the silicone type this day and then flight tested. 818 then to be positioned in the AWRE weapon assembly area, ready for loading.

Canberra PR7s. In addition to that day's sorties, aircraft available for the D-1 and D-day jobs. The courier with the 'Forth Bridge' serviceable.

Canberra B6s? Four aircraft serviceable, but new and improved drum impactors to give better collection of particle samples were due to arrive that morning and would be fitted that day.

Canberra B6 fitted for VHF radio relay? OK.

Shackletons? Sufficient aircraft serviceable for the Met, sea search, photography and ASR standby tasks.

Dakotas? Ready for tasks designated.

All appeared to be in order. The TFC had his own personal check-list, some two and a half closely typed pages listing all the necessary actions and events to be completed in sequence before approval could finally be given for the release of the nuclear bomb from the Valiant.

This check list was now completed up to the point of declaring the intention to drop the weapon in 48 hours time. At the end of the briefing, this order was so given.

The day passed quickly in a rush of organisational activity in every section of the Task Force. The TFC himself continued on a long-considered round of visits to every unit at Christmas Island, from HMS *Warrior* to the RASC cookhouse in main camp, to tell the troops in such numbers as could readily be brought together that the whole reason for their being at

Christmas Island was about to be put in action, to tell them what was going to happen and how each of their individual tasks was vital to the whole operation. These little discourses were to audiences ranging from the whole ship's company of HMS *Messina* to six cooks in the bakery in the main camp.

Perhaps the most important activity this day was in the AWRE bomb assembly compound, where the replica bomb, complete in every detail except for the radio active core, was finally completed, checked out on the test rig, installed in Valiant XD818 and checked again for correct functioning of all telemetry senders. By nightfall it was finished and an armed guard was placed round the aircraft, hidden from view behind the security screens.

Meanwhile, in the shelter of the great wind-break, the two Valiants detailed for this first live test had had their seals changed and were flight tested afterwards. After a minute inspection by the Crew Chief, and the dedicated ground crew, 818 was taxied over to the AWRE area.

There was intense activity in the 76 Squadron dispersal. Instructions had just been received from the UK that the cloud sampling aircraft should be painted with a new polyvinyl acetate-based barrier paint, to minimise radio-active contamination and to make it easier to wash off afterwards. The paint was just about to arrive at Hickam and a Canberra was sent to collect it.

On Malden Island, the scientists and sappers began the two-day task of dismantling everything other than the instrumentation sites themselves and burying it in the protective 'elephant-pits' – tents, transport, plant, fuel, tools, cook-house, the lot. The only task to be left to D-day, H-5 hours, was the starting of the generators which supplied electricity to the instrumentation sites.

The weather and upper winds in the Malden area continued favourable and at midnight an extra Shackleton meteorological sortie took off, followed four hours later by a Canberra PR7, to monitor the wind speeds and to have the results in for the eight o'clock briefing. At 04.00 six Shackletons departed to search the danger area in an extended line abreast parallel sweep at thirty miles spacing, to ensure that no shipping had strayed into the area, either by accident or design.

After the 08.00 morning briefing on May 10th, D-1 for the dress rehearsal, the TFC turned to Bill Cook.

'Assuming this was the real D-1, I reckon we go. Do you agree, Bill?'

'Yes, Wilf. We go.'

'OK with you, Ginger, and you, Guy?' – turning to the Air Task Group Commander and Captain Western.

'Yes, sir,' from both.

Turning to the two Controllers, Butch Surtees and Felix Neville-Towle, waiting tensely behind their long desk but with their glass screens moved to one side so that they were effectively part of the meeting:

'Instruct all units to proceed with the D-1 programme. Final briefing and decision at 05.30 tomorrow morning.'

May 10th, Dress Rehearsal D-1, was a curiously quiet day on Christmas Island, with less aviation noise than usual. Other than those already away on Met flights, the sea search or the run to Malden, most aircraft were being serviced and held ready for the rehearsal. Only the regular gentle drone of the Auster 'Captain Flit' spraying the camp and airfield areas with DDT and the occasional roar of an engine being run up on ground test broke the drowsy, somnolent murmur of the coral island.

Plenty of activity, of course, in engineering and domestic support sections, laboratories and offices. Amongst other happenings, late in the morning Group Captain Brousson and Lieutenant Commander Finlay, the naval signals head, came into the TFC's office.

'You will remember that in the earlier practices with HE bombs we found there was no way to stop a live bombing run during the last minute or so while the pilot and bomb aimer are on broadcast and we decided to try to set up a way of *Warrior* breaking through on the aircraft's ILS frequency in an emergency. *Warrior* didn't hold a suitable frequency crystal so we demanded one from the Carlisle Maintenance Unit three weeks ago. Now we hear it only left London yesterday and won't be at Hickam until tomorrow, early. Shall we send a Canberra to fetch it?'

'Yes, Richard. But why this delay?'

'Apparently the crystal was despatched promptly on receipt of our demand, by motor cyclist to Heathrow to save time. But the poor chap was involved in an accident and was taken into Cardiff Infirmary suffering from severe concussion. No one knew where he was. Only now have they tracked him down, found the motorcycle and the crystal and sent it on its way.'

'Can we get it to *Warrior* in time for the rehearsal, Finlay?'

'Might just make it, sir. I think our best bet is to have an Avenger standing by as the courier Canberra arrives and fly it directly to *Warrior*. Shall I arrange that?'

'Yes, please. But see that Captain Western knows what goes on, and that Air Commodore Weir and Wing Commander Hubbard are all lined up to use the ILS frequency in an emergency – if the system works!'

'Aye, aye, sir.' So it was arranged.

There were other crises, of course. At 06.00 hours on May 9th, the two courier Valiant aircraft carrying the vital explosive components for Short Granite, the first live nuclear bomb to be tested, together with their wind-finding PR7 escort, had arrived at last from Hickam. That evening Bill Cook again took the TFC on one side for a private chat.

'I'm sorry to have to tell you this, but the bad news is that the explosive supercharge shell which goes round the radio-active core of this first live round arrived cracked. Also the spare supercharge. The only explanation we can think of is that the bomb-bay heating in the courier Valiants didn't work properly and with such a long time at such low external temperatures the cold cracked the explosive material.'

'Oh, my God! We never thought of it! The bomb-bay heating, which had indeed given us some trouble earlier on but we had thought this was cured, was only sufficient to keep warm the space round a damn' great bomb case nearly filling the bay. With a tiddley little parcel like your package of explosive, there wouldn't be nearly enough heat. What the hell are we going to do now? Can you get a replacement?'

'No. We can't get a replacement in time – it would take at least six weeks. So we've stuck it together with Bostik and we'll just hope for the best. I think it better not to broadcast this in case it affects morale.'

'Bostik! All this immaculate planning, preparation and special assembly environment and now your cracker is stuck together with Bostik! Still, I agree with you about keeping it dark – let's maintain our customary air of impeturbable confidence, Bill. Now I think we need a drink, don't you? And we'll start the ball rolling tomorrow morning for the first live drop five days from now.'

After the initial shock and dismay at finding that all four of the hemispherical explosive supercharges for Short Granite were cracked, Bill Cook and the assembly team led by Dr Bean and Mr T R Roberts had decided to go ahead with the live assembly, selecting the best two of the four hemispheres. With great delicacy these were taped round to prevent the cracks opening any wider and on mating them together round the RA ball, the crack in the upper hemisphere was placed at right angles to the crack in the lower. All dimensions were then checked to ensure that, although differing from the original assembly, they were still within tolerance. The tape was then removed and the whole sphere encased neatly in a Latex bag without any trouble. Dr Bean and Mr Roberts had rehearsed this process several times before and the whole drill worked with exemplary smoothness. And then, in a thoroughly scientific gesture, they crossed fingers!

The nuclear device was then on May 11th despatched to the weapon assembly area, ready for mounting in the Blue Danube bomb case which had earlier been delivered ashore from the RFA *Fort Rosalie*.

The full dress rehearsal on May 11th, starting with the first Shackleton sortie before midnight, went well and without a hitch. Even the emergency radio-frequency crystal arrived at Christmas just after dawn and a naval Avenger aircraft took it on to *Warrior*, some twenty miles north of Malden, in time for it to be fixed in position half an hour before the Valiant's final bombing run.

Warrior's crew had done well. They had operated exactly to programme in launching twenty-seven helicopter sorties in evacuating the personnel from Malden and later returning the re-entry teams. This effort included a praiseworthy overnight engine change to have all the aircraft available at first light. The Air Direction Room had successfully maintained a continuous plot and controlled the movements of sixteen aircraft operating within sixty miles of the ship during the bombing run – a big increase in work load over all previous drills. At the same time the whole ship's company had operated under full ABCD*, State IA conditions. A very good effort indeed.

The RAF 160 Wing had performed exactly according to the plan. Snags had arisen, but had been overcome as they arose. All aircraft – Valiants, Canberras of both marks, Shackletons, Dakotas – had taken off within seconds of the appointed times and had done their jobs according to the book, all equipment being serviceable.

The personnel safety arrangements to cover the case of an accident on Valiant take off had worked satisfactorily – a great credit to the organising shepherds who had accounted for every man in the Task Force at that moment of take off.

The 'Wash-up' at the Joint Operations Centre after the dress rehearsal – a conference of heads of all participating units in which out-spoken criticism was encouraged – had confirmed that the operational plan was satisfactory and did not need any significant change; but it also showed up the fact that the Canberra PR7 squadron would be very hard pressed to provide

---

* In a state of protection against atomic, biological or chemical weapons.

the aircraft and some of the crews to deliver the cloud samples back to UK inside the specified twenty-four hours from the explosion – no mean feat in 1957 – in addition to fulfilling its essential meteorological and photographic tasks in the operation. Weir, Milligan and Brousson studied this problem and came up with the recommendation that 58 Squadron – 100's sister squadron at Wyton – should provide the cloud sample carrier service. 58 were already tasked to provide the slip crews at Travis AFB and RCAF Goose Bay, so it would be no serious problem for them to position one of their own aircraft at Christmas and so fly the Christmas-Hickam-Travis sectors as well. This change was agreed and Bomber Command were asked to implement it.

Later that evening, Ginger Weir was as usual holding court in his tent, next to the TFC's, and passers-by on their way to the 'A' mess were lured in for a drink and a chat before dinner. Freddie Milligan, who had often been caught by this over-kind hospitality, had really too much to do this evening to spend half an hour in relaxed chit-chat and so resorted to crawling on his hands and knees past the wide-open entrance to Ginger's tent, hoping to avoid detection. Observers of this little scene shook their heads, clucked in sympathy and speculated as to whether this was one of the unforeseen effects of exposure to radiation!

41

'Short Granite' – the first megaton test

The whole Task Force now moved into the final stage of the testing of Short Granite, Britain's first thermo-nuclear weapon device. On May 13th, at the conclusion of the morning briefing, the decision was given to go for a live drop 48 hours later, following the pattern of the dress rehearsal. The orders went out to the operational units of the Task Force. The outlying recording stations were alerted and warned to be ready for the 15th, as were the staging posts and slip crews for the courier Canberra.

Although it had been agreed that there should be no advance publicity or press representatives at this first shot, there was nevertheless to be present a small party of official observers to witness it.

A small British Air Ministry team, consisting of Air Vice Marshal Ronnie Lees the Assistant Chief of Staff for Operations, Air Commodore Brian Burnett the Director of Bomber and Reconnaissance Operations and Air Commodore 'Bro' Brotherhood the Director of Operational Requirements, had already arrived on May 9th in one of the special UK-Christmas Hastings flights. The TFC was naturally keen to show off a little to his late boss and drove him round to see some of the installations. Unfortunately, he didn't look where he was going, drove through a dip in the 'road' where the water from an overnight rainstorm was two feet deep and drowned out the engine. He had to call by radio for a Land Rover to come and rescue them. Ronnie Lees laughed like the proverbial drain but it was all in the day's work.

Official Government observers from Australia, Canada, New Zealand and the United States – two from each country – had been invited to witness this first test and had arrived individually under their own steam at Honolulu on May 13th. They had been collected severally and greeted by their escort, Group Captain Paul Wood and had been accommodated in an hotel, where they had expected to have to wait several days, as was the norm for such tests. They had been briefed that it was not practicable for them to stay overnight – or for several days even – at Christmas Island immediately before the test.

To their surprise, the very next morning they were hustled into a waiting Hastings aircraft, flown to Christmas, transferred immediately to a Dakota and flown to Malden. There they were straightaway embarked (or embussed?) in a DUKW and were taken out through the surf and the narrow gap in the reef to HMS *Alert*, waiting off shore. *Alert*, the despatch vessel – or private yacht! – of the naval Commander-in-Chief, Far East, had been borrowed for this very purpose by Peter Gretton on his ill-fated visit to Singapore the previous November and an excellent arrangement it was, too. Commander Edward Hamilton-Meikle, the Commanding Officer of *Alert*, made the VIPs welcome with an exemplary display of the best Royal Navy hospitality. He also put them to 'work', issuing them with fishing rods and all necessary tackle and enlisting their help in catching fish for the 'before and after' checking programme. While all these social and political arrangements were being implemented, at 07.15 on May 14th, after the briefing in the JOC on Christmas Island, the decision to drop on the 15th was confirmed and the D-1 programme was put into action. On Malden the final setting up of the recording installation was completed, as was the protective burying of all else except for the minimum requirements of the rearguard party who were to stay overnight. By 19.00 hours that evening – last light – *Warrior*, *Narvik* and *Messina* had completed the evacuation, other than the small team to be lifted off early next day, as they had done for the dress rehearsal four days previously.

On Christmas Island, the declaration of D-1 was taken as routine. After so many practices and the dress rehearsal, there was no very great sense of excitement in the main camp, just a general air of 'Ho, hum, here we go again' and a lot of light-hearted banter as to whether the cracker would be a bang or a fizzle. Nevertheless, the activity was intense and dedicated. Each man was determined that *his* job would be properly done.

Four Shackletons in line abreast at thirty miles spacing swept the danger area to ensure that no shipping had entered. Another two carried out long range 'Bismuth' type weather reconnaissance flights. Three Canberra PR7s carried out high level weather flights spaced out over the day. One Canberra B6 measured the background radiation level over Christmas as part of the 'before and after' comparison programme.

Two Hastings flights took a large proportion of the Gilbertese families to Canton Island, out of harm's way. Extra Dakota flights went to Malden, including that taking the VIP observers on their way to their spectator ship.

The two Valiant aircraft were checked and refuelled ready for the morrow, 818 to drop the bomb, 824 to play the grandstand role. After the most diligent inspection by the Crew Chief, Chief Technician Caple, 818 was taxied over to the Assembly building and handed over to the AWRE team. There the now fully assembled 'Short Granite' device in its 10,000 pound Blue Danube bomb case was loaded into the bomb bay of the Valiant and all the circuitry, including that of the telemetry senders, was thoroughly checked in an electronic environment accurately simulating that in the Malden area during the drop. The aircraft, screened off from the rest of the world, was then placed under a heavy guard until the following morning.

After the evening meal in the little 'A' mess, the TFC excused himself, leaving his visitors to the cheerful care and attention of Ginger Weir, and the others for a while. He drove himself to the airfield and went round checking all the key areas, principally to

309

let the hard working ground staffs know that he was taking a personal interest in their dedicated endeavours. All was quiet and the reinforced guard was alert in the AWRE assembly compound and in the screened-off area where the loaded Valiant was waiting. In the Shackleton dispersal, tanks were being topped up to maximum fuel load to give extra endurance to assist in any emergency which might arise, such as the drill for abandoning the Valiant in the case of an incurable bomb hang-up. The last two Canberra B6s were having the barrier paint applied. In some of the maintenance sections, technicians were working intently to rectify minor defects which had shown up during the final checks. A sense of quiet but urgent activity pervaded the whole area.

Two hours later, at 23.00 hours, D-day really began with the take-off of the first Shackleton on weather reconnaissance. This was followed by a Canberra PR7 at 03.30 and another at 04.30 to determine the last-minute high level winds to enable Ernest Hicks to make his fall-out forecast for the final decision meeting at 05.30.

Soon after midnight, the Operations Room in the Joint Operations Centre was packed with the crews of six Shackletons – nearly seventy pilots, navigators, wireless and radar operators, meteorological observers, air gunners – being briefed for the last time on their immediate task of sea search and low level photography of the atomic cloud, with the drill for emergency air/sea rescue thrown in for good measure. Every aspect of the operation was covered and then they poured out into the night, into their motor transport of various kinds and out to the airfield and the 206/240 Squadrons dispersals, floodlit now by an improvised arrangement of sodium lighting. The quiet calm of the earlier evening was swept away in the urgent bustle of pre-flight checks, loading of in-flight rations, navigation gear, parachutes, spare pyro-technics and, not least, seven or eight soldiers or sailors as passengers in each aircraft, to be spectators of the result of their labours during the past year. One by one engines were started up, spluttering a little at first and then

310

breaking into shattering roar before being throttled back to warming up revs. Twenty four Rolls-Royce 'Griffon' engines make quite a lot of noise, different from modern jets, but nevertheless very impressive.

At a quarter to three they began to taxi down the dispersal area to the holding point just off the centre of the runway. They could not use the taxi-track because it was blocked off by the loaded and screened Valiant. Then, one at a time, as cleared by the tower, they entered the runway, taxied to the western end, turned and took off. The first four departed to do their line abreast sweep through the danger area and to have this completed before the scheduled time of take-off of the two Valiants. The other two Shackletons were to make a more minute search of the danger area round Malden and then to fly each a semi-circular patrol twenty miles from ground zero to take low level photographs of the explosion.

Soon after the last Shack had gone, the first of the PR7 high-level wind finders was away and an hour later the second. The D day programme was under way.

It was also under way on Malden Island, where the rearguard of scientists and Army technical personnel were starting up the generators supplying power to the instrumentation sites and making a last check that all was in order. Most of the Malden residents had departed the previous evening, leaving only Captain Wadsworth, Ken Bomford and their small teams to switch on and leave at the latest moment which would allow *Narvik* to reach her assigned position in time.

These two groups, having completed their tasks, then assembled at 'C' site on the north-east corner of the island, the only place where there was a sufficient depth of soil to allow the excavation of an underground shelter for the last Land Rover, necessary for collecting the party together. It was also a completely flat and featureless piece of terrain, where there had been no concealment for the solitary Elsan chemical toilet which had had to serve for all the men working there. To give some

311

illusion of privacy for those private moments, the Elsan was positioned in a scooped-out hollow in the ground, leaving only the occupant's head poking up above the skyline. Poor Peter Jones of the AWRE team, having rounded up all the bodies and delivered them to the improvised helipad, marked out with hurricane lamps, then parked the Land Rover in the underground shelter and ran to join the others as the helicopter came in with the dawn's early light. In the half-dark he forgot and failed to notice Elsan Hollow, fell head over heels with a great clang and arrived at the helipad very fragrant and unpopular!

The first Wadsworth and Bomford saw of the two naval Whirlwinds was their brilliantly red exhaust pipes as they came in, one at a time, to touch down briefly, to embark first the scientists and then the soldiers, then lift off again to take the army team to *Warrior* and the AWRE party to *Narvik* at her mooring. Touching down on *Narvik's* deck in the poor light, with the ship's rigging looming in the semi-darkness only a few feet away, was an interesting experience for the passengers – and very nice flying by the naval pilot.

Now only the RAF air traffic controller and a couple of ground crew remained on Malden, waiting for the arrival of the TFC's Dakota.

At 05.00 Corporal Beall, splendid man, called the Task Force Commander and the Scientific Director with a cup of tea – kind thought – and fifteen minutes later they were on their way to the JOC.

Challens, Freeman, Hicks, Weir, Milligan, Western, Surtees, Neville-Towle all waiting for the final decision and Terry Helfer dispensing instant coffee. They checked quickly through all the parameters.

The TFC looked at Bill Cook.

'O.K.?'

'O.K.'

'We're on our way.'

As they turned to leave the Ops Room, the TFC glanced at the Air Controller whom he had seen briefing the Shackleton crews four hours earlier.

'Butch, have you had any sleep tonight?'

'No, sir. I thought I should be here.'

'Go and get three hours kip before the Valiant take-off. Jerry Roberts can manage perfectly well for that time.'

Cook, Helfer and the TFC quickly made their way out into the steamy black night – dawn was still over an hour away – and, with eyes not yet dark-adapted, were glad to be guided by Corporal Beall shining his torch on the white staff car. They climbed in and, as they drove off, switched on the VHF radio to keep in touch with JOC as they went speeding along the road to the airfield. Soon they heard Ginger Weir's voice calling Squadron Leader Hurst, sitting waiting in the cockpit of his Dakota.

'The TFC is on his way. Start engines.'

'Roger.'

Ten minutes later they pulled up alongside the Dakota, engines already running. The OC Flying, Group Captain Giles, very smartly turned out as always even at this ghastly hour of the morning, waiting to see them off safely. The three got out of the car, moved quickly to the aircraft steps and up into the bleak cabin, most of the very utilitarian seats already occupied by a miscellany of soldiers, sailors and administrative airmen coming along for the view. As they moved forward to the three seats immediately behind the flight deck, the doors clanged shut, chocks away, and Hurst taxied away to the western end of the runway. As they passed abeam of the Weapon Assembly area and glanced over the top of the security screens at the vague shadowy shape of the Valiant, gleaming faintly in the starlight, Cook and the TFC looked at each other, smiled and held up crossed fingers.

As the Dakota turned at the end of the runway and lined up, the voice from the control tower came over the cabin loud speaker:

313

'Delta Bravo. Cleared for immediate take-off. No other traffic.'

'Delta Bravo.'

Hurst opened the throttles, the aircraft rattled like an old dustbin for some forty seconds and then lifted off smoothly, wheels up, flaps up, turning gently to starboard on to the course for Malden Island. The TFC glanced at his wristwatch – 06.00.

A few minutes later, one of the 1325 Flight ground crew was hustling round with mugs of grateful black coffee. Half an hour later came the first glow of dawn in the east and then, quite quickly, the first of the sun's rays touched and illuminated the scattered cumulus clouds sailing majestically above the 'wine dark sea' beneath.

During their two and a half hour flight, the TFC and ADC from time to time ticked off on the check list the items of the long series of events as they were reported in from Squadron Leader Jerry Roberts on duty at the Controller's desk in the JOC. Reports from the sea-searching Shackletons – danger area all clear so far. Weather and upper winds – no change. Hicks' fall-out pattern – still OK. At 06.30, another Shackleton airborne to search the danger area round Christmas Island itself. All power generators to instrumentation sites on Malden started and running, all personnel evacuated except for the Air Traffic team. Squadron Leader Hammatt airborne in a PR7 at 07.30, to sit over Malden at 45,000 feet reporting wind and weather until the arrival of the Valiants. 07.45, the VIP Hastings with the Air Ministry team airborne and en route to its spectator position. Pre-flight checks by the ground crews of the two Valiants completed. Batteries in the bomb in the spacious bomb-bay of XD818 hooked up and tested by the AWRE weapons team. The stream of messages continued to come in to the TFC, in plain language but referring only to the numbered events in the check list.

Meanwhile, at Christmas Island, all personnel other than those required at the airfield to handle departing aircraft or on duty at the JOC, were assembled at various checking-in points, alongside the trucks which would move them to a safer place in the event of an accident at the Valiant take-off. Similarly, in the port area, all personnel including the Gilbertese families – other than those who had already been evacuated to Canton Island – were assembled adjacent to the two LCMs alongside the pontoon jetty. Loud-speakers kept everyone informed of the progress of events, either by relay of messages to and from aircraft or by occasional commentaries from the controllers in the Joint Operations Centre.

At 08.20 Hurst turned round in his left hand pilot's seat and beckoned the TFC to stand in the doorway of the flight deck. There was Malden Island, twenty miles ahead. Visibility good, sky clear except for a light scattering of small cumulus clouds. The voice of the Malden air traffic controller came through on the loud-speaker in the cabin, giving clearance for a time-saving straight-in approach and landing.

Hurst called *Warrior's* Air Direction Room – checking in, landing in five minutes, please inform JOC. This was acknowledged and in return reported that the Valiant crews were aboard their aircraft and ready to start engines.

08.26 – touch down on the Malden strip, landing short and turning off to port to the small reception area where the RAF ground crew and a Naval Whirlwind helicopter were waiting, the engine running and the rotor slowly turning. The door of the Dak opened, steps down; Cook, Helfer and TFC descended, walked to the chopper and climbed in. As they did so, the Dak's steps were hauled in, the doors closed and Hurst was taxiing back to the end of the runway and two minutes later was airborne and climbing away to his prescribed holding pattern twenty miles north.

Meanwhile, the RAF ground crew and controller dumped the small mobile fire extinguishers and the long lead to the VHF head-set into a pit, pulled a sheet of protective corrugated iron over it, jumped into the chopper. The naval pilot, watching from his right hand seat, turned and made an interrogative thumbs up sign to the TFC, got an affirmative and opened the throttle and they lifted off from the completely deserted Malden. No sign now of any recent human occupation, other than the airstrip, the scrapes of fresh dirt where all the equipment had been buried in the pits and the rows of instrument shelters at the south-east corner.

08.55 – the naval chopper touched down on the rope-netted helicopter platform on the foredeck of *Narvik*. As the wheels touched, the TFC was out of the cabin and running for the companionway down to the control room. Bill Cook and Helfer followed at a more discreet pace, while the chopper lifted off again and flew on to land on *Warrior*, where it was struck down to the hangar deck, out of harm's way.

In *Narvik's* control room, Ken Bomford, Wally Long his assistant, and Squadron Leader David Roberts the 49 Squadron liaison officer for the day, were waiting for them.

'Everything in order with you, Ken?' queried the TFC.

'Yes. We're ready.'

'David – all OK on the air side? All assembly for evacuation complete at Christmas? Danger area clear?'

'Yes, sir.'

'Flash signal to JOC – Valiants to take off.'

While all this had been going on in the Malden area, Ken Hubbard and his crew in Valiant XD818, with its awesome cargo, and Barney Millett with his crew in the 'Grand-stand' Valiant XD824 had just received confirmation from Air Commodore Weir at the JOC to start engines at 08.50. 818 to taxy the short distance from the AWRE weapon area to the runway and hold. 824 to follow slowly. At 08.58, the tower called 818.

'Clear to enter runway and line up.'

One minute later, the tower called again.

'818. Clear for take off. Good luck!'

'818. Thank you. Rolling – *Now*!'

With a great roar from the four Avon engines the Valiant, immaculate in its carefully washed and polished anti-radiation whiteness, accelerated down the runway. The nosewheel came

The rains came! But office work had to go on! *(Photo: AWRE)*

Would it have been better to use flying boats? Doing a pre-flight check on a Canberra. *(Photo: AWRE)*

The Forward Control ship HMS *Narvik* (left) and the aircraft carrier
HMS *Warrior* off Malden Island during the preliminary tests. *(Photo:
AWRE)*

Commander Tony Casswell, Commanding Officer of HMS *Narvik*.
(Photo: A D Casswell)

Charles Adams (unsuitably dressed!), the Deputy Scientific Director, arrives at Christmas Island. Things are hotting up! *(Photo: AWRE)*

The bomb-aiming marker on Malden Island. A fifty-yard sided concrete triangle painted with 'day-glo' paint. *(Photo: AWRE)*

Bill Cook (and pipe!), the Scientific Director, having evaded the world press, arrives safely at Christmas Island. *(Photo: AWRE)*

Bill Cook (right) and Charles Adams registering satisfaction. *(Photo: AWRE)*

off the ground – then rotation – airborne – wheels up – flaps coming up – 09.00 hours. All over Christmas Island and in HMS *Narvik* breath which had been held for forty seconds was released – 'Oouff!'

Two minutes later, the second Valiant, 824, turned on to the runway, was cleared for take off, rolled and Barney Millett climbed away to take station 2,000 feet below and one mile behind Hubbard.

The personnel who had been assembled and roll-called for a possible emergency evacuation were now released back to their duties, but most of them managed to keep within earshot of one of the many loud-speakers which continued to give news of the progress of the operation.

Next departure at 09.15 was the Canberra radio relay aircraft, bound for its orbit at forty thousand feet, midway between Christmas and Malden. This was soon followed by the first of the four B6 Canberras of the cloud sampling team, piloted by Flight Lieutenant Lindsey Cumming and carrying Air Commodore Denis Wilson, the radiation expert, as Controller of the sampling operation with the self-evident call sign 'Sniff Boss'.

The primary, secondary and reserve B6 samplers did not take off until an hour later and then with only just sufficient fuel to get to Malden, orbit and then penetrate the cloud and return to Christmas. This restriction on the amount of fuel carried would enable them to reach considerably higher altitudes, a matter of great importance to the AWRE analysts. The primary sampler – Sniff One – was flown by George Bates, the Squadron Commander. The secondary – Sniff Two – by Flight Lieutenant Barry Newton and the reserve by young Flying Officer Spatcher. These were the crews who would be exposed to most risk in this operation, although every precaution had been taken to safeguard them.

As each aircraft approached within 60 miles of Malden, it checked in with *Warrior's* Air Direction Room and then took up its designated holding position to the north west of the Valiant 'race track'. All this information was continuously displayed to

317

the Task Force Commander and the Scientific Director in the Control Room in HMS *Narvik*. In the far right hand corner of the room was an air plot screen – a vertical six foot square of heavy clear acetate sheet, marked out with a reference grid and with Malden Island shown in the centre. Behind the screen stood a young naval seaman radar plotter – white shirt, blue shorts and knee-length stockings, plimsoll shoes, headphones, a fluorescent red crayon in one hand and a duster in the other. Writing backwards – being behind the screen – he was plotting the positions and movements of aircraft and ships as the information was told to him over a radio link from *Warrior's* Air Direction Room. Permanently marked out on the screen in a contrasting colour was the 'race-track' pattern which the Valiant was to follow, one long side aligned along the east coast of Malden, the other long side parallel with the first but some five miles to the east. Seventy five miles north of Malden was the point, marked RV (for rendezvous), at which the Valiant would join the pattern and line up for the southbound run over the target marker. Five reporting points – A,B,C,D,E – were also marked in. At this time the plot showed only, on the extreme left, the parallel tracks of the sea search Shackletons sweeping the danger area and, just north of Malden, *Warrior* and *Narvik* moving slowly to their operational positions. Overhead the orbiting PR7, monitoring wind and cloud. Twenty five miles north of Malden, the other ships – *Alert*, *Messina* and *Cook*.

Whilst all this cross-checking of the air and sea activity was in progress, Bill Cook sat quietly surveying the scene, puffing away at his pipe, completely unperturbed and looking as though he was doing nothing more exciting than presiding over a discussion on the possibility of extending the staff dining room at Aldermaston. He had done his sums and had complete confidence in his calculations. He had carefully chosen a good team, from which he would quite ruthlessly have eliminated any weak element – one of his favourite sayings was: 'What hangs down gets cut off!' So he had delegated responsibility to

318

Challens and Bomford and now all he had to do was to sit and watch; but he missed nothing of what was going on in the control room.

In the far corner, Wally Long was seated at a controller's desk, laden with VHF and H/F radios, microphones and loud speakers. Standing behind him was Ken Bomford in charge of the Malden sector of the operation, microphone in hand on a wander lead. Above Long's head, on top of the radio packs, a large open face clock with a fluorescent stop/start second hand. 09.10 hours.

On the left was the telemetry receiver display, the scope face illuminated but showing only a thin horizontal black trace across the middle. Behind that, just inside the entrance to the room, were two bar stools for the TFC and the Scientific Director. For the next twenty minutes of waiting, inconsequential chit-chat and mugs of coffee.

On board *Warrior*, all except those required at action stations were assembled on the flight deck, most dressed in white overalls with hoods, being briefed once again by Commander Begg on what they were to do during and after the drop. Similarly on *Narvik*, those not required for duty and many Task Force spectators were assembled on the helicopter platform.

Soon after 09.30, the seaman plotter began to mark in the positions of the two Valiants as they approached from the north-north-west. As he crayoned in each new position, with his duster he rubbed out the one before last, so that there was continuously an 'x' showing present position and a little tail showing direction of movement. At 09.45 the radio-relay Canberra, in its elliptical orbit was shown on the western edge of the screen and a few minutes later came the plots of the Canberra sampler controller and the two Shackletons detailed for the low level photographic orbit. The PR7 overhead now moved away north to its holding position.

A few moments before 10.00 hrs came the calm, cheery voice of Wing Commander Hubbard calling *Narvik*, the whole Task

Force listening intently to the transmission either on VHF from the mike in his oxygen mask or the naval pattern throat mike on H/F.

'*Narvik* from 818. We are at point Romeo Victor (the rendezvous point 70 miles north of Malden), turning on to heading 202 degrees true and commencing navigation run. All flash screens in position except bomb-aimer's panel.'

Bomford acknowledged the message. A moment later, the 'Grand-stand' Valiant checked in, below and behind 818.

In HMS *Warrior*, the ship's air-guard radar was now tracking the two Valiants, telling their positions through the plotter in *Narvik*. *Warrior's* own position was being meticulously checked by the Navigation Officer, Lieutenant Commander Donald Watts, using all facilities available – the ship's own navigation system, the Decca Navigator equipment, radar range and bearing on Malden and a transit on two tethered balloons which were acting as leading marks. On the flight deck, the Avocado radar also was tracking the aircraft and telling it through to the Air Direction Room as an additional check.

In Valiant 818 the navigator, Flight Lieutenant Eric Hood was carefully checking his wind speed and direction at 45,000 feet, using both his Green Satin doppler (when it would 'lock-on') and Decca fixes to up-date the vector given earlier by the PR7. Five minutes later, the bomb-aimer, Flight Lieutenant Washbrook, who had the only external view from the otherwise completely shuttered aircraft, had the north-east corner of Malden Island under the graticule of his bomb-sight and began to con the aircraft visually along the well-practised line of the east coast. There was a small amount of broken cloud, but this gave him no trouble.

As the triangular target marker on the south-east corner of Malden came into Washbrook's field of view, Hubbard called *Narvik* again:

'*Narvik* from 818. Target in sight.'

Washbrook gave his pilot a small correction, 'One degree starboard 203,' and as the marker moved down the centre-line of

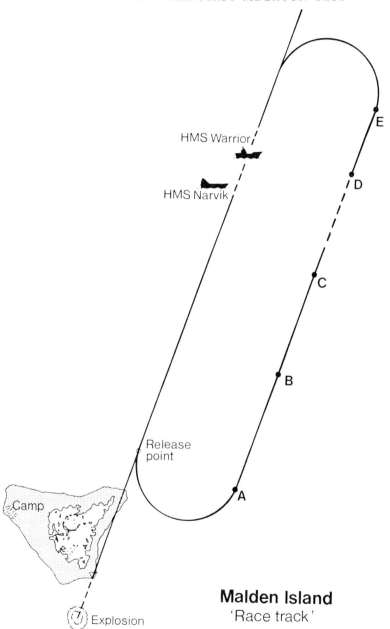

HMS Warrior

HMS Narvik

E

D

C

B

A

Release
point

Camp

Explosion

Malden Island
'Race track'

the bombsight and reached the cross-wires on the graticule, he continued:

'Steady – steady – NOW!'

Hubbard's voice: 'Turning to port,' and 818 followed by 824 curved round the semi-circular end of the 'race-track', straightened out for the northbound leg and Hubbard called again:

'818. Point Alpha.'

Calls again at points Bravo and Charlie, and then he added: 'We're ready for the Initial Run. How about you?'

Bomford had been checking all his required inputs and now referred to the TFC who had been ticking off his own list. Helfer cross-checking with him.

"OK to go ahead with the Initial Run, TFC?'

'Yes.'

'*Narvik* to 818. Next run is the Initial Run.'

'818. Roger. Initial Run.'

Hubbard called in again at points Delta and Echo, made the semi-circular turn to port and settled down again on the southbound leg. At Bomford's request, in accord with the prescribed drill, he first opened the bomb doors. Immediately there was a step in the horizontal scan on the telemetry display. Then the bomb aimer put on the master switch and a second step appeared on the scan. This satisfied Bomford, the switch was turned off and the bomb doors closed. The Valiants came over the target marker a second time and again turned to follow the race-track pattern and straighten out on the northerly heading.

Ken Bomford addressed himself to the Scientific Director.

'As far as we are concerned, Mr Cook, we're ready for the live drop.'

Bill Cook took an extra puff on his inevitable pipe. Then, turning to the TFC:

'OK, Wilf.'

The TFC looked again at the airplot. Everything was in its right place. He asked Long to speak to *Warrior* and confirm that they were in contact with all aircraft and ships in the area and that they would be ready for the live drop. The reply came – 'Affirmative'.

As Hubbard called in at point Charlie, the TFC said:

'Ken, tell him to execute the live drop on the next run.'

Bomford nodded his head.

'*Narvik* to 818. The next run will be the live drop. Good luck!'

'818 to *Narvik*, Roger – and the same to you!' replied Hubbard meaningfully.

The TFC turned to *Narvik's* signals officer who was standing by Helfer, just behind him.

'Make a signal, please – Task Force Commander to *Warrior*, repeat to JOC. Inform all aircraft under your control that the next Valiant run will be the live drop, at approximately 10.45. Acknowledge. Also inform Commander Casswell.'

'Aye, aye, sir.'

The spectators on the flight deck of *Warrior* and on the foredeck of *Narvik* who had been following the contrails of the two Valiants, were now grouped together in an orderly manner, sitting on the deck in rows, backs towards Malden, shirt sleeves rolled down, hoods of white cotton over their heads, a variety of gloves covering their hands, arms hugging their knees. Up above *Warrior's* flight deck, on the control deck adjacent to the Air Direction Room, Squadron Leader Duck the RAF liaison officer and Doctor Frank Morgan, the AWRE representative, clad in white overalls, were keeping their own check on the progress of events. Similar precautions were exercised on the three spectator ships.

In the JOC at Christmas, Ginger Weir – stop watch in hand – was ticking off the check points on a copy of the Valiant 'race-track' laid out on a table, watched by Freddie Milligan, Guy Western, John Challens and the operations room and AWRE staff. In the main camp and at the port, men strained their ears to catch every word of the transmission from 818.

It seemed to take forever for Hubbard, followed by Millett in 824, to check in at points Delta and Echo and to make the gentle semi-circular turn on to the south-bound bombing run.

Then:

'*Narvik* from 818. Straight and level on the bombing run for a live drop.'

Bomford acknowledged briefly. No more chat.

The radar plotter behind the transparent screen was working fast, continuously up-dating the positions of the Canberras, Shackletons, Hastings and the Dakota and moving the plots of the Valiants inexorably towards the point at which the bomb would be released. The TFC was watching intently both the air plot and the telemetry scope, check-list in his left hand and with his right he beckoned Squadron Leader Roberts to stand by his side. If anything were to go wrong now, action would have to be fast.

The the first step appeared in the trace on the telemetry scope – the bomb-doors had opened. In 818, Flight Lieutenant Hood again checked the wind speed and direction and fed this into the bombing computer. The Air Electronics Officer, Flight Lieutenant Laraway, set the master switch to 'on' and the second step appeared on the telemetry display in *Narvik*.

In the Air Direction Room in HMS *Warrior*, the track of the two Valiants was again being monitored meticulously. It was 'spot on' the required line and *Warrior* would not intervene unless an error developed; but Commodore Roger Hicks maintained a cool and vigilant supervision of his well-drilled team and the many aircraft for which he was at this time responsible.

The bomb-aimer in 818, Flight Lieutenant Alan Washbrook, set his face-mask microphone to 'transmit' and his voice came over the air to the listeners below and in the JOC at Christmas.

'Malden in sight, skipper. Steady on 202 degrees.'

'202,' from Hubbard.

'Arming switch on – now. Steady on 202,' from Washbrook. The third step appeared on the telemetry's display in *Narvik*. Bomford stood tensely, microphone in hand. The TFC looked again at the plotting screen, the red crosses close to the release point.

'OK, Bill?' to Cook, quietly.

'Yes.'

Washbrook again.

'Target in sight. One degree starboard on to 203.'

'203,' from Hubbard.

'Steady – steady – steady – NOW!' and Washbrook pressed the bomb release button.

Hearing this, Millett in Valiant 824 immediately went into his maximum rate turn to port and his escape manoeuvre, his bomb-aimer fixing in position the shutter over his bombing window as they went.

Hubbard in 818 maintained his steady course of 203 degrees, constant height and airspeed, for five seconds, six, seven, eight, nine, ten – then – just before eleven seconds – the computer operated the bomb-release, one and a half miles beyond the point at which Washbrook had pressed the bomb switch. The aircraft, suddenly relieved of the weight of the bomb, jerked upwards a little. In *Narvik*, the fourth step appeared instantly on the telemetry display trace.

'Bomb gone,' announced Hubbard in a matter-of-fact tone, applying full aileron, heaving back on the control column to commence the maximum rate turn of the escape manoeuvre and simultaneously closing the bomb-bay doors. In *Narvik*, Long started the second hand of the large stop-clock above his head. The 'Blue Danube' bomb case and its terrifying contents, free from the aircraft, plunged downwards on its 52 second flight to annihilation.

In Valiant 818, Washbrook quickly fixed the light-tight screen over his bombing window and the five man crew were now in a completely sealed metal can. The sensitive g-meter above the pilot's instrument panel showed a steady 1.7g and Hubbard was broadcasting a continuous commentary as he executed the turn – height, speed, g-meter reading, anything relevant to keep telling the world that all was well so far. If anything disastrous were to happen now, the TFC wanted to know instantly what, when and how.

As soon as the words 'Bomb gone' came over the loud-speakers in *Warrior* and *Narvik*, the order was given to all spectators:

'Shut your eyes now and cover them with your hands.'

Similar orders were given to all aircraft under *Warrior's* control and the pilots kept their faces turned away from Malden.

The team in *Narvik's* control room watched, listened and waited anxiously. Hubbard's calm commentary continued. The radar plotter marked in the curving paths of the two Valiants, 824 a mile and a half ahead of 818 and two thousand feet lower. Bomford, mike in hand, began the count-down.

'This is *Narvik*. Forty seconds to go.'

'Thirty seconds.'

Long pressed the telemetry sender switch to start the high speed cameras on Malden.

'Twenty seconds.'

Hubbard's voice again.

'818-rolling out of the turn on to heading zero seven zero – height forty five thousand, airspeed Mach point seven six.'

Laraway switched on the rearward facing cameras in the Valiant tail cone.

'Ten seconds,' from Bomford.

'Five seconds, four, three, two, one.'

In every listening radio set in the central Pacific came a loud click, caused by the electro-magnetic radiation from the nuclear reaction, and the steps on the trace in *Narvik's* telemetry receiver vanished, leaving only the straight base line. In the JOC on Christmas Island John Challens heard the click and exclaimed jubilantly – 'It worked!'

On the backs of all spectators on *Warrior*, *Narvik* and the other ships, came a flash of heat, as though the fire door of a great furnace had momentarily been opened behind them; and despite tightly shut eyes and hands over them, there was a sensation of brilliant light.

In *Narvik's* control room, Bomford began the count-up.

326

'Ten seconds – twelve – fourteen – fifteen seconds. You may look now.'

From *Warrior* to spectators and aircraft, the message was repeated.

'You may turn round and look now.'

Many had cameras at the ready, but for the moment they were all too staggered by the awesome sight which met their eyes – this gigantic boiling mass, filling the sky and climbing rapidly, blue and orange and dirty white, with a pure white feathery cap on the very top – the so-called Wilson effect. As they watched, the top of the cloud began to spread out sideways to form the mushroom shape and the cameras began to click.

More serious photography was also in urgent progress. The PR7 piloted by Squadron Leader Hammatt was soon circling the atomic cloud at high levels, using the sighting device which he had developed, to get excellent pictures. At the same time, the two Shackletons on low level photography were also busy recording the scene from every side. Never was anything photographed so thoroughly so quickly and from these photographs would be estimated the size of the atomic cloud and its rate of growth, leading in turn to a fair estimation of the yield of the weapon. But the best clue to the performance of the nuclear fusion device would be the analysis of the gases and particles of matter to be collected from the interior of the cloud by the Canberra sampling aircraft. These had now left Christmas, but in order to gain maximum altitude, they would not arrive until H+40 minutes.

Meanwhile, at H+30 minutes, the first of the re-entry helicopters piloted by Lieutenant Commander G W Bricker, lifted off from *Warrior* with Captain Wadsworth, RE, on board, touched down briefly on *Narvik* to pick up Doctor Ed Fuller and three of his Health Physics team and flew on towards Malden, initially at a height of one thousand feet. As they went, the scientists monitored the local radiation level but found no increase and altitude was gradually reduced. At fifteen miles, they could see a large fire burning in the main camp area and several smaller fires near the target marker, all producing a low cloud stretching two or three miles out to seaward and below which the atmosphere seemed to be tinted a light bronze colour. But no radiation.

Bricker reduced height to fifty feet as they came over the island and rubbish was burning here and there, but there seemed to be no major damage. The airstrip and the road to 'C' site seemed unaffected. There being no reading on the telemetered fall-out meters, the helicopter put down at 'C' site just one hour after the explosion. Dr Ed Fuller and his team accoutred in their fully protective clothing, left the aircraft and cautiously examined the ground and the warning instrumentation. They judged the island quite safe for the re-entry of the technical work force, so informed *Narvik* by radio and their disembarkation by helicopter began immediately.

The print-outs and other records from the instrumentation sites were swiftly collected, taken to the AWRE staff in *Narvik*, sorted, copied and helicoptered on to *Warrior*. There they were loaded into a waiting naval Avenger aircraft and flown off to Christmas Island, the aircraft being escorted by one of the Shackletons which had now finished its photographic task.

To facilitate and expedite the disembarkation by helicopter, *Warrior* and *Narvik* steamed slowly back to Malden, arriving at 15.00 hrs, four and a half hours after the explosion. *Narvik* secured to her mooring buoy, while *Warrior* proceeded to the east of the island to refuel and replenish *Pukaki*, which then continued westward monitoring upper winds and fall-out. *Warrior* lay off the island overnight and then sailed for Christmas next day.

As the TFC and Scientific Director stood on the deck of *Narvik*, checking off events after the successful drop, a signal arrived from *Alert* containing a very generously worded message of congratulation from one of the official United States observers, Major General Richard Coiner, Deputy Assistant Chief of Staff for Operations of the USAF. The TFC was very pleased, since he and Dick Coiner had been fellow students on

328

the RAF Staff College Course many years previously and he had not known that Dick was one of the two Americans.

The ships *Alert*, *Messina*, and *Cook* sailed for Christmas that afternoon, all continuing to help with the fish sampling programme. But while there was many a tasty dish of tuna or other fish served on board that night, there was no trace of radiation and contamination. Nor was there at any time.

HMS *Cook*, a survey ship when not pressed into Grapple service, took the opportunity to run an ocean depth survey on the straight track from Malden to Christmas; and in so doing, discovered an enormous sea-bed mountain which had previously been unknown. You never know what will turn up!

Meanwhile, some forty minutes after the nuclear explosion, the three Canberra B6 samplers arrived and came under the control of Denis Wilson. They immediately set about their task of measuring the dimensions of the cloud and the levels of radiation out to about four miles. Then at H+35 minutes, Wilson judged that the cloud would have cooled down sufficiently from the initial temperature of millions of degrees to a level which would permit a safe entry. Accordingly George Bates penetrated the upper part of the cloud as high as he could coax his aircraft – fifty-four thousand feet – with oxygen turned up to maximum flow, sampling equipment open and the navigator constantly monitoring the instant level of radiation and the cumulative dosage received as they passed through. The permitted safe limits were not nearly reached.

On emerging from the cloud, Bates reported to the Sampling Controller, who then ordered the secondary Canberra to go in at its allotted height, always monitoring carefully the rate of radiation and the cumulative dosage received. As soon as this was completed and no need to use the reserve, all returned to Christmas Island, landed and taxied straight to the decontamination centre, well clear of the normal taxi-track, to the southeast of the airfield. Handling crews, dressed in fully protective clothing, were waiting for them and immediately extracted the filters from the sampling equipments in the aircraft, labelled them and packed them into heavy lead cannisters.

The aircrews also were extracted, great care being taken that they did not touch the outside of their aircraft. They then stripped off all clothing, were thoroughly showered, dressed in fresh clothes and then carefully checked to see that they were now clean of any contamination. Likewise the aircraft were washed down with high pressure water hoses, which stripped off the barrier paint and also washed right through the engine intakes and the turbines. All the effluent was carefully disposed of, to ensure that no accidental contamination of personnel could occur at a later date.

A Canberra PR7 of 58 Squadron, WT503 crewed by Flight Lieutenants R E Taylor and P Bruce-Smith, was already positioned alongside the decontamination centre, awaiting the arrival of the B6s from the operation. The 'Forth Bridge' girder already fitted in the bomb-bay was quickly loaded with the cannisters containing the samples and a few minutes later Taylor started up, taxied out and took off on the first leg to Hickam and to the UK. He was immediately followed by a 100 Squadron aircraft, WT504 crewed by Langdon and Batchelor, as a stand-by in case of unserviceability at Hickam. All was well and after refuelling, 503 continued on the $5\frac{1}{2}$ hour leg to Travis.

Flying Officer Marman and Flying Officer Evans at Travis had been alerted and were poised ready to take over WT 503 for the next two sectors. Again as a reserve in case of unservice-ability, another 58 Squadron Canberra, WH790, crewed by Pilot Officer John Loomes and Flying Officer Montgomery, was ready and would follow 503. To save time, the luggage of both crews was already loaded into Loomes's aircraft.

WT503 duly arrived, was rapidly refuelled and Marman departed without delay, closely followed by Loomes. They arrived within a few minutes of each other at Namao, at about 02.30. But here there was a snag. There was only one refuelling bowser available. As was logical, Marman refuelled first, cautiously filled his wing-tip tanks as well as the main, and proceeded without delay on his way to Goose Bay, where the weather forecast was reasonable. Loomes, presumably to save time, elected not to refill his wing-tip tanks, but even so took off over half an hour after Marman.

The four and a half hour flight to Goose Bay was uneventful but the weather forecast received en route turned out to be old and inaccurate. After some difficulty in making radio contact with Goose Bay, Marman did the standard let-down through thick cloud on the NDB (beacon) and was then acquired by the GCA* for a final approach. The GCA then lost him and instructed him to home back on the NDB. He made another approach, was again acquired and then lost by the GCA and was sent back to the NDB. This happened three times and by now he was experiencing heavy icing and realised that he now had insufficient fuel to reach his alternate at Seven Islands. On the fourth attempt, in heavy snow, he pressed on below the normal limit, eventually sighted the runway and landed safely.

The next slip crew were waiting. 503 was quickly refuelled and sped on its way to the UK, to deliver the precious samples within the required time.

By this time, John Loomes and Montgomery in WH790 had arrived overhead Goose Bay and the weather had deteriorated to blizzard conditions. Radio conditions were bad and, like Marman before him, he made three approaches, only to be turned back to the beacon each time. Overshooting from his fourth attempt, about nine miles beyond the runway, WH790 dived into the muskeg. Both crew must have been killed instantaneously.

Although Loomes and Montgomery were not properly part of Task Force Grapple, their tragic loss – when it became known – was keenly felt at Christmas Island and cast a temporary gloom over the satisfaction at the success of the first test.

Meanwhile, reverting to other and contemporary events following after the bang, as soon as the all clear message was received from Doctor Fuller's re-entry team on the ground at

*The radar talk-down system to bring an aircraft down on to the runway.

Malden, the work force of scientists and army personnel were helicoptered back in and began to resurrect the domestic camp and begin preparations for the next round. Squadron Leader Hurst's Dakota which had been orbiting the spectator position to the north for the past three hours, landed back on the Malden strip to pick up the TFC, Cook, Helfer and Roberts and take them back to Christmas Island.

In the Joint Operations Centre, a few seconds after Challen's relief at hearing the click on the radio, word had been received that the explosion had taken place successfully. A message was sent immediately by the novel radio-teleprinter hook-up to the Ministry of Supply Information Office in London, in the hope that it would just catch the evening BBC nine o'clock news. Unfortunately there was no one in Ivor Jehu's office to deal with it; so the exciting news did not get to the Great British Public until the press reported it in the newspaper editions of May 16th, having been provided in advance with all the biographical details, photographs of personnel and background information to make a fair spread.

In contrast to this, the world press was thoroughly 'scooped' by the Task Force 'in house' *Mid-Pacific News*, run by a handful of enthusiastic amateurs with a mimeograph machine. They, too, had their background material already prepared but they also had an 'eye-witness' reporter present in HMS *Warrior*. Immediately after the shot, he cadged a lift in Lieutenant Commander Bricker's helicopter over to *Narvik* and at H+45 minutes he presented his script of the 'eye-witness report of the test' to the TFC for approval. By some neat underhand work in various signals offices the report was in the hands of the editor back on Christmas Island half an hour later and at 14.15 the first of 2,500 special souvenir editions of the *Mid-Pacific News* with full coverage of Britain's First Thermo-Nuclear Test was being distributed throughout Christmas Island. It was the only paper to carry the story under a May 15th dateline – and were they proud of it!

The Prime Minister, of course, had been informed without

delay and immediately wrote congratulatory letters to Sir Willam Penney and to the staff of AWRE. Aubrey Jones, the Minister of Supply, sent a similar kind message by telex to the Task Force.

So that was that, and throughout the Task Force that evening there was mild celebration mixed with some anxiety and concern about the awful business of atomic weapons, acknowledgement of their necessity and pride in a great British achievement.

Warrior set sail for Christmas next afternoon to give the crew some rest and a break ashore before the next round a fortnight later; and on Friday, May 17th, HMS *Alert* arrived back at the Christmas Island anchorage to return the VIP official observers to civilisation. The TFC sent Corporal Beall with the rapidly decaying white Super Snipe staff car to pick up the two Americans - Doctor Herbert Yorke, head of the Livermore Laboratories, and General Coiner - and the two Canadians. Doctor Yorke sat in the front passenger seat and, having been quite impressed with the British performance in the testing of the bomb, watched incredulously as Beall put the gear lever into first and then engaged the clutch by hauling on a yard of half inch rope tied round the clutch pedal. It worked fine. After a moment, Yorke found his voice and ventured a remark.

'Say, is this a *British* car?'

'Yes, sir,' replied Beall, cheerily and proudly.

'Oh!'

All the VIPs were taken to the 'A' mess and entertained to drinks and as good a lunch as could be provided – not quite what most of them were used to. But it was all very cheerful, loaded with bonhomie and there were sincere expressions of thanks for all the help which the Task Force had received from those countries. Dick Coiner chatted freely with Ginger Weir, whom he had known for many years. The TFC overheard him say:

'Congratulations on your wonderful organisation, Ginger, and how wise you were to begin with a small yield and work up.'

So! The yield of Short Granite probably wasn't up to Bill

Penney's hopes. Nevertheless, it was an extremely good start.

After lunch, the visitors were shown round the airfield and evinced particular interest in the immaculate and impressive gleaming white Valiant aircraft. The Americans and Canadians then left for Honolulu and home. The Antipodeans stayed on for another day and caught a southbound Hastings to Fiji and Amberley.

That night 49 squadron decided to celebrate the success of round one with a beach party, fishing in pockets of the reef for crayfish by the light of Tilley pressurised paraffin lamps and then roasting them over a beach fire. The Air Ministry visitors and some of the 'A' mess residents were invited to join in the fun, which at one point came near to being not funny at all. 'Giloh' Giles, standing knee deep in the dark, was caught out by a freak wave and was being swept out rapidly over the reef. He reached out to grab anything to check his movement and found himself clutching a strongly protesting human leg – on the other end of which was Air Vice Marshal Ronnie Lees! Air Marshals do come in useful, sometimes!

Four days later a photograph of the atomic cloud – not a very good one but nevertheless a photograph – appeared in the *Daily Express* and a major row broke out between Brigadier Jehu's Information Department in the Ministry of Supply and the press in general. What about the undertaking given by the Task Force Commander that there would be no release of pictures until the press representatives could witness the second test? Querulous signals flashed back and forth between Castleford House, Task Force Rear Link and Christmas Island, demanding explanations, replying that it couldn't be true, reviewing the security procedures and orders to the troops. Mystification.

Only much later did the truth come out. A very smart seaman cook, an enthusiastic photographer, had been in the crowd on the flight deck of HMS *Warrior* during the first live drop, had taken a snapshot of the cloud – which was permitted since it was judged that such could not be available in the UK before the second test – had rushed below and developed and printed the shot, popped the print into a letter to his father awaiting posting. The letter went into the homeward mail bag. An eager beaver rating in charge of the post room took the opportunity of the Avenger with the Malden records going to Christmas Island to send on that bag of mail, which fortuitously went into the Hastings shuttle leaving for Hickam that very night. At Hickam the mail had as usual been handled expeditiously by the Field Postal Unit, went swiftly on its way to the UK and was delivered three days later. The father, being every bit as smart as his son, sold the snapshot for £100 to a sceptical *Daily Express* who printed it for fun in disbelief of the cook's father's story. At the time it all took a lot of living down and the Task Force HQ had a very red face. Eventually, not much harm was done and it was all forgotten.

The mail bag with the clandestine snapshot was not the only important passenger leaving in the Hastings that evening. Air Commodore Wilson, scarcely back from controlling the sampling at Malden, also went back to the UK carrying the records from the instrumentation sites to marry up, two days later, with the samples already delivered by the Canberra PR7 with the 'Forth Bridge'. Within a few days he was on his way back to Christmas as one of the two escorts to the radio-active core of the next device to be tested.

42

Drama in the Assembly shed

After a forty eight hour stand-down, all necessary arrangements were rapidly pushed ahead for the testing of the second thermo-nuclear device code-named 'Orange Herald', the target date for which was now brought forward by ten days and at which press representatives would be present. HMS *Alert* would again be used as accommodation and observation platform for the visitors, who had been briefed that it would not be possible to accommodate them on Christmas Island.

The operational pattern of the first test had been entirely satisfactory and would be followed again. But on this occasion, in order to spread the experience of such operations, Air Commodore Weir would go forward to the control ship, HMS *Narvik*, to control the drop while the TFC stayed in the JOC to 'look after the shop'.

Orange Herald was different in concept from Short Granite – another possible way of achieving the required result; and as early as February 1957 it had been realised that the Orange Herald components with very different packing and transportation requirements, would not go into the bomb-bay of a Valiant. The Weapon Development Policy Committee had therefore agreed that they should go out to Christmas Island in three loads, each in a separate Hastings aircraft.

Some three months previously, in February, all the planning factors had indicated that there had to be a five week gap between the firing of the first and second live tests. Under pressure and encouragement from Bill Cook the AWRE teams at Aldermaston had made the most strenuous efforts to reduce this time and to their credit the main components of the device were unloaded from a Hastings aircraft at Christmas Island at 21.30 hours on Monday, May 13th. It was transported with great care to the Assembly Building the same evening and the process of dismantling, checking and partial re-assembly continued until Saturday, May 25th.

The third Hastings with the heavily protected radio-active core and Air Commodore Wilson again acting as Escort, arrived on Sunday morning May 26th. It was monitored and checked for correct dimensions by Mr Clark and Mr Barker and assembly of the whole Orange Herald device was to be completed the next day.

Bill Cook suggested to the TFC that he might like to watch the final assembly. He accepted with alacrity, not having witnessed such an operation before, since he had himself observed the same 'need-to-know' restrictions as were current throughout the Task Force.

So middle morning the two of them went along to the tall Assembly Building and were provided with a couple of chairs, while they watched the very capable RAF Warrant Officer Humphries, with his RAF and AWRE assistants, carefully placing the hollow hemispherical explosive sections round the radio-active core. Then two copper hemispheres were placed round the explosive sphere to contain it exactly, one below, then the other on top. Round the diameters of the hemispheres were two small flanges, male and female, each with a fine screw thread. The Warrant Officer carefully fitted the flange of the upper hemisphere over that of the lower one and then gently rotated it clockwise to engage the screw thread. So far, so good. He continued to rotate the upper hemisphere delicately – one complete turn – one and a half – and then it stuck! It needed another six and a half turns.

So he tried to reverse the movement to undo the flange threads and start all over again. Nothing to get excited about.

337

But he could not move the top hemisphere. It was firmly stuck. Forwards again – no movement. Backwards again – no movement. The smiles raised originally by this small contretemps vanished. The situation was no longer amusing. Several times more the WO tried, gradually increasing the force applied to what was supposed to be a very delicate operation.

The next move was for one of the assistants to hold the lower hemisphere firmly while the WO with two hands applied more force to unscrew the upper. No movement. None.

Time was passing and the two spectators, with other pressing commitments, felt they couldn't stay much longer; but neither could they go, leaving John Challens and the Warrant Officer with this increasingly worrying problem unsolved.

An hour passed by. Bill Cook refilled his pipe and puffed away, outwardly unperturbed. The TFC felt great sympathy for the Warrant Officer who was maintaining a superbly calm exterior, but was beginning to sweat, despite the air conditioning of the building.

Another hour gone. The WO stood back, wiped his hands on the seat of his shorts and turned to Challens and Cook.

'In my experience of this sort of engineering problem, sir, there's only one thing left to do – clout it!'

Cook and Challens looked at each other in dismay. The TFC, although only a visitor with no right to a voice, added:

'I think he's right.'

'OK,' said Cook, less calmly than usual. 'Clout it!'

WO Humphries went over to his tool box, rummaged around and fished out a small seven-pound copper-headed sledge hammer. He positioned an assistant with hands supporting the upper and lower hemispheres to absorb the shock, took a deep breath and gave the flange round the middle of the sphere a moderate thump with his hammer. Sharp intakes of breath all round. He put down the hammer, put both hands round the upper hemisphere while the assistant did the same below and tried to rotate it. It moved as smooth as silk. Six and a half turns more – the assembly of the heart of Orange Herald was complete.

'Thank you very much,' said Cook to the WO. 'Well done.' Turning to his companion and looking at his watch he added:

'I don't know about you Wilf, but I have a date in the Mess – in the bar! Shall we go?'

Later in the afternoon came the word that the assembly of the bomb with its core, electronics, power supply, telemetry, and all was now complete. It was then transferred to the Weapon Functioning Group for final testing before being ultimately loaded into Squadron Leader Robert's Valiant XD822.

Meanwhile, immediately after the short break to recover from the successful first live drop, the RAF Technical Wing hustled to get all aircraft back to a state of full operational readiness. They weren't helped in any way by a resumption of the severe flooding of the Technical area consequent on further heavy rains. Nevertheless, on May 19th the Shackleton and Canberra PR7 meteorological flights were resumed at full intensity and all preparations for the second live round were in full swing. *Warrior* and *Narvik* sailed again to take up their operational stations off Malden. All the recording out-stations were resupplied, the New Zealand flying boat squadron made their regular visit and the USAF C54 made its transit through Christmas to support their monitoring team on Penrhyn. The TFC was very pleased to note the excellent co-operation and mutual support between the USAF and RAF detachments at Penrhyn.

At the same time as all these preparations for the second test were going on, with only some five or six weeks to go before the end of the test series, equally intensive efforts were being made to plan and organise the withdrawal and return to the UK of the whole Task Force at the end of June. Extra clerical and other staff had to be brought in to cope with all the packing and required documentation.

Meanwhile the battle against the weather and increasing

deterioration of aircraft continued relentlessly. The programme of inert and high-explosive test weapon drops necessary before the second live drop was delayed by these problems; but on May 23rd time was made up by dropping two test weapons in the one day on the Malden range, requiring great efforts by the AWRE teams and the Navy and RAF operations units. Two days later, in a mini-dress rehearsal, the last test high-explosive weapon was dropped, supported by Shackleton danger area search and Canberra sampling practice. Everything was ready for the full dress rehearsal.

The administrators backing all this front end activity had their problems too. At Malden the fly menace had become very much worse and a 22 Squadron helicopter had to be fitted with insecticide spraying gear and lent to the Navy. A Hastings loaded with perishable food went unserviceable at Hickam and a Shackleton had to be sent to rescue the cargo. The crew of another Hastings were all seriously ill on arrival at Hickam and it was feared that there was another outbreak of food poisoning. Happily this turned out to be only Asiatic Flu caught on the Australia run. And so on.

Despite all these and other little troubles, the full dress rehearsal on May 28th went like clockwork, with David Roberts and his crew in Valiant 822 doing the drop and Arthur Steele in 823 flying the Grandstand role. The operation had been made a little easier by it having been considered unnecessary to exercise the precautionary evacuation drill at Christmas.

So, on May 29th the decision was made to go for the second live drop on May 31st and this was confirmed at the morning decision meeting the following day.

43

The Press and 'Orange Herald'

As agreed long ago, representatives of the press and BBC were invited to witness this second live test and were carefully scheduled to arrive after the dress rehearsal and so just in time for the actual drop. Special arrangements were made, however, for two official representatives from Fiji, whose Government and Armed Forces had been particularly helpful in the early days of establishing the base on Christmas Island. At that time they had provided a working party of sixty army personnel who had been a great help. Later, a party of 39 Fijian Royal Naval Volunteer Reserve ratings had embarked in the RNZN ships *Pukaki* and *Roititi* when they sailed from Suva on March 19th en route to Christmas Island. This detachment was now embarked in HMS *Warrior*.

On May 26th, the two Fijian observers, Lieutenant Colonel Ratu Penaia Ganilau and Commander S P Brown arrived in a RNZAF aircraft and stayed overnight in 'B' Mess. Colonel Penaia was a magnificent figure of a man, six feet five or more in height and built like the Rock of Gibraltar, smartly dressed in a British Army tunic with the Fijian version of the kilt. He had an excellent Korean war record and looked the part. He and Bill Cook rapidly found a mutual interest in whisky and the drinking thereof. This soon developed into a contest to see who could drink the most without weaving. In the end it was declared a draw!

Next day, May 27th, Colonel Penaia and Commander Brown

flew on to Malden, where they were lifted by helicopter to *Warrior* and were greeted by a Fijian Ceremony of Welcome, laid on by the FRNVR ratings. Two days later, the whole Fijian team performed a traditional Veiqaravi Vakavanua ceremony of appreciation and thanks to Commodore Hicks and the ship's company of HMS *Warrior*. Speeches were made, gifts were exchanged and group photographs were taken on the flight deck, to feature in family albums for years to come.

While the Fijians were enlivening the hum-drum ship-board life on *Warrior*, the representatives of the press and the BBC invited by the Government to be present at the second test were arriving individually at Honolulu. They were collected together by John Claridge, the CO of the 160 Wing Staging Post, who explained to them that it was not practicable for them to be accommodated overnight at Christmas. It was quite a distinguished party and included that eminent defence correspondent Chapman Pincher, who had helped in the plan to fend off possible intruders, and William Connor ('Cassandra') of the *Daily Mirror* famous for his astringent comments on men and affairs, as well as other well known journalists.

Early next day, May 30th, D-1 for Orange Herald, they were herded into the Hastings and arrived at Christmas mid afternoon. They were taken to the Joint Operations Centre for a briefing on the Task Force set-up and the programme for the drop – plus a cup of coffee – and were then emplaned in a Christmas Airways Dakota, flown to Malden, loaded into two DUKWs and taken out to HMS *Alert*, the spectator ship, where PRO Ivor Jehu awaited them. Edward Hamilton-Meikle was now well versed in this drill and lost no time in providing them with fishing gear. After refreshment in the ward room those who had the inclination were put 'to work', as had been the VIPs a fortnight previously, catching fish for sampling.

Brigadier Jehu had packs of background information for the press and radio correspondents and the Task Force made every effort to give them all the information they needed – other than details of the bomb itself. Arrangements had been made for the press photographs and copy to be flown to Christmas Island in the same Naval Avenger that would carry the records collected from the Malden instrumentation sites; and a Canberra would take these on to Honolulu where the Staging Post would express them on to London for the earliest possible publication.

While all this Public Relations activity had been going on, the Task Force had been fully occupied with the D-1 programme – and other problems. On Christmas Island, May 30th had dawned hot and drier than usual. There had been, remarkably, no rain for several days. The morning briefing meeting had confirmed the go-ahead for the second live drop the next day, although there were some operational difficulties with shortage of serviceable aircraft. There was, for instance, no available reserve Shackleton.

Mid morning, Freddie Milligan came into the TFC's office, looking a little pale under his sun-tan.

'We have a bush-fire on the edge of the airfield, sir, and all too close to the AWRE Assembly Building. John Woollett is turning out all his chaps to deal with it and Ginger has put the RAF fire tenders under his control.'

'That's not very funny, Freddie, is it? A nice thought! A fully assembled squib inside and a fire outside! You stay in charge here while I go and see what's going on. You can contact me on the radio, if necessary.

This was no time to observe the local speed limits aimed at conserving the roads and ten minutes later there was the scene. All the scubby vegetation to the south-west of the airfield was ablaze – flames and thick smoke billowing upwards – some of it only a couple of hundred yards from the Assembly Building, John Woollett organising teams – mainly army but with some RAF if one could spot the small difference. Lines of men beating out the flames with shovels, sacking, blankets, bits of tent canvas supported by a couple of hose pipes.

Woollett, grimy and less immaculate than usual, came up for a moment.

'We're short of water, sir. The 'banana hole' which we banked on for this sort of thing has run dry – we've been drawing on it too heavily for domestic purposes. I don't want to use the RAF foam unless the situation gets desperate. I think we can contain the fire by beating it out like this.'

'OK, John. I leave it all to you.'

Air Commodore Weir had joined the discussion and as it broke up he asked:

'I've got a problem of aircrew safety and I'd be happier if you made the decision. Can you spare the time to come and talk with George Bates and Wing Commander Geoffrey Dhenin from the Institute of Aviation Medicine?'

'Sure thing, Ginger. Let's go.'

Geoffrey Dhenin, an RAF medical officer and specialist in aviation medicine, was also a keen and very competent pilot, currently qualified on Canberras. He had recently arrived at Christmas Island to take part in the cloud sampling operation and had brought with him some experimental pressurised flying helmets – fore-runners of the 'bone dome' – in the hope of trying them out.

The Institute of Aviation Medicine at Farnborough had been concerned about the risks to the crew of a possible explosive decompression at the heights at which the 76 Squadron Canberras were doing the cloud sampling and Dhenin was insisting, for safety reasons, that the crews should wear these new helmets. George Bates, the outspoken CO of 76, had tried it out and had found that, after some time at the low temperature at 50,000 plus feet, on returning to land the visor misted up heavily and there was nothing he could do about it. Very dangerous, he thought, and he would rather take the risk of explosive decompression.

Bates, Dhenin, Weir and the TFC met in the 160 Wing Offices, discussed at length and finally agreed that the new helmets would not, for the time being, be used on the sampling operation; but all reasonable opportunity would be taken to experiment with the new helmet and to try to cure the misting up.

The hours of D-1 rushed on relentlessly, filled with many little problems and their solutions, and then it was D day again. After the 05.30 confirmatory briefing, Air Commodore Weir and the Scientific Director went forward to Malden and HMS *Narvik*, to control the drop, leaving the Task Force Commander with the JOC staff to oversee the whole operation.

The well rehearsed programme worked out smoothly and the sky was cloudless, for a change. The spectators had a perfect view of the aerial ballet as Roberts and Steele in Valiants 822 and 823 painted the clear blue sky with their Rinso-white contrails, round and round the race-track pattern, while the B6 and PR7 Canberras knitted a different design in their holding orbits to the north west.

David Roberts and his crew made a good and accurate drop on the first bombing run; but this time, on the turn-away into the escape manoeuvre things went awry. The sensitive g-meter above Roberts' instrument panel chose that moment to malfunction, under-reading. He pulled the aircraft into too tight a turn and found himself in a high speed stall and then a spin before noticing the instrument error. With consummate airmanship, and while continuing his broadcast commentary without a tremor in his calm voice, he recovered from the abnormal attitude, reverted to the standard g-meter inconveniently located elsewhere on the instrument panel, re-orientated the aircraft more or less on the correct heading and continued the escape manoeuvre. Although he had lost separation distance, there was no serious ill-effect when the shock wave hit 822.

In *Narvik's* control room, Weir and Cook had watched the indications of arming, release and explosion on the telemetry scope. The operation appeared to have gone perfectly and twenty seconds later they emerged on to *Narvik's* deck, unaware of the momentary drama in Robert's cockpit above their heads, to survey the awesome results of their efforts and the rapid development of the mushroom cloud. It was obviously a very satisfactory answer to Sir William Penney's sums.

At Christmas Island, in the JOC, the listeners heard the click of the radio-flash superimposed on the relay of Robert's commentary and sent word to London of another successful test. Half an hour later, over Malden, the sampling operation proceeded as for the previous round, Denis Wilson controlling it, Geoffrey Dhenin observing and monitoring radiation as passenger in the Canberra B6 primary sampler.

Again Commodore Hicks and the efficient crew of HMS *Warrior* operated faultlessly the helicopter re-entry procedures. Dr Fuller again found Malden free of any radiation affect and the work force returned to collect records. The Canberras returned to Christmas with their samples, the Avenger aircraft from *Warrior* with the records. The cloud samples were swiftly packed in their containers into the 'Forth Bridge' in the waiting PR7 and this time there was no hitch or tragedy to mar their safe and timely arrival at Aldermaston, only 24½ hours after the explosion.

While all these post-bang activities were in progress, the press and BBC correspondents were transferred from *Alert* to *Warrior*, where they were given a run-down on the operation as seen from the aircraft carrier, and were then given the free run of the ship to talk with any of the ship's company whose opinions they might wish to seek. They also took the opportunity to send their advance copy and photographs back to Christmas and so on to UK and Australia. Duty done, they were then refreshed with Duty Free in the wardroom before being returned to *Alert*.

After completing their several tasks, the ships and most of the AWRE team returned to Christmas for a short break before the next test. *Alert* arrived at the Christmas Island anchorage on the morning of June 2nd and landed her passengers and fish. Special arrangements had been made with Cable and Wireless, who provided two operators in the JOC to expedite the lengthy fuller reports which the correspondents wished to send both to the UK and to Australia.

The press were given any interviews they wished with the

senior HQ staff and with the CO of 49 Squadron and others. Then after a conducted tour of the airfield and the main camp, they were taken back to Honolulu and so home.

44

A weekend off

It had been a tough month for everybody in the Task Force, albeit highly successful, and a long week-end break was decreed before starting on the last lap. As many as possible of the key people were sent off somewhere for a refreshing change of environment. Alexander of the Islands, capo de Shackletons, sent every available aircraft to out-stations to collect micro-barograph, seismic and fall-out records, each aircraft being fully loaded with extra passengers. The USAF helped too by taking some in their weekly C54 supply trip to their own recording station on Penrhyn. The Christmas Airways did equal service, keeping only one aircraft for the daily run to Malden. *Messina* and *Salvictor* took full loads of enthusiastic fishermen to Fanning and Jarvis Islands. *Narvik's* hard-worked crew went to Penrhyn for a short twenty-four hours of recreation.

Bill Cook was asked to go to Rarotonga, that delightful island which was at one time the home of Robert Louis Stevenson, on the rather flimsy excuse of paying a courtesy call on the charming and intelligent Queen of Rarotonga. He stayed with G Nevill, the genial and hospitable New Zealand Commis-sioner, and got on very well with the Queen, a highly attractive and cosmopolitan lady. This resulted in some leg-pulling at a later date.

There was one quite unexpected bonus from the long week-end break. In Fiji, Samoa, Rarotonga, Tahiti et al, the sight of so many obviously fit and healthy aircrew and other personnel

After the explosion the Re-entry team leave HMS *Narvik*. *(Photo: AWRE)*

Dr Ed Fuller and his team examine the ground on Malden Island for any contamination. *(Photo: AWRE)*

Britain's first thermo-nuclear test – the 'Short Granite' cloud at about H+5 minutes. *(Photo: AWRE)*

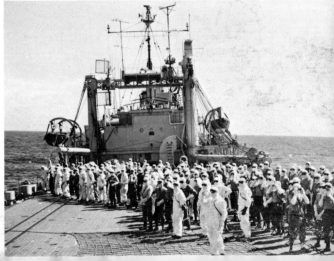

'You may turn round and look now.' HMS *Narvik's* spectators view the cloud in silent amazement. *(Photo: AWRE)*

The Task Force Commander and the Scientific Director transfer from Malden Island to HMS *Narvik*. (Photo: AWRE)

'Shut your eyes now and cover them with your hands.' Spectators, backs turned, on the deck of HMS *Narvik* awaiting the explosion. (Photo: AWRE)

The Task Force Commander and the Scientific Director arrive at Malden Island for the first test, 'Short Granite'. *(Photo: AWRE)*

Underground shelter for the last Land Rover before the first 'live' test. *(Photo: AWRE)*

completely allayed the anxieties of the local people about the possible harmful effect of radiation or fall-out on their peaceful lives. The world news media had been making much of this. But this happy state of affairs was almost upset when one of the aircrew visiting Bora-Bora suddenly got a severe and painful rash on the back of the neck. This occasioned great concern at first; but it turned out that the poor chap was allergic to shellfish, of which delicacy he had eaten too well and unwisely. He recovered in a couple of days.

The ship's doctor of *Warrior*, Surgeon Lieutenant Commander Pugh, went with the package tour of Aitutaki, that earthly paradise, where he did a very interesting genetic study of the Masters family. Their story is probably well-known, but may be worth repeating. It appears that at about the turn of the century, a trading schooner was wrecked on one of the islands of the Tubai group and some dozen of the crew got ashore, only to be made captive by the local residents. Inter island warfare, in which they were almost consistently losers, had reduced them to cannibalism, and one by one the captives disappeared, until only one was left – John Masters (not the famous novelist!) a handsome, well built, muscular seaman, who philosophically reckoned his number was up next day. That night, to his astonishment, one of the local maidens snuggled up to him to comfort him he supposed. So, what the hell, why not be comforted and enjoy his last hours? Next morning, again to his surprise, instead of the head chef he was greeted by a substantial breakfast, borne in by another of the local beauties. This programme was repeated every night for the next year, when he was hauled before the chieftain, who explained that, to break the series of continuous defeats in battle, they had to improve their bloodstock. This John Masters had now done. Thanks very much. Would he like to stay as an honoured member of the tribe, or would he prefer to take some women and a canoe and move on? He cautiously chose to move on, taking with him a comely matron with two teenage daughters.

Now his grandson, with fifty wives and innumerable

children, occupied this very pleasant island, Aitutaki, and lived pretty handsomely by collecting conch shells, burying them in the sand to be cleaned out by ants and selling the clean shells at $5 a time to Honolulu. Commander Pugh knew the story and wanted to see what all this continuous in-breeding had done to the family. To his astonishment, he found them all entirely healthy and intelligent, although extremely dirty, with no sign of degeneration.

Then back to work. The pressure was on to bring forward the date of the next shot and June 19th was fixed as the target. Meanwhile the administrative staff were already working at top pressure on plans and preparations for the withdrawal and return home of the Task Force at the conclusion of the tests. With the return to Christmas Island of the personnel and salvageable equipment and stores from all the out-stations and the planning of the run-down of personnel and the loading of much precious equipment into ships at Christmas, this was a task as great as that of the initial landings.

Furthermore, in discussions with the TFC, Bill Cook had broached the idea that Christmas might be a much better place to do some of the future kiloton tests planned at that time to take place in Australia, particularly if public or political opinion in Australia should become less enthusiastic about the present plans. This seemed common sense and the TFC asked Colonel Woollett to investigate the possibility of constructing a Dakota strip, like the one on Malden, at the south-east tip of Christmas Island, near the target marker. At the same time a more detailed photographic survey was made by a Shackleton, to facilitate any necessary triangulation by the sappers at a later date.

45

'Purple Granite' – the 'last' test

Early in June a decision was given that there would be only one more shot, code-named 'Purple Granite'. This was just as well, thought the Task Force HQ staff, since everything was beginning to wear out, corrode away or be used up at a faster rate than had been envisaged. In pursuit of the Minister of Supply's firm directive to exercise the greatest economy, the whole operation was, in relation to the enormous task to be performed, run 'on a shoe string' and there was not much to spare of anything.

Fortunately the team work and inter-service co-operation within the Task Force was superb, morale was high and there were occasional lighter hearted moments to off-set the dreary slog of long working hours in uncomfortable conditions. This was also helped by the feelings of satisfaction at triumphing over difficulties with brilliant improvisation and self-help.

One incident which caused some ribald amusement occurred when Wing Commander Bob MacVicar, the CO of 5 RNZAF (Sunderland) Flying Boat Squadron, came into Christmas Island to discuss the progress of his fish and flora sampling operations.

The TFC, an old flying boat enthusiast himself, thought it would be courteous to go over to St Stanilaus Bay to greet the helpful New Zealanders and invited Denis Wilson and Group Captain Hutchinson, the Head of the UK Service Liaison Staff in Wellington who had been present at the second test, to go with him. So they set off across the lagoon in an open launch and, half way there, disturbed an enormous manta ray, basking near the surface. This creature, with a wing span of about fifteen feet, could easily have flipped over the launch with a flick of its tail. Fortunately, it just grumbled and moved off to a less over-populated part of the lagoon.

Somewhat sobered, they continued on their way and a few moments later the visiting Inter Tropical Front deluged them with an extremely heavy shower of rain. On arriving at the small jetty, with its general use nissen hut alongside, they were dripping and looked as though they had swum all the way in their clothes. So they stripped off their clothes to dry off a little and for the moment could only wait around stark naked. Wandering around the hut they found a dart board and some darts; so to while away the time the TFC and Denis Wilson played a game. Hutchinson stood by and kept the score. One dart, thrown with more strength than skill, struck a wire, ricocheted off and ploughed into Hutch's ample right buttock. The poor chap with a wail of anguish went hopping round, the dart quivering in his ill-used flesh. Protocol and discipline prevented him from saying in plain Anglo-Saxon what he thought of the thrower and he bravely restricted himself to a series of 'Oh! Oh!! Oh!!!', while the others tried to stifle their laughter and to look suitably sympathetic and contrite. Hutch was a good sport and caused roars of laughter in the mess that night with his highly embroidered account of the episode. All cause for merriment was a boon on Christmas Island.

Meanwhile, the clothes had dried off and the party, suitably attired, were waiting on the jetty to greet the crew as the Sunderland touched down in the lagoon. At first, the keel of the hull gently kissed the aquamarine surface of the water, tracing a tiny white feathery wake, which gradually deepened into full-blooded foaming bow waves as the hull sank deeper. The aircraft came to rest, turned and taxied slowly back to the mooring buoy, an air crew man standing in the bow cockpit with his boat-hook poised ready to pick up the strop. Then a neat and quick job of mooring up. It was a lovely nostalgic sight, needing a combination of Neville Shute and H de Vere Stacpoole to do it descriptive justice, the flying boat riding gently to the mooring bridle against the backdrop of the turquoise amethyst or aquamarine water – depending on the nature of the lagoon bed at any particular point – and beyond that the dazzling white strip of coral on the further shore, with the waving coconut palms serrating the skyline. All it lacked was a bevy of shapely chocolate-coloured maidens, but these were not part of the local inventory, alack-a-day!

But back to business. There was no sign of radio-active pollution anywhere in the area, so far.

Wing Commander MacVicar and his crew stayed the night in the accommodation at the St Stanislas Bay detachment, and went on their way next morning.

On June 6th, one of the precious Hastings transport aircraft took a party of forty AWRE scientific staff to Nandi, Fiji, for a few days rest and recuperation before the next test. They had been working overtime on the results of the previous test and unable to take advantage of the general stand-down. Otherwise the week-end break was almost forgotten and preparations were being pushed ahead energetically and rapidly both for the execution of the final test and for the evacuation and return to Britain of the entire Task Force.

The communications experts of both light and dark blue vocations tackled a problem which had appeared intermittently during the various inert and HE test drops and also during the Orange Herald live test. There appeared to be a blind spot in *Warrior's* VHF transmissions and in one sector both Valiants and Canberras had difficulty in reception at high altitudes. So a special series of Valiant and Canberra sorties, using up precious flying hours and fuel, had to be made now to try to eradicate the trouble. Some improvement was made. Otherwise the drill for the work-up to the 'drop' of Purple Granite was now well established and ran very smoothly; but 160 Wing was feeling the shortage of serviceable aircraft and available flying hours, despite the heroic efforts of Ron Boardman and his Technical Wing. These shortages were inevitably aggravated by the occasional intrusion of Murphy's Law or other para-normal phenomena. A Canberra returning from a long sortie couldn't get the undercarriage down, despite every procedure in the book. When fuel was down to emergency level, the OC Flying decided to put it down, wheels up, on the old original coral strip which now served as vehicular access to the airfield. Time was short, there was no one else immediately available and the TFC, who had been visiting the station, found himself smartly detailed off by the forthright Group Captain to go and hold up the traffic approaching the old runway while the landing took place. Very sensible, too, and typical of the way in which everyone in the Task Force would pitch in to do any job necessary, regardless of rank or service. But now they were one Canberra short, until the Tech Wing could get it restored.

The para-normal came into it, too – or so it might appear. Despite all appearance of jollying about on week-end jaunts, Shackleton flying hours were precious and were carefully conserved. So much depended on the regularity of aircraft arriving back from the UK after major servicing and it was a great relief to begin, on May 29th, the movement of the Shackletons through the shorter northern route through Canada. One aircraft was delayed en route by a series of technical troubles and was over two weeks late when it eventually arrived on June 11th, with some unlikely explanation about this having been due to 'The Witch's Curse'. The story will keep to a later chapter.

Extra commitment of Hastings aircraft to the Australia shuttle, with additional calls to pick up scientific records from Samoa and New Caledonia meant that Shackletons had to do both the Penrhyn re-supply run and the Honolulu shuttle. Then 58 Squadron were unable to provide a stand-by Canberra for the next sample-courier, so one of 100 Squadron's precious PR7s had to be positioned at Travis AFB on 10th June. And so it went on.

Nevertheless, everything was ready just in time, and the dress rehearsal took place without any snags or hitches on June 16th; and on June 19th, the anniversary of the first arrival of the Task Force on Christmas Island, the last live drop was made with complete success. Arthur Steele in Valiant XD823 made a good and accurate drop, with Barney Millett in XD824 flying the 'Grandstand' role for the second time. There was very nearly a drama when *Warrior* flew off the Avenger to take the instrumentation records from Malden to Christmas, with the usual Shackleton – albeit a very much patched-up one – providing the safety escort. Half way home the Shack lost one engine. So? Then it lost another. H'm! Fifty miles short of base, a third engine had to be shut down. So the pair of aircraft arrived with the Avenger providing safety escort for the Shackleton!

By 15.30 hours that afternoon, the cloud samples were on their way to Hickam and the UK in a 58 Squadron PR7. By early evening all other aircraft were safely on the ground and in the JOC the cry went up – 'Bed-time for Hicks!' – the signal that there was no longer any need to monitor the progress of the atomic cloud which was all that was left of Purple Granite.

The task of the Task Force was complete and nearly four thousand men, with relief and satisfaction at their different jobs all having been well done, looked forward to being home again soon, many of them after a year in the islands.

46

Back to the drawing board

It was a quiet evening, rather than one of rowdy celebration, with a general feeling of reaction and let-down after a long period of strain. After the evening meal, Bill Cook cornered the TFC.

'Wilf, can we talk?'

'Sure, Bill. Let's take a couple of chairs out on to the patio.'

They settled down with a drink apiece outside the dining tent and Cook began:

'We haven't got it quite right. We shall have to do it all again, providing we can do so before the ban comes into force; so that means as soon as possible.'

'Like how soon, Bill?'

'Say, three or four months.'

For a few moments the TFC was flabbergasted and at a loss for words. His thoughts ranged swiftly over the exhausted state of the naval and air force elements, the need to replace many of the personnel and train the replacements, the low level of supplies of every description, the worn-out motor transport and what else. In conformity with the directive to exercise the greatest economy plus the old adage that 'he travels fastest who travels lightest', the Task Force had been set up with just enough of everything to do this test series, with only a small operational reserve which in many cases had already been used up. For days now they had, so to speak, been straightening and re-using bent nails and joining up bits of string. Not so far fetched, this last one, for several of the Shackletons had had fuel tanks repaired by stitching them up with needle and thread and sticking a patch over it.

Then he voiced a thought which had been at the back of his mind after watching the first and third shots and his realisation that these megaton nuclear explosions were manageable after all.

'Bill, although I must check with Guy Western, I'm sure it's out of the question for *Warrior* to go on here for another four months and equally so to get another aircraft carrier in that time. So Malden is out.

'But there is an alternative. From here to the south-east tip of the island is nearly thirty miles. I reckon we could do the live drops at eight thousand feet, one and a half miles beyond the point, with only very minor blast damage to the camp and the airfield. What do you say to that?'

Cook puffed at his pipe and took a long pull at his whisky and soda.

'I agree. That's OK from my point of view, if you are happy on the operational side.'

'OK. We'll have a staff meeting tomorrow to set up an outline plan. I'm afraid it means we have to abandon our trip home in *Warrior* round South America. A great pity, that – it would have been fun and very interesting for me to meet old friends. Too bad!'

'Yes. I'm sorry about that; and I'd like to go back to Aldermaston as quickly as possible. Could you fix that for me?'

'Of course, Bill. How would you like to go to Hickam – in a Canberra or in a Shackleton?'

'You say, Wilf. You're the boss.'

'Um! The Canberra is uncomfortable but it's quick. The Shack is more comfortable but slow – and I'm not too happy about their serviceability at the moment after this afternoon's near miss. It had better be the Canberra. I'll ask Ginger to fix it up for you. Please excuse me if I don't see you off myself, as I must leave for Nandi and Australia straight after the staff meeting tomorrow.'

Then another thought occurred to the TFC.

'Bill, can you honestly say that, if we can just scrape through another test in October/November, that will be the end? Or are you going to want more after that?'

Again Cook considered the question before replying.

'I know it's a change from the original concept, and we haven't even asked yet for political or financial approval which we might not get; but I think we shall want to go on improving and testing until a test ban stops us. It's important for Zeta – the industrial application thing – as well as for weapon development.'

'In that case it won't do just to scrape up enough resources to get through one more test in the autumn. We'll have to start some long range planning. But please get Bill Penney to hustle with getting authorisation for this next bang, because until I get orders to the contrary, I have to carry on with the evacuation; and I don't want to tell my logisticians and movements people until we have some reliable new instructions.'

So that was agreed. What a way to go to bed after a successful last test!

At the staff meeting early next day, June 20th, the TFC broke the news that there would probably be another test later in the year, but that the news would not be released outside that immediate circle until some official word was received from London. The test would take place off the south-east tip of Christmas Island, using the same overshoot bombing technique as had been used at Malden. He asked Colonel Woollett to put in hand immediately the construction of the 1,000 yard Dakota airstrip for which a survey had very recently been done. In view of the probable time scale, a road journey of $4\frac{1}{2}$ hours each way was not acceptable as the standard mode of access. Also, he wanted a survey done to provide, in that same south-east area, a second Class I Valiant runway. It was not sensible to carry on indefinitely with no diversion airfield within 800 miles. Twenty

358

five miles wasn't really enough for a diversion, but it would be a great deal better than nothing.

The Decca station would have to be moved – possibly to Malden? – and he planned to ask for an up-to-date Type 80 radar, to perform the monitoring role played by *Warrior* during the drops at Malden. The whole of the Malden instrumentation set-up would have to be recreated near the new target area and outline planning for this should begin between Ken Bomford's team and John Woollett's staff as soon as some official word was received from London.

There would have to be major changes in personnel. In principle, no one should be asked to do more than one year at Christmas, although in a few cases it would be necessary to extend this to the end of the year. In such cases, proper home leave should be given.

Meanwhile, 49 Squadron would return to the UK as planned. 76 would return to Edinburgh Field and 1325 Dakota flight would follow them as soon as the evacuation of Malden and Penrhyn was completed, to take part in the next test at Maralinga – code named 'Antler'.

The TFC then addressed all the personnel of RAF 160 Wing, assembled together in the Bessoneaux hanger, to thank them for their efforts, noting the many occasions on which ground crews had worked all through the night to change engines or do other work to ensure that no sortie was ever late or missed. Air crews likewise had performed exactly to programme and with commendable efficiency. He then left by Shackleton for Nandi; thence by TEAL to Wellington to thank the New Zealanders. On June 22nd, George Bates, en route to Edinburgh, picked up the TFC and his ADC at Ohakea and flew them overnight to Laverton, whence they rushed to Canberra and Melbourne to thank the Australians similarly. And so back to Christmas by the Hastings shuttle.

Meanwhile, several hours after the TFC had departed from Christmas Island on June 20th, Ginger Weir had carefully packed Bill Cook and Denis Wilson and their baggage into a 76

359

Squadron Canberra for what should have been a short and uneventful flight to Honolulu. But it turned out slightly differently. On nearing the Hawaiian islands above solid cloud, the pilot – Peter Nichols – had radio trouble and was unable to make contact with any ground station for the customary let-down guidance. This trouble was compounded by the navigator – Ray Davies – being unable to get an astro fix at that time, the sun being too low and the stars not yet visible.

At their estimated time of arrival over Hickam, Nichols went into a holding pattern and shut down one engine to conserve fuel, while he tried to sort out the situation. Most fortunately, after some considerable time and increasing anxiety about the fuel state, a US Weather Service WV2 Constellation aircraft heard Nichols's fruitless attempts to make radio contact and intervened to help. The WV2 located the Canberra by radar and talked it down through the cloud, clear of the thirteen-thousand feet high volcanic peaks on Hawaii and Maui. Then through a break in the cloud, Wilson spotted a point of land and, since fuel was by now desperately low, urged the pilot to go down immediately and make a wheels-up crash landing on any possible piece of land rather than risk ditching in the sea. As Nichols broke through the cloud base and looked around hastily, there, off to one side, was a thousand yard dirt airstrip which had been scraped out by some film company on location and was now being used for rural aviation. With great flying skill and still on only one engine, Nichols positioned the Canberra for an approach and made a good landing. As the aircraft came to a stop, so did the one engine. They were out of fuel.

This little airstrip turned out to be Kahului on the island of Maui and also accommodated a unit of the National Guard, whose Commanding Officer, Colonel Almedo, went out to greet the unexpected visitors. Under some high-level pressure from Bill Cook he called in a passing US Navy aircraft, which picked up the two VIPs and took them on to Honolulu International Airport and a safe journey home to the UK. So all was well in the end, but there were some very red faces in 160 Wing, not to mention the TFC himself when he heard what his decision had led to!

Five days later the Task Force Commander arrived back from his courtesy calls in New Zealand and Australia to find instructions from the Air Ministry that Christmas Island, instead of being completely evacuated, was to be reduced to a Care and Maintenance basis and would be so maintained for six months. The RAF would take over from the Army the responsibility for administering and supplying the island and two Hastings aircraft would remain based at Christmas to fly in twice-weekly supplies of fresh food from Honolulu.

The TFC also found that during his absence in Australia and New Zealand, the rumour had gone around the force that there were to be further tests and that they would have to remain much longer at Christmas. This was apparently confirmed by the preparations to build the air strip in the south of the island. The cheerful put-up-with-the-snags-and-get-on-with-this-important-job attitude of all ranks was changing to a sullen resentment. The troops of all three services had had a pretty miserable time, despite all efforts to the contrary, but had been buoyed up by the belief that the task was of great national importance and the sooner they got the three tests done, the sooner they could go home. Now maybe that was just 'flannel'.

This situation could go badly wrong; so Guy Western was sent home in a hurry. Flight Lieutenant Barry Newton flew him up to Hickam in a Canberra to catch a through flight to London, where he immediately went to see the Minister of Supply. Three days later he was back at Christmas with a firm assurance that no man would be asked to do more than a year at Christmas, unless he volunteered to do so. The TFC explained and emphasised this point in making addresses to the troops of the Army Task Group and to ships' companies, thanking them for their splendid efforts over the past year, as he had done to the RAF. Morale was restored.

The recovery of all equipment from Malden and Penrhyn went ahead at full speed, both by air lift and by HMS *Messina*.

This was all completed by the end of the month. All on Christmas Island except that needed to support the small Care and Maintenance party – now planned to be about 200 men – was packed up, documented and loading into ships began.

The operational aircraft began to move either to the UK or to Australia, just two or three each day in order not to overload the Staging Posts. The 22 Squadron helicopters embarked in *Warrior*, 1325 Dakota flight left for Edinburgh Field and Operation Antler on July 10th. A steady stream of Qantas and TEAL chartered aircraft arrived, embarked ground crews for Australia and time-expired men for UK, and departed without delay. Precious and scarce aircraft spares and component servicing equipment and AWRE technical equipment were loaded into RFA *Fort Rosalie* and HMS *Narvik*. *Messina*, fully loaded with all the gear from Penrhyn, also sailed for home. The run down proceeded apace and the Organisation staffs had some worries as to how they were going to keep the men happily occupied until the arrival of troopships to supplement the airlift.

Very soon after his return from Australia, the TFC was summoned back to London, to report to the Chief of the Air Staff as early as was practicable. With the briefest of courtesy calls at Hickam, Travis, Ottawa and Washington, he was back in London four days later and making his way up to the sixth floor of the Air Ministry building. He was promptly shown into the office of the Chief of the Air Staff, Air Chief Marshal Sir Dermot Boyle, a very tall, very handsome Irishman of great personality and charm, but with a very steely hand inside that very velvet glove.

'Hello, Wilf. Welcome back – and congratulations on your fine achievement. I believe you already know Fred Brundrett?' – turning to the third person in the room.

'Thank you, sir. Yes. How do you do, Sir Frederick?'

'Now, Wilf, we want you to go back and do it all over again – and as quickly as possible. Within three months?'

CAS indicated a chair with his hand and the TFC sat down. For a moment he looked at the two eminent men. Brundrett he knew as being a first class adminstrative scientist, a mover in high Government Defence circles as Chief Scientific Adviser to the Ministry of Defence and Chairman of the Defence Research Policy Committee, which had originally recommended to the Government the development of a thermo-nuclear weapon and its urgent testing. Flight Lieutenant Boyle had taught him to fly at Cranwell nearly thirty years previously and he had worked for Air Commodore, Air Vice Marshal, Air Marshal and now Air Chief Marshal Boyle at various periods, with ever increasing respect and admiration. But at the same time he recognised that neither of the two men facing him had any idea of what they were asking him to do in a matter of a few weeks. In no way was he going to say it couldn't be done, but at the same time he had better make it clear now that it was going to be difficult and some exceptional measures would be necessary. So –

"We'll try, sir. I don't have any doubt about the actual operation but the logistics will be difficult. I shall need an immense amount of air transport which may be beyond the capability of the air charter companies. There are some second-hand 'Constellations' for sale at Heathrow and I may need to ask the Ministry of Supply to buy them. I presume we could crew them at a pinch?'

'I'm sure the Ministry of Supply will do anything they can to help, just so long as you get the job done,' replied CAS.

'On that point, sir, wouldn't it be better to have someone else take over from me for this next test, to spread the experience more widely?'

'No, Wilf. The Ministry of Supply has asked that you should run this next operation and I have agreed.'

'Very well, sir. Then I'd better go and get on with it.'

So, from the oxygen level of the sixth floor down to the 'Dungeon' and the Grapple offices in the below-ground 'citadel', to confer with the splendid Jack Stone and the rear-link people who had supported the Christmas Island end so very well during the past five months. Warm greetings all round.

'Jack, I've just had the definite instruction that we are to do another test series in October/November. I don't know how many shots, yet. But we're going to do it at Christmas, not Malden, and I want the sappers to get on right away with the construction of a new air-strip and the new instrumentation site. I've asked John Woollett to start on the airstrip, but I imagine 28 Regiment will have to be replaced immediately?'

'Yes, sir. We've already had a warning that this might be on and I've arranged that 25 Regiment will take over the work and Lieutenant Colonel Gatward will take over from John Woollett as CRE on August 6th. All the 25 Regiment chaps will have to fly out, I suppose, and 28 Regiment come back in the same aircraft? There'll be a bit of an accommodation problem if there's much overlap.'

'That's right, Jack, and Doug Longley must arrange all that as soon as he gets back. Meanwhile will you please tell Christmas Island to stop the back-loading of all equipment, spares or whatever and to retain the 22 Squadron helicopters which were to have returned home in *Warrior*.

There's a lot of detailed work to be done and we can't go on ad hoc or we'll get into a muddle. As soon as Ginger Weir, Freddie Milligan and Guy Western get back – any day now – we must have a staff meeting to put the show on the road in an orderly fashion; then I want all staff returning from Christmas to take a week's leave before we start on this frantic rush to have the Task Force on Christmas back up to full operational readiness by October 1st. I'm going to take a long weekend off, but I'll keep in touch in case you want me and I'll be in on Tuesday. Tuesday? We must start the weekly AWRE meetings again the following Tuesday. So long, Jack.'

47

U-turn for Grapple-X

On Christmas Island, Tony Jillings was looking out of the entrance of the tent which he had, until recently, been sharing with his sapper friend Keith Bean. He couldn't believe his eyes! There was the *Messina* going the wrong way – returning to Christmas! What went on? Two days earlier he had taken a farewell drink – or two? – with Commander Harry De Vere, who was intensely looking forward to seeing his wife and family again after a long separation. In reply to an unofficial signal of enquiry, De Vere sadly responded:

'Spring will be a little late this year!'

The first two weeks of July had been fully occupied with the hectic activity of packing up and loading everything not needed for the Care and Maintenance party and either air-freighting it to Australia or shipping it to the UK. Air Commodore Weir had departed for the UK, leaving Group Captain Richard Brousson in command as Senior Officer, Grapple Area. By the 13th the loading of *Narvik* and RFA *Fort Rosalie* with RAF and AWRE technical stores had been completed and they sailed for the UK without delay.

On July 16th instructions were received from London to stop the back-loading of aircraft spares and component servicing equipment. *Narvik* and *Fort Rosalie* were ordered to return to Christmas and unload the technical stores. At the same time chartered Qantas aircraft were arriving, embarking personnel for return home or to Australia and running down the

Christmas Island population at a great rate. The 22 Squadron helicopters which had embarked in *Warrior* were flown ashore again.

Then the tide turned. The new RAF personnel to man the Care and Maintenance force were to travel from the UK, to Edinburgh Field in the new RAF Comet transport aircraft, thence to be taken on to Christmas by the Hastings shuttle service, which would now be augmented instead of being reduced as planned. On July 25th official word was received that further megaton tests would take place in November and volunteers were called for to continue at Christmas until the end of the year. The response was good. Otherwise, all 160 Wing personnel would be repatriated as originally planned. Replacements would arrive in August and all aircraft and component servicing bays were to be opened up again as quickly as possible. Malden Island was to be reactivated as a meteorological and Decca station – more tasks for *Messina*.

Lieutenant Commander Walliker and his hard-working crew in *Salvictor* had already sailed for home and to make a call at the US Navy base at San Diego, giving them a break before continuing through the Panama canal. *Warrior*, soon after her return from the last shot at Malden, had gone up to Pearl Harbour to pay farewell calls on the very helpful US Navy and in so doing took a considerable number of army personnel for a break. These were men overdue for return home but who could not go until their reliefs from 25 Regiment arrived a month later. *Warrior* then finally sailed from Christmas on July 20th, to make flag-showing calls at Rarotonga, Pitcairn Island, Callao and other points in South America.

The crew of *Messina* were relieved and Commander Harry De Vere handed over the ship to Commander Douglas Williams – another cheerful, competent seaman.

By the first week in August, the change-over of personnel was in full swing. In five days the New Zealand airline TEAL flew the 400 men of 25 RE Regiment from Honolulu into Christmas. The three principal Australian airlines flew in a large quantity of

AWRE freight and personnel. 1325 Dakota flight returned from Australia on August 24th and recommenced their standard Grapple operations. By the end of the month, all the original Task Force personnel had been replaced, other than those volunteering to stay on to the end of the year and some 200 still awaiting the arrival of their reliefs. During all this movement, Britain chalked up 'one for the book' in operating the first jet passenger aircraft – an RAF Comet – through San Francisco international airport.

At the Grapple HQ in London there were many and serious problems, mainly of an administrative or logistic nature, to be contended with. It seemed to the TFC that the first of these should be the well-being of the personnel on Christmas Island and he went to see the Air Council Member for Personnel, Air Chief Marshal Sir Francis Fogarty. Very bluntly the TFC explained that, in successfully accomplishing the first series of tests, the Government had traded on the loyalty and enthusiasm of carefully hand-picked men for an important task which originally had a certain glamour. This was no longer the case. The general run of troops would find life on Christmas miserably uncomfortable, the food quite unsatisfactory and the hours of work quite unacceptable in a peace-time environment. There had to be some financial inducement, perhaps a Local Overseas Allowance, and a better scale of rations. This was not the way for a relatively junior officer to talk to AMP, but 'Joe' Fogarty was a 'good type' and miraculously a Local Overseas Allowance for Christmas Island was approved from August 1st. The catering would improve.

Next, it was now clear that AWRE and the Ministry of Supply were working on several more series of tests after this one in November; so it was time to consider changes in the top management. He went to see the Air Secretary, Air Chief Marshal Sir Denis Barnett, who was responsible for senior RAF appointments, and proposed that he himself, Ginger Weir and Freddie Milligan should be replaced at the end of the year; and if that were to be so, then the new boys should join as soon as possible to understudy during the forthcoming test in November. Denis Barnett agreed, but the problem would be to find suitable people for these rather exotic appointments. It was soon agreed that Jack Roulston, a rather dour but very competent South African, should take over from Weir and John Mason from Milligan.

A good name was suggested for the top job and the TFC went to see him, an old acquaintance, to explain all about it; whereupon the officer chosen felt himself unfitted for the post. This happened a second time. Finally the Air Secretary discussed it again and said the only solution he could propose was that Air Commodore John Grandy, at that time a student on the Imperial Defence College course, should leave the IDC prematurely, understudy for Grapple-X and take over at the end of the year. This suited the TFC very well indeed. John Grandy was well regarded both as a first class aviator and a good commander, a rising star as his later career proved. October 1st was agreed as a suitable date.

The daily morning 'fix-it' meetings started up again in the Grapple HQ as soon as the senior members were back from Christmas Island and a few days leave. The most urgent problem in time was the major re-supply of the island – tents, bedding, barrack equipment of all kinds, clothing, construction supplies, motor transport and an endless list. It was almost as big a task as the initial planning a year previously, but at least they now had the advantage of experience and instant communication with the Garrison Commander on the spot. But the more serious problem was to ensure that the decision to carry out the live tests at Christmas Island instead of at Malden was not a foolish one. So requirement number one was a radar facility to monitor the aircraft carrying out the drop. The TFC wanted the new Type 80 radar, but Douglas Lovelock was taken aback when informed of the cost of supply and installation. He would have to get Treasury approval.

'Get it, then.'

So David Serpell, one of the very bright under-secretaries in the Treasury, came over to join a meeting with the TFC, Weir, Stone, Milligan and Lovelock. He listened carefully to the explanation of why the live drop now had to be made on Christmas Island itself, the narrow margin of safety, the consequences of the bomb dropping significantly away from the correct point, the reason for choosing the Type 80 as the solution and the cost thereof. Then he said, simply:

'Yes. That is agreed.'

It was quite un-nerving! So unlike the conventional picture of the Treasury!

There was the slight problem of getting it manufactured, tested, delivered to Christmas, installed, calibrated and commissioned in time. It had to be accepted that this might not be possible, but the Type 80 would in any case be equally necessary for any later test series.

So what to do as a back-up for Grapple-X, as this next test was now officially called? The Army had, for Anti-Aircraft gunnery fire control purposes, a radar plotting system known as Number III Mark 7. One had already been used with some success at Orfordness during the 'Fly-over' bomb evaluation tests and this could be made available. There was just about enough time to get it to Christmas Island and set up for the test.

The primary method of dropping the weapon accurately would still be by visual bombing, at which 49 Squadron had proved themselves to be so very good; but this would be backed up by the now well-proven Decca system and again by the Mark 7 radar. It also had to be considered that the weather factor at Christmas had proved to be not nearly so good as at Malden and it might be necessary to resort to a 'blind' drop. Bearing in mind the first point, however, it was essential to keep the selected crews of 49 Squadron up to scratch in their visual bombing and this would be virtually impossible in UK weather. It was arranged, therefore, that these aircrews would go to the bombing range at El Adem in Libya for a period of intensive practice. This turned out very successfully.

Another problem to be considered by the Grapple planners

was how to provide for the heavy traffic between Main Camp at Christmas and the instrumentation sites dispersed over the south-east 'tail' of the island, both during the hectic construction phase immediately ahead and then during the operation. The new Dakota strip was going to be a great help, but movement from there to the dispersed sites would be very slow by wheeled vehicles. So a further six Whirlwind helicopters had to be won from somewhere and shipped out as a high priority. The air and ground crews could be flown out.

At one of the weekly Aldermaston meetings, the AWRE team asked if they could do their own messing as they hadn't been very happy with the army standard of catering. This request was hastily agreed by the TFC before they could change their minds! It would be a great relief not to have the customers grumbling about the service! Arrangements were made for the scientists to have their own dining and kitchen accommodation, wherever they would like to have it sited. In the event, it was noticeable that many of the old hands continued to use the officers' 'B' mess, but they were very welcome and not a word was said about it.

With only three months from the official 'go' to the required live test date and a six week voyage from England to Christmas via the Panama Canal, any kind of shipping was a real problem, and this applied equally to Royal Navy ships. With no *Warrior*, *Salvictor*, *Alert* or RNZN frigates, something had to be done quickly to provide a means of forcing any intruder out of the danger area. Guy Western worked fast and succeeded in getting an old destroyer, HMS *Cossack*, detached to Christmas Island for that role. Royal Fleet Auxiliaries had to be diverted from other planned tasks to continue to supply the Task Force; a cargo ship – the SS *Somersby* – was chartered to get the new supplies of tentage, domestic equipment and other stores out there almost in time. For a few days troops were reduced to taking it in turns to sleep in a bed or to use mess cutlery, cups and plates, but then *Somersby* arrived in the nick of time.

Doug Longley had worked miracles in chartering aircraft

from USA, Canada, Australia, New Zealand as well as from all the charter companies in Britain. RAF Transport Command gave tremendous support also, both in providing extra Hastings and in putting their new Comet jet passenger aircraft on the run to Christmas, both eastabout and westabout. In five weeks he had moved 2,000 men out of Christmas and a similar number plus a great deal of air freight back in again.

Wing Commander T Stevenson had taken over command of Royal Air Force, Christmas Island, in its status as a Care and Maintenance unit. Now he was saddled with this vast movement of personnel and stores, and the problem of feeding and accommodating too many men with too few facilities. By early September the worst was over and Christmas Island was once again working up to a state of operational readiness. On September 11th, *Messina* delivered the meteorological and AWRE monitoring equipment to Malden Island, together with the first party of RAF and Met personnel. Arrangements were made with Cable and Wireless Ltd to accommodate Met and AWRE observers at Fanning Island and *Messina* delivered them on September 22nd. The detachments on Penrhyn and Jarvis were re-established. It was all beginning to fit together again quite neatly.

48

The Witch's Curse

In mid-September, HMS *Warrior* arrived back at Portsmouth and the TFC invited Commodore Roger Hicks to come up to London to have lunch at the 'Senior' – the United Service Club in Pall Mall.

It is necessary at this point to go back to early June, when there was a serious shortage of Shackleton aircraft at Christmas Island. Because there had not been time or capacity to provide second-line servicing for them in 160 Wing, when each Shackleton had flown about one hundred hours since its last major overhaul it had to return to its home base at Ballykelly in Northern Ireland for the next overhaul. So throughout Operation Grapple there was a constant stream of Shackletons flying the westabout route out to Christmas, performing their tasks and then returning for overhaul and to start all over again. The 206 and 240 Squadron air and ground crews prided themselves on keeping exactly to schedule and it was rare even to be one day late in consequence of some temporary technical snag. So when, back in June, two aircraft had been over a week late arriving at Christmas there was great chagrin and a demand for an explanation.

It appeared that, one sunny afternoon in late May, a young ground crew technician who was due to go with the next Shackleton to Christmas the following morning, went for a walk to the top of that mountain to the north of the Ballykelly airfield known to most aviators as 'Ben Twitch' on account of the anxiety which it causes during approaches in bad weather. As he strolled along the top, his eye fell on an unusual object, a small yellowish skull with a hardwood stick firmly stuck through the top. He picked it up and swung it to and fro as he made his way back to camp via the village of Limavady. Despite it being Sunday evening and the fronts of the public houses all firmly closed, he went round to the back of his favourite, knocked three times and was duly admitted. After ordering suitable refreshment, he turned to the numerous company there present on similar social duty, showed them the skull and stick and enquired if anyone knew what it was. At that there was a sharp intake of breath amongst the local residents. This was a 'Witch's Curse', a very powerful device indeed, and he had better be very careful what he did with it.

This amused our young technician considerably and he took it along with him. It might be just the thing to brighten life on Christmas Island, which from accounts received was pretty dull.

At five o'clock the following morning, he queued up with the rest of the passengers, climbed into the back of the Shackleton and threw his suitcase and the Witch's Curse into that dark tunnel in the tail which leads to the rear gun turret. Then thought no more about it. Oddly, however, this particular aircraft, instead of doing five quick sectors in five days to Christmas, had troubles right from the start. Technical troubles and delays over four days; then struck by lightning, radar and radio knocked out, two engines failed and the crew felt themseves pretty lucky to be able to make a landing at Bismark, Texas. The Chief Technical Officer at Ballykelly, furious at this reflection on the work of his technical wing, despatched another Shackleton with a replacement engine, radio, radar and what else, plus his best technicians with orders to get that adjectival aircraft on its way with no more delay.

Meanwhile, a thought had occurred to our young technician. But no! That's a lot of nonsense! But was it? Just suppose . . . ?

373

When the relieving Shackleton with a spare of everything arrived, he quietly took the Witch's Curse out of the first aircraft and popped it into the second. From that moment on, the first had no more trouble and rushed on to Christmas. The second limped back to Ballykelly, was turned round quickly and struggled out to Christmas, arriving two weeks late, after many technical delays.

On the asphalt dispersal, Wing Commander Ron Boardman, the irate and harassed Chief Technical Officer, explosively demanded of Flight Lieutenant Williams, the Shackleton Captain:

'Where the hell have you been?' You were due here over a week ago!'

'It wasn't my fault, Chiefie,' replied Williams, waving the Witch's Curse in his hand and offering that as an explanation.

'Give me that damn' thing!' and Boardman stomped off down the tarmac to report this unlikely story to Ginger Weir, who had been chasing him for more aircraft. As he did so, he heard a small and unusual noise which he eventually traced to his wristwatch, a beautiful Omega which had been a wedding present from his wife, twenty five years ago. Something in the escapement had broken and the hands were whizzing round!

Ginger Weir later retailed this story to the TFC and went on:

'How about tying this on to Purple Granite and see if it makes it work better?'

'No, Ginger. We have more than enough trouble without fooling around.'

'Well then, how about taking it with you to Malden when you go for the live drop and dump it in the sea? We might get a new volcano.'

'No. Absolutely not!'

'I'm surprised at you! You're a spoil sport.'

'So I am! No! I don't believe it but I'm not going to tempt fate.'

A lot more joshing went on – all quite light-hearted.

After the third drop, Ken Hubbard and a team of 49 Squadron

went out to *Warrior* in the Christmas anchorage for a farewell party, taking the Witch's Curse with them, concealed. Choosing his moment, Hubbard popped the Witch's Curse behind the picture of the WAAF over the wardroom fireplace, the party went on exuberantly and the tale eventually reached the TFC.

So now, beneath the picture of Lord Roberts in the dining room of the 'Senior', having placed their lunch order with Mr Moss, the Head Steward, the TFC enquired of Roger Hicks had he had a good trip home? What a pity he'd missed the voyage. Hicks paused for a moment and then:

'I've never had such a bloody awful trip in all my life!' It had all started well enough visiting Ratotonga and Pitcairn Island. But then came a series of calamities. His boat had been stolen in Callao! They'd had a very rough passage round the Horn. At Buenos Aires, the splendid ceremony of 'Beating the Retreat' laid on by the Royal Marines at the special request of the ambassador had been a disaster in a torrential rainstorm. In Rio a lot of the ship's company had had a stand-up fight with the police and that took some laughing off. Then they had come through that hurricane which had sunk the famous German sailing ship *Pamir* and caused immense damage to *Warrior* particularly to a lot of stuff in the ward-room on which the insurance had lapsed. No! Not at all a good trip home!'

This did not seem a suitable moment to tell the story of the Witch's Curse.

To complete the tale, some time later the *Warrior* was sold to Argentina, to become the flagship of the Argentine Navy as the *Independencia*. This was followed by the Minister for Marine and the Commander-in-Chief losing their posts, it was said on account of irregularities in the deal.

A year later, there was a great sensation that a Russian submarine was suspected of entering Argentine national waters without authorisation and was hunted by a naval task group including the *Independencia*. The naval authorities confidently stated to the press that they had the submarine pinned down in

St George's Bay in Patagonia and it was only a matter of a few days before it would be compelled to surface – to face the music. Six weeks later, the hunt was quietly abandoned and careers were blighted.

At this, the former TFC, now in another post, thought something had better be done; so he invited the Argentine Naval Attaché in London to lunch at that same table beneath Lord Robert's benign gaze and told him the foregoing tale. The NA turned quite pale and asked:

'Do you suppose it's still there?'

'I don't know, but it might be worthwhile looking.'

And that is the end of the story, as far as it is known.

49

Round-C

By Mid-September it looked as though everything was going to work out all right after all. The daily staff meetings showed that construction of the new facilities on Christmas Island would be completed in time, the radio and Met reporting network would soon be re-established, the New Zealand Air Force had resumed the collection and delivery of fish and vegetation samples, the re-activation of microbarograph and fall-out monitoring stations was proceeding satisfactorily. Even the leaflets to drop on any ships entering the danger area were already to hand, but that did raise the question of whether the warning 'Notice to Mariners', advising all shipping to keep clear of the danger area, had actually been published. Guy Western went over to the Admiralty to get a copy, which would be better than any bland telephoned assurance, but came back with the astonishing and worrying news that the Minister of Defence had refused to allow the Notice to be issued. Why on earth not? This was serious.

The Task Force Commander made an appointment and went across Whitehall to see the Minister, was shown into the imperial office and got a fairly cool reception from the unsmiling character behind the desk. After the usual courtesies, he explained that he understood that there might be some problem over the issue of this vital Notice to Mariners and enquired if there was anything he could do to enable it to be issued immediately. Time was of the essence.

Nothing wrong with the draft Notice. The Minister

considered it much too early for it to be issued. A month before the test would be soon enough. The TFC explained again that while this might be adequate in Europe or the North Atlantic, in the vast and loosely organised island chains of the Pacific ocean, it could take weeks for the Notice to come to the attention of masters of ships, many of whom made voyages of two or three weeks between ports. It was already very late for the issue of the Notice. The Minister was unmoved. No. Early October would be soon enough. Good morning.

Stony faced, the TFC returned to tell the Grapple team that they would just have to cope with the problem themselves, if it arose. This, after all, was probably not the most important thing they had to worry about.

By October 1st the re-build up of the Christmas Island base was almost complete and the operational aircraft began to flow westward. An RAF Comet positioned slip crews on the westabout route and continued to Christmas Island to deliver key technical personnel. The Shackletons from Ballykelly began to stage through and were followed by 49 Squadron Valiants a couple of days later. Wing Commander Hubbard in the first Valiant arrived on October 11th and was quickly followed by Millet and Steele. 58 Squadron had now absorbed No 100 and the first three of their Canberra PR7s arrived and commenced weather reconnaissance flights. The fourth PR7 was held at Hickam to fly wind-finding sorties on the Travis-Hickam leg for the fourth Valiant, captained by Flight Lieutenant Bates, who had been delayed by strong headwinds.

Air Commodore Weir, accompanied by the staff of the Joint Operations Centre, had arrived on October 11th and again assumed command of the Air Task Group. Two days later, Captain Western and Colonel Stone followed on the next inbound shuttle from Hickam, the former to resume direction of naval operations including the destroyer HMS *Cossack* which had now joined and Jack Stone to oversee the activities of 25 Regiment, Royal Engineers. Milligan remained in London to look after the Rear Link.

No time was wasted. On October 16th the Valiant aircraft began 'Flyover' trials for the testing of the new instrumentation sites and calibration bombing and this was continued intensively. The results from the radar plotting table were quite good – not good enough yet for blind bombing, but certainly good enough to ensure that nothing went disastrously wrong with the visual drops.

The Shackletons played their low and medium level roles complementary to the Canberra PR7s' high level sorties in twice daily weather reconnaissance and also backed up the Dakotas in delivering scientific recording equipment and the operating scientists to Kwajalein, Canton, Aitutaki and Samoa.

The Canberra B6s of 76 Squadron arrived back from Australia October 21st and 23rd and began to rehearse again their sampling drill. It was all coming together again quite quickly.

John Grandy, who was to take over as Task Force Commander at the end of the year, had joined in London on October 1st. Wisely and considerately he confined himself to watching and learning, not getting in the way of the hard-pressed 'old hands'. Now he had arrived at Christmas Island and was familiarising himself with the Grapple area, with test procedures as they had evolved so far and with local operating conditions. There was a lot to learn before he assumed overall responsibility in a few weeks time.

The Task Force Commander and Terry Helfer arrived on the 26th. As they arrived at five o'clock that morning at Honolulu, the ever hospitable General Sory Smith had met them, driven them to breakfast at his home and then taken them to the waiting Canberra. By mid-morning they were back at work in their old offices in the Joint Operations Centre at Christmas.

Two days later there was a full scientific rehearsal, to bring the whole Task Force team up to speed quickly. The sea search by Shackletons, the dropping of an inert but instrumented bomb by a Valiant, the monitoring of the bombing run by the Mark 7 radar equipment, high and low level photography and a dummy sampling operation were all exercised and various troubles were sorted out. Detailed plans for the safety control of all personnel on the island were refined and practised piecemeal. All this was going on while a new main camp site was being set up with the new tentage and other accommodation equipment landed from the SS *Somersby*.

As usual in Grapple, the serious side of life was often relieved by some flash of light-hearted humour. Since the administration of the island was now being run by the RAF instead of the Army, a question arose as to who should run the TFC's 'A' mess. No one was eager to act as President of the Mess Committee, Bar Officer, Treasurer or anything else. Finally, Guy Western said he would do it, but only on condition that he could do it the only way he knew and using the naval mess system. This was readily agreed. So when the TFC arrived, he found a notice board above the entrance to the hut, bearing the legend:

G Western and A Young
Proprietors
Licensed to sell beer, wine, spirits, tobacco and cigarettes

Leading Seaman Young was Western's steward and it all worked most satisfactorily. But what the Air Ministry auditors made of it on their first formal inspection six months later is unknown.

John Grandy accompanied the TFC on his tour of the new facilities and his many checks on readiness for the imminent live test. The new Dakota airstrip on the south-east tip of the island was well done and in busy use. The Army had done a great job in getting all the array of instrumentation sites prepared and in helping the equally efficient AWRE teams to set up and test their recording equipments, much the same as they had been on Malden Island six months previously. In lieu of the control ship *Narvik* there was now a heavily protected forward control post, consisting of three intercommunicating rooms each made of inch thick steel sides and roof, with the same communications

The Re-entry team being checked for any health hazard on return to *Narvik*. *(Photo: AWRE)*

Checking Canberra B6 sampling aircrew after careful decontamination. *(Photo: AWRE)*

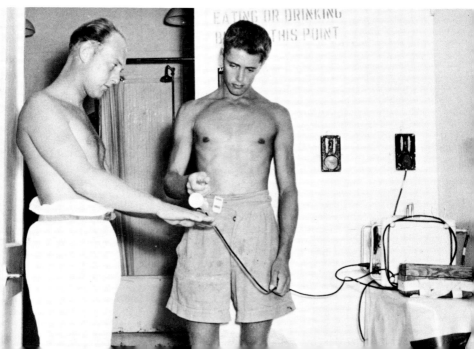

Decontaminating the Canberras which penetrated the radioactive cloud. *(Photo: AWRE)*

Washing off the barrier paint with high pressure hoses. *(Photo: AWRE)*

Colonel Jack Stone, the Army Task Group Commander, at Christmas Island. *(Photo: K Bomford)*

The 'Yellow Cab Company' – 22 Squadron RAF helicopters providing rapid transit between Main Camp and the South East Point instrumentation sites. *(Photo: AWRE)*

Success! Round 'C',
8th November 1957.
(Photo: AWRE)

The South East Point
Dakota airstrip at
Christmas Island.
(Photo: AWRE)

and control equipment as had been in *Narvik*. The entrance to each section was through a small heavy steel door of the type set in water-tight bulkheads in naval ships; and one had to be careful to duck one's head going through the doorway or suffer a mighty crack on the forehead. Ken Bomford had it all very well organised and when Bill Cook, the Scientific Director, arrived on the 31st October he expressed himself well pleased with the new set-up.

Most personnel transport between the main camp and the south end was made by helicopter and 22 Squadron really earned and justified their nick-name the 'Yellow Cab Company'. Heavy equipment and supplies went by road – or track – which had been greatly improved by the army engineers, but it was still a long and wearying journey. When available, the occasional Dakota also made the short shuttle trip between the main airfield and the southern strip. Extravagant perhaps, but a most valuable time saver.

Once again, information had been received that there might be attempts to block the impending tests by the intrusion of small shipping into the danger area; so on October 30th, the full-scale sea searches were commenced.

The weather factor at the morning 'go/no go' briefings was much more difficult than it had been back in May, and it seemed that it would be necessary to take advantage of relatively short periods of suitable weather conditions in between relatively long times of unacceptable cloud cover and winds. On November 1st, everything was ready on the starting line, including the High Explosive version of the live round to be tested. Freeman felt fairly sure of a clear break of a few hours next morning, so the decision was given to go for a full scale dress rehearsal next day, November 2nd.

The programme allowed the TFC a couple of hours of sleep before the final decision in the early hours, but no sooner had he lost consciousness on his bed than the telephone awakened him. The control tower at the airfield.

'Sorry to bother you, sir, but we have an unidentified

American aircraft in the circuit, asking permission to land. Is that OK?'

Very odd. It was quite a frequent occurrence for USAF or USN aircraft to pass through Christmas, but they had always been meticulous about sending flight plans.

'Ask the aircraft what is the purpose of his visit?'

A few minutes later came the answer.

'He says he has a Doctor Crocker on board, sir.'

Allen Crocker! For Heaven's sake, what was this about?

'Clear the aircraft to land, lay on whatever facilities the crew need and have a vehicle of some kind to bring Doctor Crocker to my tent.'

This was a bit of a problem in the middle of all the activity of a rehearsal D day, but anything goes to help Allen Crocker. Twenty minutes later a young duty officer showed the visitor into the TFC's tent. Sincere greetings between good friends. Surprise! Coffee? Drink? Nothing, thanks – just some help with a problem.

'Wilf, I have a team at Palmyra Island to monitor your test and we're in trouble with some of our equipment. It would help us enormously if you could let us know the approximate time of the drop. Is that possible?'

'Sure, Allen. Today is just the rehearsal and we hope to do the live drop in three days from now. But the weather is troublesome and we may have delays. The best thing would be for us to radio you when we decide to go. How much warning do you need?'

'Oh, a couple of hours would be fine.'

'Right. If you will let us know what frequency to call you on, we'll send you a signal when the final decision is made. That'll be about three hours before the bang. Now, is there anything else we can do for you? Would you like to stay the night? Or a meal, or what?'

'No thanks, Wilf, I prefer to get back right away. But I hope you'll come and stay with us again on your way back through Washington. So long, for now.'

382

And the burly figure vanished into the night and the waiting Land Rover.

Three hours later, at 6 o'clock, there were the old gang, the TFC shadowed by John Grandy and Ginger Weir by Jack Roulston, with Bill Cook, John Challens, Guy Western, Jack Stone, Mr Freeman, Ernest Hicks and all the others, making their final decision in the JOC. It all looked in order, so the 'GO' was given. On this new programme, based on the drop at Christmas instead of 400 miles away at Malden, the TFC now had some time to spare before going to the Forward Control post. So he and John Grandy took a helicopter tour round all the units on the island. All personnel, other than those specifically detailed for handling aircraft or for the JOC, were being assembled and roll-called at various sites. Windows were firmly fastened wide open in all hutments, to minimise the effect of blast. All loose equipment in tents was firmly stowed away so that it could not be blown about and cause further damage. All aircraft not scheduled to be airborne were parked tail to the south and controls firmly locked.

Then a quick look at the AWRE self-catering site to see that it had been properly shut down. Finally to several well-protected manned recording sites, in one of which they found a gloomy, depressed scientist not getting on with his job.

'It's no good, TFC. You'll have to cancel the rehearsal. I can't do it.'

'I'm sorry to hear that. Why not?'

'I haven't had any breakfast and I feel awful. I just can't do my job like this.'

'How come you haven't had any breakfast? You chaps chose to do your own catering so that everything would be just as you wanted it.'

'Yes, I know. But we had to close down our kitchen early and those of us who were late had to fix ourselves a sandwich. So I did, but I can't eat *that* . . .' – indicating a monstrosity on a plate on top of a rack of electronic equipment. The worthy man had evidently cut himself – unskilfully – two wedges of bread, each an inch and a half thick at one end and paper thin at the other. Between them a slice of corned beef, but the bread was so arranged that the two thick ends were together, making a sandwich over three inches thick at one end and nothing at the other. Truly a gastronomic problem.

The TFC, determinedly trying to look serious, picked up the radio hand-set, called the JOC and asked for Air Commodore Weir.

'Ginger, this is a real emergency and I joke not. Call in one of your choppers, find a cook in the cookhouse assembly point, tell him to fry up some bacon and two eggs in a hurry and fly it down here to site D3. Explanations later.'

Twenty five minutes later the famished scientist was bolting down his breakfast, courtesy of the Royal Air Force, and the rehearsal could now go ahead. John Grandy's comment – 'I just can't believe it!'

The TFC, who also had had no breakfast, eyed the wedge sandwich speculatively, took off the top and turned it round 180 degrees and then wolfed the thick but otherwise reasonable sandwich as they went on their way.

The rehearsal was completely successful and full advantage was taken of the temporary clearance in the weather for Flight Lieutenant Bates, in Valiant 825, to do some practice overshoot bombing, his first experience of this drill. That same evening two official American observers, Rear Admiral Patrick, USN, and Brigadier General J W White, USAF, arrived from Hawaii to witness this next test. They were very congenial and knowledgeable characters and were warmly welcomed into the 'A' mess circle. Another late arrival was Group Captain John Mason, who was to take over Freddie Milligan's job and had come to see how it all worked. There wasn't much time for socialising, but it was a very pleasant evening meal and Admiral Patrick endeared himself to all by claiming to have been at Christmas Island long before any 'johnny-come-lately' Brits. Challenged to substantiate this, he explained that his father had been master of one of the last clipper ships and, with his wife and baby son on board his ship the SS *Aeon*, had been driven ashore on Christmas Island in a great storm. Which is why that bump on the east coast of the island was called 'Aeon Point'.

This was treated as a leg-pull, but Patrick persisted. So next day, Ginger Weir, Guy Western, Jack Stone and Patrick took a jeep down that terrible track to Aeon Point and actually found bits of the old wreck. It was true after all!

The 'wash-up' after the rehearsal showed everything satis-factory, operations OK, the safety procedures worked smooth-ly. The courier Canberra with the imaginary cloud samples in its 'Forth Bridge' carrier departed on time for Hickam, but had to return with engine trouble. Ron Boardman would see to that. So it was planned to go for a live drop three days later.

But at the decision meeting on November 4th the weather was so hopeless that a delay of 24 hours was declared. The same thing happened on the 5th. And on the 6th. A worried Ginger Weir came into the TFC's office.

'Boss! We can't go on for long like this. We're using up Shackleton and PR7 hours at a hell of a rate running the D-1 programmes.'

It was agreed that the Task Force would have to come to full readiness and stand-by through all the daylight hours, to take advantage of any break which might occur in the weather.

At the morning meeting on November 7th, it looked as though after a night with a fair amount of cumulo-nimbus cloud and occasional thunderstorms, there should be a clearance for some hours the following morning. The winds were satisfactory as they affected the fall-out pattern. The live 'Round C' weapon was ready, the necessary number of serviceable aircraft available. So the TFC and the Scientific Director decided to go for a live drop next day, November 8th. The sea search Shackletons and the first pair of low/high level weather reconnaissance aircraft were already airborne and half way through their D-1 sorties. Most of the Gilbertese families had already been evacuated by sea and now the remainder were packed into two Hastings aircraft and sent off to Canton Island, not very happily this time; but they just had to be out of any harm's way with this first live test over Christmas itself.

What was by now the almost routine D-1 programme continued through the afternoon and the later Shackleton and PR7 meteorological flights supported the estimate that there would be a period of clearer weather soon after dawn the next morning. Millett's Valiant XD824 was taxied over to the AWRE Assembly building area and loaded with the improved thermo-nuclear device. Everything seemed to be proceeding pretty well.

At midnight the crews of the Shackletons detailed for the danger area sea search and for the early low level weather flight were being briefed in the Joint Operations Centre and by 01.15 they were boarding their aircraft and ready to taxi out. As soon as they were all airborne and D day was well under way, the TFC and John Grandy went back to their tents to get some sleep. An hour later, Guy Western woke the TFC with the news of a Liberian ship in the danger area and heading towards Christmas Island. This could foul up everything.

Twenty minutes later, the TFC, Weir, Western and Surtees were grouped in discussion round the chart spread out on a table in the Operations Room. The destroyer *Cossack* had just reported that she was under way and sailing to intercept the Liberian *Effie*. The plot showed that *Cossack* might make it in about four hours with a fair chance of turning *Effie* away in time.

Any information about *Effie*? The only thing was an entry in Janes' *All the World's Shipping* showing her as an old World War 2 Victory ship, operating under the Liberian flag of convenience. No conclusion could be drawn as to whether this intrusion was accidental or a deliberate ploy. The plot on the chart showed that there could be no question of a live drop that day if *Effie* continued on her present course and speed. The 206 Squadron Shackleton which had found the ship was still keeping her under observation but so far had got no response to all efforts to arouse the crew; but if she could be turned away in the next three hours or so, the live drop could still be on. With the rare chance of a break in the cloudy weather and in view of the critical supply situation plus the worrying shortage of aircraft flying hours, the TFC decided against delaying the operation at this stage. They would stick to the programme in the hope that either *Cossack* or the Shackleton would succeed in diverting *Effie* in time.

That flaming business of the Notice to Mariners not being issued in time! It had only been out from London three weeks previously and *Effie* had probably sailed from Sumatra or somewhere before that. If only they had had a depth charge available to drop in the sea to make a loud bang a few hundred yards from *Effie* to wake up the crew! Nothing to do now but wait.

At 04.00 hours the Canberra PR7 detailed for the first high altitude wind-finding recce departed. At the same time, all personnel on the island not engaged on specific duty were awakened and soon began to assemble at their designated points and to answer their roll-calls. Motor transport was arranged at each point in an orderly fashion, ready to move off in convoys to the port area should a general evacuation be necessary.

In the Operations Room, Corporal Beall, who had by then caught up with the TFC, moved round from one small group to another, dispensing the welcome hot black coffee. At five o'clock, finding the bird flown from the tent and his thoughtful cup of tea superfluous, he had temporarily purloined a Land Rover, picked up Terry Helfer and taken him to the JOC.

While the driver helpfully did the coffee rounds, the ADC, unobtrusively at the side of the TFC, was now methodically ticking off the items on the vital check-list. Every fifteen minutes the assistant Controllers, Squadron Leader 'Dickie' Bird and Lieutenant Commander Finlay, updated the plot on the chart while Freeman and Ernest Hicks did the same with the weather and fall-out pattern. With great difficulty the TFC restrained himself from questioning them more frequently, as the dawdling minutes brought no good word about *Effie*. All factors about the operation were gone over so often and so thoroughly, that when the whole team for the briefing meeting arrived at about ten minutes to six, it was a quick and informal business. The Valiant with the live 'Round C' was loaded and ready to go. The 'Grandstand' Valiant and all other supporting aircraft were ready and waiting. The instrumentation set-up was ready for switching on. Winds and weather were going to be acceptable. The only snag was *Effie*.

At six o'clock, pitch black and raining outside the JOC, the TFC looked at Bill Cook.

'Bill, I propose that we go ahead with the programme, but inject a delay of half an hour to give us just that little bit of extra time for *Effie* and the weather. Do you agree?'

'Yes, Wilf. That's OK with me.'

The order was given and the Valiant and Canberra crews crowded into the Operations Room for final briefing – Barney Millett for the drop, Bob Bates' crew for 'Grandstand', George Bates and his four Canberra B6s for the sampling, Squadron Leader Monaghan, the new boy in command of the 58 Squadron Canberra PR7 detachment for the final wind finding, high level photography and the courier with the samples home to the UK.

At 06.15 the first break came – a signal from the Shackleton tracking the Liberian ship.

'*Effie* turning south.'

Evidently the Shackleton captain had at last succeeded in waking up the crew and successfully dropped some of the warning leaflets on her deck. A few minutes later, a follow up signal.

'*Effie* steering 180°T. Speed 12 knots.'

The TFC looked at Guy Western.

'Twelve knots? – a Victory ship?'

'They must have the cabin boy sitting on the safety valve!' replied Western. Evidently the master of the good ship *Effie* had taken the leaflet to heart and at that rate she would be clear of the danger just in time.

06.20. A report in to the JOC that all non-essential personnel on the island were assembled in their assigned positions and accounted for – except for one man, who would doubtless turn up soon. It was raining lightly and there was still heavy cloud over the airfield but the two aircraft circling the dropping area still reported clearer weather approaching with another band of heavy cloud to the north-east of that.

06.30. Another Shackleton – 'Lookout 3' – airborne to report continuously weather in the target area and, hopefully, for low level photography after the burst.

06.40. AWRE Weapons team reported batteries connected – the last item for the weapon itself.

07.00. Valiant pre-flight checks complete and crews waiting in their aircraft. Signal to Allen Crocker at Palmyra Island – estimating 08.30V.

07.20. Valiants ordered to start engines. An unusually anxious Ginger Weir cornered the TFC in the Ops room and asked, quietly: 'Aren't you pushing it a bit, Boss?'

'Yes, Ginger, but if we stop now it'll take us a month to get ready again. I reckon it's just about all right and we'll press on to the last moment before calling it off. Tell Millett and Bates to go ahead as per programme. But where the hell can that missing man be?'

07.25. Another report from the Shackleton escorting *Effie*. '*Cossack* now in company.' Also a hurried message from the main camp. The missing man had turned up. He had fallen asleep leaning against the off-side wheel of a Bedford truck and no one had noticed him until that moment.

07.35. Butch Surtees, the air controller reported:

'Valiant 824 lined up and ready for take-off, sir.'

'Take off.'

Thirty seconds later came to the listeners in the JOC the roar of the four Avon jet engines as Millett drove 824 down the runway and up into the semi-darkness of a very heavily-clouded daybreak. As the sound faded away to the east there came a great flash of lightning and a terrific clap of thunder. The TFC's heart skipped a few beats before he realised that it was indeed only thunder and lightning and then Millett's calm voice came through on the Ops Room loudspeaker.

'824, climbing to the north-east. Weather improving.'

Two minutes later the second Valiant took off to take position below and behind 824. Five minutes later, the first of the Canberra B6s, the primary sampler, to go for the maximum altitude possible at H+10 minutes. Then the wind-finding PR7 and the B6 Sampling Controller, Air Commodore Denis Wilson flown by George Bates, the 76 Squadron CO, again with the self-explanatory call-sign 'Sniff Boss'. Sniff Two and Three followed in quick succession.

As soon as the second Valiant was airborne, the TFC, Bill Cook, John Grandy and Terry Helfer were into the tired old white staff car and off to a helipad a few hundred yards away, where a 22 Squadron Whirlwind was waiting for them, engine running. Ten minutes later they were put down alongside the sheet steel and earthworks Forward Control bunker, half way down the peninsula towards Ground Zero. Here the sky was much clearer, patches of blue showing between lumps of alto-cumulus cloud, beginning to shine white in the light of the rapidly rising sun. Even as they watched, the cloud was beginning to disperse – probably not much more than three eighths at that time.

Into the bunker to be greeted once again by Ken Bomford, the Scientific Superintendent of the Forward Area, Wally Long at the Controller's desk, a message coming over the loudspeaker from Ginger Weir at the JOC.

'Signal from *Cossack*, *Effie* clear of area. All heads down.'

Relief!

'Lookout Three', Squadron Leader Church in the Shackleton circling the area round Ground Zero, was now reporting only two eighths of cloud and dispersing. Valiant 824 at 40,000 feet and still climbing, following the 'race-track' pattern.

08.15. 824 began the Navigation Run, starting from a point well north of the airfield, over the northern marker at the north east tip of the island, across the Bay of Wrecks and over the southern marker at the southern tip of the bay. Then over the Target Indicator on the south shore of the peninsula and the turn back on to the northerly heading. How was the weather now? Bill Cook anxiously went out through the bunker door to look, forgot to duck his head and suffered an almighty crack on his forehead from the top of the door frame. Protesting vehemently he said he would use the other door and did the same thing again. Poor Bill! It really wasn't funny, but he soon recovered. And the weather was fine – only a few wisps of cloud.

08.22. Shackleton 'Lookout Three' ordered to leave target area and take up its orbit 35 miles west. Check with the JOC. All personnel, all aircraft on the ground, all facilities ready for the live drop. Bomford reported all instrumentation working correctly, except for the ultra high-speed cameras at the last moment.

08.26. 824 commenced the Initial run. Bomb doors open. Telemetry working correctly. Bomb aimer conning the aircraft along the correct bombing line. Mark 7 radar confirming the line. Navigator's Green Satin confirming the wind vector passed by the PR7. Over the target marker, close bomb doors, turn away for the reciprocal course. Points Alpha – Bravo – Charlie.

TFC to Scientific Director. 'OK, Bill?'

'Yes, OK.'

'Foxtrot to 824. Next run is to be the live drop.'

'824. Roger. Live drop next run.'

In the port camp, main camp, airfield and AWRE areas, on ships in the anchorage, in the JOC itself, some 3,000 men awaited in their assembled groups with interest and not a little trepidation for their first experience of a megaton explosion, albeit at a distance of some thirty miles. All had heard, over the nearest loudspeaker the order and the acknowledgement that the Valiant was now about to drop the weapon.

Again on the Tannoy loudspeaker, the controller's voice from the JOC.

'All personnel now turn your backs to the south, as previously rehearsed. When you hear the Valiant has released the bomb, close your eyes and put your hands over them.'

In the Forward Control bunker, the heavy doors were now closed and latched. In the dimmed light in the control room, the large luminous clock over Long's head and the scope of the telemetry receiver glowed gently. Over on the left, away from the overhead light, a two-foot square of white cardboard on an easel was brightly illuminated by the light coming through the tiny hole in the steel wall – the classic mediaeval pin-hole camera, in which a picture of whatever was outside appeared, inverted, on the white screen inside a darkened room. This, of course, was directed at the point in space at which the bomb would explode and was in the charge of Peter Jones, he of the unhappy close encounter with the Elsan on Malden on the first test and as yet quite unaware that one day he would become the Director of the Atomic Weapons Research Establishment, in the footsteps of Sir William Penney.

Forward Control, using the call sign 'Foxtrot' which is the aviation phonetic jargon for the letter F, again called the JOC to check that all supporting aircraft airborne were in their correct orbits.

08.43. Valiant 824 at point Echo at the northern end of the race-track, turning onto the bombing run. Millett and his bomb-aimer, Flight Lieutenant Frank Corduroy, now going on to continuous broadcast.

'Northern marker in sight,' called Corduroy, 'steer 162 degrees.'

'One six two,' responded Millett. 'Air speed point seven six mach, height forty-five thousand.'

The drill was by now quite familiar to the crew of 824, who had done two 'Grandstands' on live drops as well as many practices. All was calm and controlled – no drama.

The captains of the three 'Lookout' Shackletons and the Canberra PR7 at high level adjusted their orbits to be in a position to get good photographs despite the considerable cloud

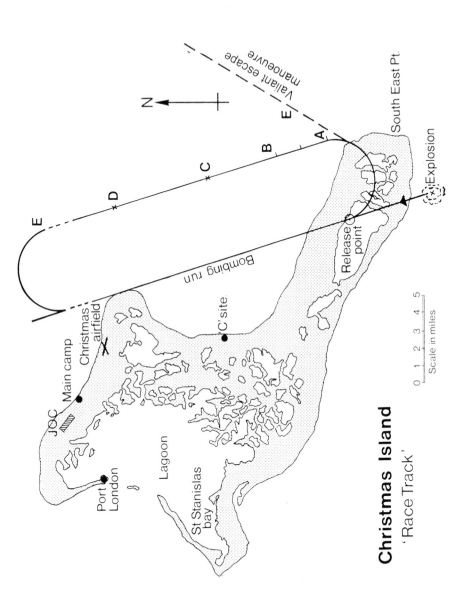

Christmas Island
'Race Track'

only a little west of the bombing run. Bates in Valiant 825 was firmly in position 2000 feet below and one mile astern of 824.

The bomb doors of 824 were opened and the first step appeared in the trace on the telemetry scope in the Forward Control. Then the master switch in the aircraft went on and the second step appeared. Then the arming switch and the third step.

'Southern marker in sight – visibility good – steer one six three,' called Corduroy. Millett acknowledged.

The TFC looked at Bill Cook and raised his eyebrows interrogatively. Cook just nodded and puffed at his pipe.

'Target indicator in sight. Steady on one six three,' from Corduroy.

A few seconds later, with all the Task Force listening intently –

'Steady, still on one six three – steady – steady – NOW!' as he pressed the bomb release. Millett held straight and level for the overshoot. Bates turned away for his escape manoeuvre, his bomb-aimer fitting the flash-shield over the bombing panel as he did so.

Ten seconds later the computer operated the bomb release. The fourth step appeared on the telemetry trace in the Forward Control room. Millett went into the escape manoeuvre and began his commentary. Flight Lieutenant John Tuck, the Air Electronics Officer in 824 switched on the rear-facing cameras in the tail.

In the control room the broadcast went out:

'Shut your eyes and cover them with your hands.'

Long switched on the ultra high speed cameras in the instrumentation site and Bomford began to count down.

'Thirty seconds – twenty – ten – five, four, three, two, one...'

The white screen of the pinhole camera in the control room suddenly showed a bright point of light, which expanded rapidly into a brilliant pink and gold chrysanthemum and then into a gaudy sunrise. Simultaneously the four steps on the telemetry scope vanished. Satisfaction all round. But then Peter

Jones stared at the pinhole camera screen in horrified disbelief. The image of the new sun was *sinking* to the bottom of the screen, instead of rising! Two seconds later he realised his mistake – the picture was inverted, of course.

Bomford was broadcasting the count-up.

'Ten seconds – fifteen seconds – you may turn and look now.'

The three thousand spectators, still uncomfortably aware of the momentary flash of heat which had warmed their shoulders at the moment of detonation, now turned and stared with amazement at the southern sky, full of the pink and brown candy-floss cloud shooting up heavenwards at great speed and acquiring a topping of snowy sherbet. Too awed for speech, there was utter silence for some seconds, apart from the remote drone of aircraft and the rustle of coconut palm fronds in the breeze.

As the count-up had reached fifteen seconds, the TFC and John Grandy rushed out into the open to observe the visual results of the Task Force's endeavours and to get some first hand experience of the blast wave. A minute later they got just that, as the shock hit them and bowled them over like scraps of straw in a gale. It was worse than being at the bottom of a Welsh rugby scrum in a needle game! So now they knew!

At the airfield and the JOC, the shock would be much less on account of the inverse square law; but had the confident decision to do the test at Christmas Island itself been justified – or not? So back into the control room to telephone the JOC. Was all well?

Ginger Weir, in a hurt and plaintive voice:

'Don't *ever* do that to me again!' – and a great laugh. 'But seriously, Boss, apart from a good shaking we seem to be OK. I'll check round.'

The damage was in fact minimal, the most serious being that some helicopters parked near the JOC had had their hatches and windows blown out, but were otherwise undamaged. No damage at the airfield or main camp. It had worked out all right in the end.

Bill Cook was looking very pleased.

'As you know, we can't tell until we do the proper analyses, but at first sight it looks as though we've got what we wanted.'

Ten minutes after the detonation, Denis Wilson and his team of Canberra samplers began to measure the cloud at various heights and to check the radiation levels at different distances from the cloud. After twenty minutes, Sniff One, the primary sampler, made the first penetration, to be followed by Sniff Two and Sniff Three at other levels. Their missions accomplished, the B6s returned to the airfield, to the decontamination centre where the samples were extracted, potted and loaded into the waiting 58 Squadron PR7. It took off at 13.10 hours and, thanks to the smooth and efficient operations of slip-screws and Staging Post teams, arrived in England 24 hours and a few minutes later. Meanwhile, the B6 crews and aircraft were decontaminated and returned to circulation. The Task Force had done what it had been asked to do, but no thanks to that stupid refusal to let the Notice to Mariners be sent out in good time. Possibly over-reacting both to the finally successful outcome of a very dicey operation and to the problem itself, the TFC boiled with fury as he reviewed the quite unnecessary risks and difficulties which had been imposed on the Task Force. As soon as the chopper had picked up him and the others at the Forward Control and delivered them back to the JOC, he sent off a signal to Eric Jackson in the Ministry of Supply in London.

'For Jackson from Oulton.

'After the most strenuous efforts to overcome heartbreaking difficulties we had a fleeting chance to fire this morning. This opportunity was very nearly lost through the lunatic policy on issue of Notices to Mariners. Everything happened as I had forecast and I wish to register the strongest possible protest against such gross interference with a Task Force Commander charged with such a difficult and dangerous duty.'

Then he felt better, blood pressure back to normal, and got on with the day's business of thanking the staff for their splendid efforts and congratulating Ken Hubbard, who had been with

Ginger Weir listening in to events in the Ops Room, on yet another accurate delivery by 49 Squadron.

The *Mid Pacific News*, published as usual a superb Souvenir edition devoted to this November 8th test. It included an excellent article by one of the AWRE scientific staff, which ended with the following paragraph:

'This was a Joint Operation linking all three services and the civilian scientists. What has been said above should serve to underline how utterly essential to final success the close collaboration between these elements has been. Indeed it is a pleasure to take part in and see the beneficial effects of these extremely friendly relations which exist on every side and which surely are a credit to all concerned.'

50

Task completed

That's Grapple X – that was! – to misquote a once famous Shell petrol advertisement; but much remained to be done. Christmas Island and the central core of the Task Force to be run down to a gentle tickover and at the same time start preparing for the next series of tests under new management.

Half an hour after the detonation of Round C, the re-entry team were being lifted into the instrumentation sites by the helicopters (without windows!) of 22 Squadron. The records were collected and were homeward bound in the next Hastings shuttle to Hickam.

The Air Task Group began immediately to prepare aircraft for return to UK or Australia. At a rate of two or three a day, the Valiants and Canberra PR7s departed between November 11th and 16th. Charter aircraft and Comets of RAF Transport Command came in and collected squadron ground crews and 160 Wing servicing personnel. 76 Squadron returned to Edinburgh Field.

After a quietly celebratory dinner in the 'A' mess, Admiral Patrick and General White were taken back to Honolulu next day in a 206 Squadron Shackleton.

Malden and Penrhyn detachments were quickly withdrawn in a combined effort by 1325 Dakota Flight and HMS *Messina*, the latter then going on to evacuate the Decca team from Jarvis, and the Met and scientific equipment and personnel from Fanning Island. The Dakotas also brought in the records, equipment and personnel from all the outlying recording stations. The New Zealand flying boat crews brought in their last samples of unpolluted fish and vegetation.

Early on Sunday, November 9th, Air Vice Marshal John Grandy, the new Task Force Commander designate, departed in a Hastings aircraft to make his initial courtesy calls on the authorities in New Zealand and Australia. Bill Cook was shipped off to Hickam in a Hastings shuttle to connect with a commercial flight home and his next lot of sums.

Suddenly the TFC found himself with nothing much to do for the first time in nearly two years, and mid-afternoon wandered over to the 'A' mess 'lounge'. Not another soul about anywhere. On the table in the corner was the dusty old record-player which Freddie Milligan had coaxed out of Harvey Schwartz when the Decca Company had first been brought into the Grapple planning. He remembered now that he had been asked were there any particular records he would like to have and he had asked, if it were possible, for Rachmaninov's Second Piano Concerto or César Franck's Symphonic Variations. He sorted through the little pile of record sleeves and there was the César Franck. Blowing off most of the coral dust, he put it on to play and sat back in an armchair. Rather scratchy, but soothing with that restrained but grandiose opening phrase, a bit like the start of the Grapple story, and gradually working up to an absolute frenzy – yet a tightly controlled frenzy, also like Grapple.

Musing gently over this Christmas Island epic and the heroic efforts of the four thousand characters from cooks to captains who had made the final success possible, he just hoped the world realised that the end purpose was not simply to make a frightening bang, without doing any damage to either people or planet, but more importantly to ensure that ordinary decent folk might live ordinary decent peaceful lives.

And as the last exhilarating variation wound up to its overwhelming climax, to his astonishment and discomfiture he found tears streaming down his face. Good Lord! This wouldn't do. What would the cohorts think if they saw their leader now?

So back to work! Many different folks, of many nations, of different coloured uniforms and even different coloured skins had worked together in unwonted harmony to make the operation possible. It was time to thank them and say goodbye. Speeches of congratulation and thanks to the troops of three services, to the AWRE and RAE teams, to the Gilbertese islanders. Finally, although it was a bit of a 'jolly', on November 13th a Shackleton took the TFC, Ginger Weir and 'Gilo' Giles to Rarotonga to thank the ever helpful and genial Geoffrey Nevill, the New Zealand Commissioner for the Cook Islands and to pay respects to the Queen.

'Your visit couldn't have been better timed,' said Nevill.

'We have a party tonight – a party to beat all parties. The local parliament has been sitting for the past three weeks and ends today. It only meets once a year and the Queen allows absolutely no consumption of alcohol during that period. So starting this evening, all restraint will be off.'

He then went on to explain, with a twinkle in his eye, that Rarotonga was the only place in the world where women got ulcers. Why? Well, the local social custom was that it was quite in order for a girl to have any number of babies by any number of young men until she got married. But after marriage, absolute fidelity was the rule and no fooling. This left every girl with a serious problem. If she continued to lead a wild life for too long, she would miss altogether the chance of marriage and a secure old age. If she married too soon, she would miss a lot of fun which her friends would still be having. For a people unaccustomed to problems this was a great worry and caused the ulcers!

It also caused him a social problem, since he was the local judge and would have to deal with the divorce problems which would inevitably arise as a result of this night's frolics, and he couldn't risk being involved. So he hoped his guests would all come to the Queen's party and stay as long as they wished; but

400

he, like Cinderella, would have to leave on the stroke of midnight.

It was indeed a great party. A beautiful tropical palace setting, music, flowers and exotic perfume, lots of good drinks, a gay and happy people, pretty girls in brief flower-printed cotton or silk dresses – the combination of white, polynesian and 25% chinese blood was quite overwhelming in some cases. The Queen too, very attractive in something simple from Paris, was all set to throw off the cares of State for one night. By midnight the palace itself seemed to be doing a hula as the music got wilder and the TFC decided he'd better go home with the Commissioner.

So, next morning, goodbyes and warmest thanks and a very muted Shackleton crew as they droned and drank black coffee all the thousand miles back to Christmas. There the final packing up and looking under the bed in the tent to see if anything had been left.

November 15th. Number One uniform. RAF Christmas Island paraded on the nearly empty tarmac of the airfield, flanked by Percy Roberts and a very smart platoon of Gilbertese Police.

Formal inspection by the Task Force Commander, stopping to speak to many of the men. Then – 'Goodbye'. Salutes and into the waiting Hastings. And so home through a series of 'thank you and farewell' calls in all the watering places on the route to London, there to write the final report.

Some cracker!

Postscript

During 1958, two further series of British atomic tests, Grapple-Y and Grapple-Z, were carried out at Christmas Island under the command of Air Vice Marshal John Grandy. For the benefit of any readers who may be interested in the total programme of British atomic tests in the atmosphere, a tabulation of these events follows. Additionally, a United States test series was carried out at Christmas Island in 1960.

In 1979, Christmas Island ceased to be part of the British Crown Colony of the Gilbert and Ellice Islands and became part of the Republic of Kiribati, whose capital is Tarawa and which comprises the Gilbert Islands, the Phoenix Islands (round Canton) and the Line Islands (Christmas, Fanning, Palmyra, Jarvis, Washington, Starbuck and Malden). The former Christmas Island now rejoices in the name of Kiritimati and has a flourishing and increasing permanent population of over 1200, mainly of Gilbertese origin. Nuclear tests and military matters are long forgotten and their attention is devoted to a peaceful pursuit of commerce, mainly in fish, copra and salt, but rapidly increasing in tourism. The former Task Force Officers 'B' mess has now been reconstituted as the 'Captain Cook Motel' and caters for a steady flow of bird-watching enthusiasts and big game fishermen who arrive and depart by a regular airline service from Honolulu, using the original Grapple runway.

Malden and Jarvis islands remain deserted.

Penrhyn, Raratonga and Aitutaki remain prosperously as part of the Cook Islands dependency of New Zealand. Their inhabitants lead happy and peaceful lives – except for a very rare typhoon – and are relatively well equipped with free health care in hospitals and dispensaries, free education in primary and secondary schools, with a sixth form college on Raratonga. Able students go to universities in Fiji or New Zealand. There is a fairly flourishing but partly subsidised economy, mainly agricultural for home consumption, but including export of canned fruit and the products of cottage industries. It is worth reading the Cook Islands entry in the Encyclopaedia Britannica, Micropaedia, Volume 3.

TABLE 1: UK OVERSEAS ATMOSPHERIC NUCLEAR WEAPONS TESTS, 1952–1958

TABLE 1(A) UK ATMOSPHERIC NUCLEAR WEAPONS TESTS IN AUSTRALIA, OCTOBER 1952 – OCTOBER 1957

OPERATION AND LOCATION	DATE AND TIME (GMT–Z)	SITE	TYPE	HEIGHT (m)	APPROX. YIELD (kilotons – kT)
HURRICANE Monte Bello Islands Western Australia	3 Oct 1952 0000Z	Lagoon of 12 m depth	CSB: in HMS Plym	–2.7	25
TOTEM Emu Field South Australia	14 Oct 1953 2130Z	T1	NSB: MS Tower	31	10
	26 Oct 1953 2130Z	T2	NSB: MS Tower	31	8
MOSAIC Monte Bello Islands Western Australia	16 May 1956 0350Z	G1: Trimouille Island	NSB: Al Tower	31	15
	19 June 1956 0214Z	G2: Alpha Island	NSB: Al Tower	31	60
BUFFALO Maralinga Range South Australia	27 Sept 1956 0730Z	One Tree	NSB: Al Tower	31	15
	4 Oct 1956 0700Z	Marcoo	CSB: At ground surface	0.2	1.5
	11 Oct 1956 0557Z	Kite	Airburst: Freefall	150	3
	21 Oct 1956 1435Z	Breakaway	NSB: Al Tower	31	10
ANTLER Maralinga Range South Australia	14 Sept 1957 0505Z	Tadje	NSB: Al Tower	31	1
	25 Sept 1957 0030Z	Biak	NSB: Al Tower	31	6
	9 Oct 1957 0645Z	Taranaki	Airburst: Balloon–System Borne	300	25

NSB: Near Surface Burst   CSB: Contact Surface Burst   MS: Mild Steel   Al: Aluminium Alloy

TABLE 1(B) UK ATMOSPHERIC NUCLEAR WEAPONS TESTS IN THE SOUTH PACIFIC, MAY 1957 – SEPTEMBER 1958

OPERATION AND LOCATION	DATE AND TIME (GMT)	SITE	TYPE	HEIGHT (m)	YIELD RANGE
GRAPPLE Malden Island	15 May 1957 1937Z	Off-shore, South Approx 1.7 kilometres from land	Airburst: Freefall	2400	Megaton
	31 May 1957 1941Z	Off-shore, South Approx 1.7 kilometres from land	Airburst: Freefall	2300	Megaton
	19 June 1957 1940Z	Off-shore, South Approx 1.7 kilometres from land	Airburst: Freefall	2300	Megaton
GRAPPLE X Christmas Island	8 Nov 1957 1747Z	Off-shore, South East Point Approx 2.5 kilometres from land	Airburst: Freefall	2250	Megaton
GRAPPLE Y Christmas Island	28 Apr 1958 1905Z	Off-shore, South East Point Approx 2.5 kilometres from land	Airburst: Freefall	2350	Megaton
GRAPPLE Z Christmas Island	22 Aug 1958 1800Z	Balloon site South East Corner	Airburst: Balloon–System Borne	450	Kiloton
	2 Sept 1958 1724Z	Off-shore, South East Point Approx 2.5 kilometres from land	Airburst: Freefall	2850	Megaton
	11 Sept 1958 1749Z	Off-shore, South East Point Approx 2.5 kilometres from land	Airburst: Freefall	2650	Megaton
	23 Sept 1958 1800Z	Balloon site South East Corner	Airburst: Balloon–System Borne	450	Kiloton

D/AWRE/SFS/A/26(YD)
16 June 1986

The above table is reproduced by kind permission of the compiler, Mr W N Saxby and of the Director of the Atomic Weapons Research Establishment.

Glossary

A & AEE	Aircraft and Armament Experimental Establishment, Boscombe Down
ABCD State	Operating condition when HM Ships take all precautions against Atomic, Biological and Chemical Warfare.
ACR7(D)	A small, portable airfield radar for guiding aircraft down to the runway in bad weather.
ADC	Aide de Camp — personal assistant to a senior officer.
AFB	Air Force Base (United States Air Force).
Air Formation Signals	The British Army organisation which provides land line and telephone communications for the RAF.
Antler	A kiloton (fission) atomic test at Maralinga in 1957.
AOG	'Aircraft on Ground', a designation for a replacement item without which one aircraft cannot fly, ie urgent.
ASR	Air Sea Rescue.
ASRE	Admiralty Signals Research Establishment.
AUDE	Admiralty Underwater Development Establishment.
Avgas	The gasoline fuel used in piston-engined aircraft.
Avtur	The kerosene type fuel used in aircraft jet engines.
BFPO	British Forces Post Office.
Bismuth patrols	A standardised pattern of meteorological flight.
Bowser	A large fuel tank on a wheeled chassis.
Buffalo	A series of atomic tests at Maralinga, 1956, including the first British air drop.
CINCPAC	The US Navy Commander-in-Chief Pacific, at Pearl Harbor, Hawaii.
Constellation	A Lockheed piston-engined passenger aircraft.
CR/DF	An equipment to display automatically on a circular screen the direction of an aircraft transmitting on Very High Frequency radio.
CRE	Commander, Royal Engineers.

C54	An American four-engined transport aircraft.
CTO	Chief Technical Officer, in charge of the aircraft maintenance wing of a RAF station.
DCAS	Deputy Chief of the Air Staff in the Air Ministry (1956).
DCIGS	Deputy Chief of the Imperial General Staff, War Office.
DCNS	Deputy Chief of the Naval Staff in the Admiralty.
Decca Navigator	A system for determining the position of an aircraft.
Dieso	Diesel fuel.
DNC	Director of Naval Construction.
DRPC	Defence Research Policy Committee, which advises the Government on Defence Matters.
DUKW	An amphibious vehicle, a boat hull on wheels.
Emu	An early atomic test in Australia.
Eureka	A radar beacon. See 'Rebecca'.
Fission	The release of atomic energy by the splitting of heavy atoms, e.g. uranium.
Fusion	The release of atomic energy by the combining of light atoms, e.g. hydrogen.
GCA	Ground Controlled Approach. A system for giving directions to an aircraft to guide it to land.
Green Satin	An airborne doppler radar used in navigation.
H-hour	The time set for an event — such as a nuclear explosion — to take place.
High Speed Stall	A condition in which the wing of an aircraft flying at high-speed ceases to provide lift.
H/F radio	High Frequency radio used for communication between aircraft and ground stations over long distances.
HT	The designation of an official troop transport ship.
IFR	Flight according to Instrument Flight Rules, ie when there is no sight of the ground.
ILS	Instrument Landing System. System of landing in bad weather without help of a controller on the ground.
ITF	Inter Tropical Front — bad weather zone near Equator.
LCM	Landing Craft (Mechanical Vehicles). A boat with a ramp at the front end which can be lowered on to a beach to allow vehicles to drive ashore.
LST	Landing Ship (Tank). A ship with a bow door and a ramp which can allow tanks or other exceptionally heavy or large vehicles to be driven ashore.
MEXE	Army's Mechanical Engineering Experimental Estab.
MF Beacon	A medium frequency radio beacon on which a bearing can be taken with a radio compass.

405

MFV	Motorised Fishing Vessel.
Mosaic	A kiloton (fission) atomic test at Monte Bello Is's, 1956.
NAAFI	Navy, Army and Air Force Institute, which provides recreation, amenity supplies and other facilities for the Armed Forces and their families.
NCO	Non-Commissioned Officer, e.g. Sergeants.
N.mls.	Nautical Miles — longer than statute miles.
NDB	Non-Directional Beacon (radio) — see MF Beacon.
OCU	Operational Conversion Unit, where trained aircrew change to a new type of aircraft.
OKW	Oberkommando Wehrmacht, the German Army High Command Planning Staff in World War II.
OTU	Operational Training Unit, where aircrew learn to apply their recently acquired flying skills.
Plant	Heavy equipment of every kind used by the Royal Engineers and civil engineers.
POL	Petrol, Oil, Lubricants for engines of every type.
PRO	Public Relations Officer.
RAE	Royal Aircraft Establishment, Farnborough.
RAOC	Royal Army Ordnance Corps.
RASC	Royal Army Service Corps.
RE	The Corps of Royal Engineers.
REME	Royal Electrical and Mechanical Engineers.
Rebecca/Eureka	A short-range radar position-finding equipment for aircraft, Rebecca in the aircraft, Eureka on the airfield.
RSM	Regimental Sergeant Major.
Sappers	The informal name for the Corps of Royal Engineers.
SM	Sergeant Major.
USAF	United States Air Force.
USN	United States Navy.
VFR	Visual Flight Rules. Flight conducted by visual reference to the ground.
VHF/DF	Direction Finding by manual methods, using Very High Frequency radio.
WO	Warrant-Officer.
W/T	Wireless Telegraphy, by Morse Code, not voice.
Zeta	A proposed method of obtaining industrial energy from nuclear fusion.

Index

407

INDEX

PARTICIPATING UNITS

Royal Navy

HMSs	RFA
'Cossack'	'Fort Beauharnois'
'Cook'	'Fort Constantine'
'Messina'	'Fort Rosalie'
'Narvik'	'Wave-Prince'
'Salvictor'	'Gold Ranger'
'Warrior'	

Army

25 Field Engineer Regiment RE
28 Field Engineer Regiment RE
12 Field Engineer Squadron RE
55 Field Engineer Squadron RE
71 Field Engineer Squadron RE
64 Field Park Squadron RE
51 Port Squadron RASC
REME
Royal Signals
RAOC
504 Postal Unit

Royal Air Force Squadrons

22 (ASR) – Helicopters
58 – Canberra PR7
76 – Canberra B6
100 – Canberra PR7
1321 Flight – Valiants
49 – Valiants
24 (Commonwealth Sqdn) – Hastings
1325 Flight (Dakotas)
206 – Shackleton
240 – Shackleton

New Zealand

HMNZS 'Pukaki'
       'Rotoiti'
5 Squadron, RNZAF